SUPER NATURA

An introduction to the make-up and workings of the body's immune system, with advice on natural ways of increasing its efficiency.

SUPER
NATURAL
IMMUNE
POWER

How to keep your natural defence
mechanisms in peak condition

STELLA WELLER

THORSONS PUBLISHING GROUP

First published 1989

© Stella Weller 1989

British Library Cataloguing in Publication Data

Weller, Stella
   Super natural immune power.
   1. Man, Immune reactions
   I. title
   616,07'95

   ISBN 0-7225-1623-1

Published by Thorsons Publishers Limited, Wellingborough, Northamptonshire NN8 2RQ, England

Printed in Great Britain by Richard Clay Limited, Bungay, Suffolk

10   9   8   7   6   5   4   3   2   1

Dedicated to
Lottie and Humphrey

CONTENTS

Acknowledgements   8
Introduction   9
1   Meet Your Body's Defence Agents   11
2   How the System Works   29
3   Eating for Protection   36
4   Mind Against Malady   58
5   Strategies for Stress Control   69
6   Exercising for Immune Fitness   81
7   The Immunity Connection   95
8   Notable Immune Boosters   114
Glossary   125
Bibliography   135
Index   140

ACKNOWLEDGEMENTS

Several individuals have contributed to this work by providing me with help, encouragement and inspiration. Mention of their names below is my way of saying many thanks: John Hardaker, Dhana Homan, Frankie Leibe, Marjorie Nelson, Judith Smallwood, Bee Walters, David Weller, Karl Weller, Walter Weller.

INTRODUCTION

Of all the body's resources for defending us against damage from harmful agents, the immune system is undoubtedly the most important. Although much has been discovered about its workings in recent years, it is so very intricate that there is still a great deal to be learned about it.

Advances in research have made it increasingly clear that a knowledge of immunology – the study of how the body protects itself against disease and other foreign agents – is vital to an understanding of a wide variety of health disorders, from the common cold to cancer.

The current revival of interest in the immune system, though, is not only because of the crucial part it plays in guarding the body against the agents of infection and the spread of malignant cells. There is also a new surge of curiosity as to why the same cells that identify and destroy foreign material can sometimes turn on the body itself to produce such abnormal conditions as rheumatoid arthritis and systemic lupus erythematosus.

Because more and more individuals are taking greater responsibility for their well-being, they are eager for information on the workings of the human body, the nature and cause of certain health disorders and ways to prevent them. Often, however, available research is couched in difficult language not readily grasped by lay persons. Trying to comprehend the immune system is an excellent example: the terms used to describe its components and mechanisms can be very intimidating indeed.

This need no longer be the case: I have presented an overview of the system in clear, simple language to make it easily understood. Chapter 1 describes the components of the system and how it functions. As you read further you will appreciate, perhaps as never before, how factors such as exercise, nutrition and stress can influence immunity for good or for ill. You will also discover a little-known role played by the skin – our largest organ – in protecting the body from invasion by foreign agents. You will also learn simple, effective, enjoyable ways of strengthening your body's natural defences.

The suggestions offered will in no way interfere with any medical treatment you may be having. They are not intended to replace such therapy. Because they are perfectly natural, they will complement, as well as enhance, whatever regimen you may be following for a particular health problem.

There is growing awareness that every departure from good health – from allergies to AIDS – comes under the influence of the immune system and that this system *can* be cared for through natural methods and fortified against attacks from potentially destructive organisms.

This book provides an introduction to your body's natural defence system: the components of which it is made up, factors influencing its harmonious operation and strategies for buttressing it against enemy agents. Armed with this knowledge, you will see your body in a new light and respect it as perhaps never before. You will be equipped to choose and use with wisdom the tools best suited to help the system work optimally for you. You will be better prepared for boosting your natural immune power.

1 MEET YOUR BODY'S DEFENCE AGENTS

Your immune system is part of your body's natural protection against an environment that constantly threatens your well-being.

Your body – your personal terrain – is like a country that has not only an army but also a navy and an air force to defend it. But it possesses a much more marvellous defence system: one that is unequalled by any army devised by humans; one composed of diverse, highly-specialized components superbly designed and programmed to carry out exceedingly sophisticated functions.

The body's defence agents are neither randomly scattered nor concentrated in a single area. They are, on the contrary, organized into admirably coordinated units which are positioned at highly strategic key points. Moreover, in the healthy body they are constantly reinforced by new recruits that are efficiently trained to perform their very specialized duties.

Foreign Agents

The environmental factors that threaten our well-being may be divided into two broad categories: (1) physical and chemical and (2) microorganisms. Heat, cold and pollutants fall into the first category. In the second come bacteria (sing. *bacterium*), viruses and fungi (sing. *fungus*). Some of these live in harmony with you, the host, as part of the body's normal flora (literally, plant life). Examples are the 'germs' that colonize the skin's surface and actually discourage the growth of other, potentially dangerous organisms, and the colon bacilli that inhabit the intestines and are thought, among other functions, to contribute to the synthesis of B vitamins.

Those microbes that are not part of this resident population are collectively known as antigens. They can enter the body in a number of ways, such as through breaks in the skin caused by scrapes, cuts, punctures, burns or eruptions and can cause varying degrees of dysfunction.

First Line of Defence

Certain mechanical barriers form the body's first line of defence against foreign agents that are alert and ready to invade. They include epithelial (outer skin-layer) surfaces, which usually prevent penetration by large molecules, and mucous fluids of natural body openings such as the eyes, nose, mouth, opening to the bladder (urethra), anus and vagina. These fluids (mucus) consist of proteins, salts, water, epithelial cells and leucocytes (white blood cells) about which more information will be given later. Their acidity and immunological characteristics provide the body with remarkable protection.

Although some poisons can be absorbed through the skin, most invading foreign agents (e.g. bacteria or viruses) are unable to advance past this front line of natural defences if the body is healthy.

Skin's protective role

Skin is more than just a covering: it is the body's interface with an external environment teeming with potentially dangerous microorganisms. It is your largest organ, representing about 15 per cent of your body weight and measuring approximately 21 square feet or 2 square metres. It is also an active participant in the workings of the immune system.

The skin's surface is never sterile. It is colonized by flora which include a variety of germs. There is substantial evidence that these resident organisms, far from being harmful, actually discourage the growth of other, potentially dangerous ones. Moreover, the skin's uppermost layer is coated with a fatty film that has bactericidal properties, that is, it can destroy harmful organisms. On this surface, too, dying cells combine with chemicals and sweat to kill bacteria before they can injure the body.

Exciting research done by Richard L. Edelson and colleagues at the US National Institutes of Health supports the probability that the skin may be an integral component of the human immune system. Edelson and fellow researchers discovered certain specialized skin cells that have interacting roles in response to invasion by foreign organisms. Their findings led them to the conclusion that a significant population of T-cells must be resident in the skin. (T-cells are a variety of white blood cells, the immune system's principal warriors. You will be reading a great deal about these later.)

Edelson then began to consider an exciting possibility: might not the skin, like the thymus gland, be a site where some T-cells mature? (The thymus, about which you will read more later, is the gland from which T-cells obtain their name, and where they are processed for immunological characteristics.)

The subsequent discovery that a major T-cell population existed in human skin suggested that skin might have functions comparable with the thymus gland – an implication you'll better appreciate as you read on.

A further clue to the link between skin and thymus appeared under the electron microscope. Some thymic epithelial cells possess distinctive granular structures seemingly identical with those seen in *keratinocytes*, the major cells of the epidermis, or outer layer of skin. (Keratinocytes synthesize keratin, an extremely tough substance, the primary structural protein of the skin's outer coat.)

Further experiments at Columbia University College of Physicians and Surgeons, in conjunction with research at Memorial Sloan-Kettering Cancer Institute, seemed to confirm that keratinocytes were responsible for the skin's impact on T-cell maturation. Understandably, this discovery produced a great deal of astonishment because it was previously thought that keratinocytes were primarily responsible for producing keratin. Now it appeared that they could play an important part in T-cell biology.

Moreover, researcher Tung Tien-Sun and his colleagues at New York University Medical Center examined epithelial cells from human and rodent thymus glands, and were able to identify quantities of this skin cell protein (keratin). These findings, of course, strengthened the case for a skin-thymus connection.

To summarize: exciting similarities have been found between the epithelial cells of the thymus gland and those of the skin. These discoveries are compelling evidence in favour of skin as an integral part of the human immune system.

Since skin is evidently of major importance to an optimally functioning immune system, its care becomes much more than mere cosmetic concern. (I have given a wealth of information on the structure and function of skin, as well as all aspects of care, in my book *Silky*,

Smooth and Strong, see Bibliography for details.)

Other mechanical barriers

Lung tissue provides another mechanical barrier to would-be invading organisms, but because this is only a thin one, the body compensates by providing *cilia*. These are hair-like processes projecting from epithelial cells, such as those forming the lining of the bronchi (branches of the windpipe). Cilia propel mucus, pus and dust particles upwards. They are associated with the *cough reflex*, which comes into play in response to certain irritants. Noteworthy is the fact that smoking damages the cilia, thus impairing the body's defences against disease.

As added reinforcement, all epithelial tissues produce secretions, such as *mucin*, a sugar-protein substance found in mucus, which is found in various parts of the body and in body fluids, including saliva, bile, eye secretions and skin. Also highly bactericidal is *hydrochloric acid*, secreted by the stomach, while *digestive enzymes* can eliminate some organisms. (Enzymes are complex proteins capable of inducing chemical changes in other substances without being changed themselves.)

Second Line of Defence

Your body's second line of defence against foreign agents is what is technically known as *phagocytosis*. From Greek *phagein*, to eat, and *kytos*, cell, it literally means ingestion and digestion of bacteria and particles by phagocytes. *Phagocytes* are white blood cells which have the ability to ingest and destroy foreign matter. They are of two classes: *macrophages* and *microphages*. Macrophages are large cells that engulf and ingest dead tissues and cells. They are the first white blood cells to challenge invading organisms. If they cannot overpower the enemy, they promptly signal for reinforcements, and when these arrive they work with them in more complex fashion to fight infection and cancer. Microphages swallow and digest bacteria. Phagocytosis, or 'cell eating', is thought to provide transitory protection for the body until the immune system is adequately activated.

According to the famous playwright George Bernard Shaw in his play *The Doctor's Dilemma*, there is only one scientific treatment for all diseases, and that is to stimulate the phagocytes – the 'cell eaters' – to devour and destroy all disease germs!

When a microorganism, usually a protein, penetrates the body's surface defences, it activates a series of mechanisms. The most important of these are phagocytosis and immunity (protection from disease) reactions associated with the so-called reticuloendothelial system (RES).

The RES, or more accurately the Tissue Macrophage System, is a term applied to those cells scattered throughout the body which have the power to ingest, or phagocytose, particulate matter such as bacteria and colloidal particles. They differ in appearance and name according to their location in various tissues. For instance, they are called *Kupffer cells* in the liver, *tissue macrophages* in the spleen and bone marrow and *microglia* in the brain. These types are known as fixed reticuloendothelium cells but, under certain conditions (e.g. inflammation), they may become actively motile, or wandering. RES, then, is the name given collectively to the combination of fixed tissue macrophages and mobile macrophages.

Diseases of the RES include Hodgkin's Disease, a disorder of unknown cause, in which there is enlargement of lymphoid tissue, spleen and liver, with invasion of other tissues.

According to Dr Ridgeon in Shaw's *The Doctor's Dilemma*, the phagocytes won't eat microbes unless they are 'nicely buttered' with *opsonin*. Opsonin is a substance in blood which acts upon microorganisms and other cells to facilitate phagocytosis.

Third Line of Defence

The immune system, the body's chief specific defence system, represents your third line of protection against a hostile environment. Its action is sometimes described as resistance against 'non-self' substances (invaders) as opposed to 'self' substances (your own healthy cells). It is made up of specialized organs and cells and is under the overall supervision of the brain, a fact worth remembering.

As you read about this system, you will encounter a number of technical words and terms. Don't let them intimidate you. Make the effort to become acquainted with them. They will be explained in the text, as well as in the glossary at the end of the book. Once you understand the components of the system and how they work together, you will better be able to care for it intelligently and so increase your chances of attaining and/or maintaining the best possible health. If illness strikes, you will have paved the way toward recovery.

Cellular components of the immune system

The various parts of the immune system are so organized and interrelated that they can, and usually do, work with amazing synchronization and flexibility.

The white blood cells

Chief among the system's fighting forces are the white blood cells (WBCs), or *leucocytes* (also spelled 'leukocytes'), from Greek *leukos*, white, and *kytos*, cell. They are scavenger cells, and a key part of the body's protective system against invasion by foreign organisms. They are formed partly in bone marrow, partly in lymph tissue, but after formation are conveyed in the blood to different parts of the body, as required. So important are they that leucocyte studies, that is, WBC counts and WBC differential counts, help doctors and nurses to evaluate the strength of the immune system.

There are five types of WBCs, each performing a specialized protective function. These are, in turn, classified as either *granulocytes* (because of granules in the cytoplasm) or *agranulocytes* (because it was once thought that granules were absent from their cytoplasm). The former include neutrophils, eosinophils and basophils and, because of their multi-lobar nuclei, are also known as polymorphonuclear leucocytes, or polys. They are formed in the bone marrow and are markedly phagocytic. The latter have only one nucleus (mononuclear leucocytes) and include lymphocytes and monocytes.

Neutrophils, the most abundant of the WBCs, albeit rather short lived, are the first to arrive at a site of infection. When an infection is severe, the demand for neutrophils is so great that immature neutrophils (called bands, or stab cells) are released into the blood-stream from the bone marrow. This release is called a 'shift to the left' and is highly indicative of infection. On the other hand, when there is an increase of mature cells, it is known as a 'shift to the right'. This is seen, for example, in allergies and burns or in a myocardial infarction (heart attack).

Eosinophils fight allergies such as asthma as well as parasitic infections. They increase during the healing stage of inflammations and are very active in the later stages.

Basophils are released in chronic inflammations and in the healing stages. They help fight blood diseases and certain abnormalities of the bone marrow and spinal cord.

Lymphocytes are formed in the lymph nodes and help combat viral infections. Unlike the granulocytes, however, they are not phagocytic. They appear in chronic inflammation and in the early and late stages of the inflammatory process. You will be reading a great deal more about these WBCs, which are considered the chief fighting component of the immune system, and of which there are about a trillion in the healthy human adult.

Monocytes are formed from cells of the capillaries (minute blood vessels) of various organs, perhaps principally the spleen and bone marrow. They prepare tissues for healing, and fight chronic infection by ridding the body of damaged and dead cells.

WBC counts

The normal adult has between 4,300 and 10,000 WBCs in a cubic millimetre (cu. mm) of blood. This represents his or her total number of circulating WBCs. A leucocyte count is usually done, for example, before a surgical operation if an infection is suspected. A count may also be taken after surgery to determine the development or otherwise of wound infection.

A WBC count greater than 10,000/cu. mm (*leucocytosis*) suggests acute bacterial infection or inflammation. It could also occur in haemorrhage, tissue injury, circulatory or malignant disease or in persons using certain drugs such as quinine, lithium, phenylbutazone or erythromycin.

A lowered WBC count (below 4,000/cu. mm) is called *leucopenia*. It is seen in viral infections, in bone marrow depression caused by heavy metals, in alcoholism and diabetes and in individuals using such medications as antibiotics or cancer chemotherapeutic agents.

WBC differential counts

WBC and WBC differential counts are usually used together. The differential count reveals percentages of the five types of WBCs just described. Since leucocytosis generally results from an increase in only one type of WBC, the differential count is useful in pinpointing the probable causes of an underlying problem. For instance, if the differential count shows that the leucocytosis is a result of an increase in lymphocytes, the cause may be infectious mononucleosis (glandular fever) or whooping cough, while in lymphatic leukaemia lymphocytes may increase to as much as 90 per cent.

The differential count also indicates the maturity of the cells and the degree of shift to the left or right. It therefore furnishes specific information about the stage and seriousness of a disease as well as the body's ability to conquer it.

Here is a short table of WBC differentials:

Neutrophils	50% – 70%
Eosinophils	1% – 4%
Basophils	0.5% – 1%
Lymphocytes	20% – 40%
Monocytes	2% – 6%

Laboratory results show differentials as percentages of the WBC count. To interpret them, simply multiply each percentage by the WBC count.

One further piece of information on WBCs is worth noting. All are manufactured by a particular cell known as a *stem cell*, located in bone marrow, principally that of the breast bone (sternum), the crest of the hip bones and the long upper bones of the arms and legs.

More about lymphocytes

If the macrophages – part of the body's second line of defence – fail to overpower invading foreign agents, they quickly signal the lymphocytes, by chemical and electrical means, to initiate a more sophisticated form of combat.

Lymphocytes are of two types: T-cells and B-cells. Both are derived from bone-marrow stem cells, but the stem cells that produce T-cells have passed through the thymus gland (more on this later), whereas those that produce B-cells have not.

T-cells

T-cells (or T-lymphocytes) are lymphocytes that have been conditioned by the thymus gland (thymus-dependent cells), hence their name. They are highly specialized lymphocytes and play a major role in the body's defence against fungi, viruses and some bacteria such as those responsible for tuberculosis. They also attack tumours and transplanted cells. They represent the body's cellular, or *cell-mediated immunity*, and regulate the activity of the immune system as a whole.

Within the class of T-cells are additional subdivisions, each concerned with a specialized immune role.

Helper T-cells (or inducer cells) are those T-lymphocytes which, when stimulated by antigen, promote the differentiation of B-cells and other T-lymphocytes. They are also involved in delayed hypersensitivity reactions by secreting factors (lymphokines) in response to antigenic stimulation, which in turn activate macrophages.

Suppressor T-cells form a second class of T-lymphocytes. They recognize antigen or other lymphoid cells, but rather than boost immune response, they inhibit it.

Helper and suppressor T-cells work closely together to maintain a healthy, albeit delicate, balance in the immune response. They may be thought of as 'switch' cells, turning immune reactions on or off. For example, helper T-cells may influence B-cells (to be explained shortly) to respond to the presence of foreign substances, or they may stimulate other T-cells into action. Suppressor T-cells, by contrast, 'turn off' certain cell activities. For instance, they may inhibit the activity of B-cells or of helper T-cells.

Why are there two opposing forms of T-cells? Without the regulatory capacity of the suppressor cells, the immune response would continue, unchecked, and the attack against invaders would progress to an assault on the body's own healthy tissues. The consequences would be fatal.

In health, the ratio of helper T-cells to suppressor T-cells is approximately 1.8:1. Ratios that are substantially higher or lower signal impaired immunity. AIDS victims, for example, have a ratio of 1:1 or less, an indication of serious malfunction, in which the suppressor cells actually destroy the body's immunity. In systemic lupus erythematosus (SLE), there is a ratio of about 1.51 (helper T-cells): 1 (suppressor T-cells).

Cytotoxic T-lymphocytes compose the third class of T-lymphocytes. Upon appropriate stimulation, they can bind directly to agents that threaten the health of the body and kill them.

There are, as well, other lymphoid cells with surface markers not characteristic of either B- or T-cells. Such cells, frequently classified as 'null cells', include two functionally important groups: *killer* (K) *cells* and *natural killer* (NK) *cells*.

K-cells bind and lyse (literally, dissolve) antibody-coated cells in a reaction known as antibody-dependent cell-mediated cytotoxicity

(ADCC). K-cells are different from cytotoxic T-lymphocytes in that they do not depend upon previous immunization and do not require antibody as a co-factor.

NK-cells, which are also not induced by overt immunization, are capable of destroying blood cells and tumours.

B-cells

B-cells are lymphocytes which take their name from an area in the intestines through which certain WBCs pass. This area has been identified in chickens (it is known as the *avian bursa*) though not in humans. In humans, B-cells arise in the bone marrow (bone marrow-dependent cells) and are vital in the body's defence against pus-producing bacteria. When stimulated, they divide to produce *plasma cells* and *memory cells* (more on this shortly). Plasma cells manufacture protein molecules called *antibodies* which bind bacteria and viruses and either neutralize them or make them vulnerable to attack by immune cells. Antibody is generated when foreign agents (*antigens*) invade the body. These various substances provide *humoral immunity* (humoral pertains to body fluids or substances contained in them).

Antigens and antibodies

The first *antigen* was unwittingly discovered by an eighteenth-century English milkmaid. It was she who brought to the attention of Edward Jenner, a Gloucestershire doctor, that milkmaids who had caught cowpox (vaccinia) from a member of her herd never subsequently contracted the much more serious smallpox.

Jenner was impressed. He injected human beings with fluid drawn from cowpox sores (inoculation). This produced mild discomfort only, but conferred on the subjects protection from the potentially lethal related disorder – smallpox.

Despite Jenner's successes, immunity research lay dormant for a century because this was an age when no one knew the true nature of infection. Notwithstanding, the work of this British doctor was so important that we now label all immunization procedures as *vaccination* in recognition of Jenner's pioneering work (see also Chapter 2).

The first vaccine contained vaccinia (cowpox) virus, although Jenner was unaware of it. Today, vaccines contain a variety of different molecules which provoke the appearance of *antibodies*. Because they generate antibody production, therefore, we call these molecules *antigens*.

More on antibodies

On Christmas Eve of 1891, a little German girl lay dying of an acute infectious disease known as diphtheria. In a bold and unprecedented experiment, the renowned German scientist E.A. von Behring did something that saved the child's life and earned him, ten years later, the first Nobel prize in medicine.

Experimenting with animals in the previous year, von Behring and a colleague had discovered substances called *antikörper* in the blood-stream after infections, and had found that these could neutralize poisons. They had inoculated a sheep with diphtheria antigen, and now von Behring instructed the child's physician to inject some of the sheep's serum (fluid portion of a blood clot) into the terminally-ill child. Within hours the child began to revive.

This transfer of antibodies made by one person or animal to the blood-stream of another is known as *passive immunity* (see also Chapter 2).

Types of antibodies

All antibodies are found in the globulin fraction of blood proteins and are therefore referred to as *immunoglobulins* (Ig). There are five basic classes: IgG, IgA, IgM, IgD and IgE.

IgG is the major Ig in the blood. It is able to squeeze between cells and enter tissue spaces where it neutralizes harmful microorganisms. It is this ability that permits it to pass through the placenta and thus provide protection for the foetus. It also passes into the mother's milk and thence to the breast-fed baby.

IgA is found in large quantities in the blood-stream and is concentrated in body fluids such as saliva and tears, as well as in the mucous secretions of the respiratory (breathing) and gastrointestinal (stomach and intestines) tracts, thereby giving immunity to body entrances. It also appears in breast milk and is thus transmitted to the nursing infant. Here we have a superb example of the specificity of the immune system's components. Although IgAs guard body entrances, those at each orifice have their own special characteristics for dealing most effectively with the particular organisms most likely to be attracted to that particular entrance.

IgM, the largest of the antibodies, tends to remain in the blood where it effectively kills bacteria.

By analysing the number of IgM and IgG antibodies, doctors can often determine the stage to which a disease has progressed. If there are more IgMs than IgGs, the disease is in an early stage; if there are more IgGs, it is in a later stage.

IgD is currently the subject of research to determine its real role. It is known, however, that it is almost exclusively found in cell membranes and regulates the behaviour of the cell. It is also found on the surface of some T-cells and helps them to lock on to antigens.

IgE binds to the surface of specialized immune cells in the skin (mast cells). It releases *histamine* and summons lymphocytes and polys to do battle with invading parasites. This is the antibody implicated in allergic reactions such as hay fever, hives and asthma.

Complement

This is the name coined by Paul Ehrlich in 1900 for the assorted serum protein components that play an integral role in the immune process. They interact independently with cell-bound antibodies to enhance lysis of bacteria, thus complementing the complexing of antibody to cellular antigens. In this way they enhance reactions initiated by antigen-antibody complexes and therefore play a crucial role in resistance to infections.

Characteristics of the Immune System

Immunologic responses are, according to the editors of *Clinical Immunology*, classically divided into those mediated by humoral antibodies and those mediated by cells. (These terms have already been explained in the sections dealing with B-cells and T-cells respectively.) In each case, the hallmark of the immune system is its specificity.

Specificity

This means that the immune system has the ability to recognize an antigen as foreign and to respond by synthesizing specific Igs (immunoglobulins, or antibodies). Thus, a chickenpox antibody will attack an invading chickenpox virus but not, say, an invading mumps or influenza virus. Each microscopic invader has its own antigenic characteristics, and each elicits a specific antibody response. The immune system is able to produce millions of different kinds of antibodies, each reacting to a particular antigen. This brings us to another characteristic of this truly amazing system: memory.

Memory

Memory is the system's ability to remember its enemies. When a B-cell is stimulated, it divides to produce *plasma cells* and *memory cells*. The latter are cells that retain the ability to secrete antibodies to the same antigen which previously invaded the body. Once an antibody has been produced in response to an invading antigen, it will again, rapidly, make quantities of identical antibodies should the same antigen ever enter the body in future. If, for instance, you have had measles, you will be immune to, or protected against, measles for many years, perhaps forever. The degree of immunity depends on the kind and amount of an antigen and how it entered the body. This capacity for immunologic memory, like that of antigen recognition, is fundamental to the specific nature of the immune response.

Self-recognition

This is the third trait characterizing the specificity of the normal immune system. It is the ability to differentiate between 'self' and 'non-self' substances, thus affording protection to the body against self-destruction. In health, the WBCs will track down and destroy all invaders but will not harm those structures belonging to the host. (*Host* is defined as the organism from which a parasite obtains its nourishment. The host is you. The parasite is any organism that lives within, upon, or at the expense of the host without contributing to the host's survival. Antigens may be considered parasites.)

Immune surveillance

There is yet another characteristic of the immune system, that of *immune surveillance*. As mentioned earlier, the immune system is capable of distinguishing self from non-self substances. Tumours are transformed cells bearing tumour-associated (non-self) antigens. The immune system therefore maintains surveillance and rejects malignant cells as they appear.

Formerly, T-cell immunity was believed to mediate this surveillance mechanism. The evidence to support this view has weakened, whereas the possible role of natural immunity (see Chapter 2) is receiving increased attention.

In support of the immune surveillance theory is the fact that animals whose immune systems are suppressed are more vulnerable to cancer-causing viruses. Humans, too, whose immune system is impaired, have shown a tendency to tumour development. In this connection, I recall reading in a drug reference book that physicians prescribing the drug Imuran, which is an immunosuppressive agent, should be aware that it could increase the risk of tumours. (This drug is sometimes used to treat rheumatoid arthritis in adult patients. It is also known as Azathioprine.)

Other Components of the Immune System

Apart from cellular components which are transported in body fluids, there are other structures involved in the human immune system. These include the bone marrow, the thymus gland, the lymphatic system, the spleen, tonsils and adenoids, Peyer's patches and, some scientists suspect, the appendix as well. All are closely interrelated with other body systems, a fact worth bearing in mind.

Bone marrow
Bone marrow is the soft tissue that fills up the hollow spaces in bones. It is found in the insides of long bones (such as those of the thighs), although these contain mainly fat. More important are the hollows and crevices in the extremities of such bones, as well as in the pelvis and vertebrae (bones of the spine).

Marrow may account for as much as 5 per cent of adult body weight. There are two types: yellow and red. The former is thought to have little to do with blood formation. The latter, found in the ends of long bones and those of the spine and pelvis, is coloured red. G.J.V. Nossal has referred to bone marrow as the source of raw recruits for immune battles, as well as a school for lymphocytes, where these cells are produced, processed and exported. Gina Kolata, writing in the September 1987 issue of *Discover*, likens bone marrow to a massive factory that makes all the machinery a country needs to defend itself: tanks and bombers, trucks to carry supplies to the front and ambulances to treat and transport the wounded. Bone marrow also turns out red cells, granulocytes, monocytes and platelets (involved in blood clotting).

The thymus gland

The thymus gland, sometimes called the sweetbread, is an organ that lies in the chest cavity, just beneath the breast bone, in front of and above the heart. It consists of two flattened, symmetrical lobes which are further subdivided into tinier ones (lobules). Each lobule is composed of a cortex (outer portion) and a medulla (inner part). The cortex is made up of dense lymphoid tissue containing a great many cells called *thymocytes*. The cortex, in fact, contains over 98 per cent of these cells, which are a type of lymphocyte.

On average, the thymus weighs 13 grams at birth. It grows rapidly during the first two years of life, attaining a weight of about 30 grams at puberty. Thereafter, it gradually decreases in size and weight, and in extreme age may be barely recognizable.

The thymus is important in early life for the development and maturation of cell-mediated immunological functions.

It is interesting to note that the thymus, *at any age*, will shrink very rapidly if an individual is seriously ill or has been subjected to great stress.

It now seems clear that this structure plays a vital role in immunity. First, it is the original source of lymphocytes at birth. Soon afterwards, it begins to secrete a hormone that stimulates lymphocytes to develop into plasma cells (these synthesize antibodies).

According to G.J.V. Nossal, so little was known about this organ even as recently as the 1950s that medical books devoted a mere half-page to it. By the mid-1960s, however, so much information had been amassed that international scientific symposia on it were being held and massive books published.

We know more about the thymus in mice than in humans through experiments by researchers such as Dr J.F.A.P. Miller at the Chester Beatty Research Institute in London. Findings indicate that although the thymus itself does not form antibodies, it nevertheless plays a crucial part in the development of the immune system.

G.J.V. Nossal refers to the thymus as a military training school as well as a factory for T-cells. In adult life it produces new T-cells and exports them to other parts of the body, at least until it atrophies (wastes away) late in life. Thus, the main function of the thymus seems to be the production and export of immunologically competent T-lymphocytes (T-cells) to other body structures, notably the spleen and lymph nodes.

The importance of the thymus for normal development of a competent immune system (immunocompetence) was recognized in the 1960s, following experiments with mice, rabbits and chickens. When their thymus gland was removed shortly after birth, their immune response became impaired later in life. In mice, immunocompetence could be restored by grafting back the thymus into the animals.

In *Medical Microbiology*, edited by Samuel Baron (see Bibliography), the thymus has been described as an epithelial organ. Epithelial refers to epithelium, the layer of cells forming the epidermis, or outer layer, of skin. Here we again have a glimpse of the similarity between the thymus gland and the skin, which was discussed earlier in this chapter. Both structures are of immense immunological importance.

The lymphatic system

This system is composed of structures involved in conveying lymph from the tissues to the blood-stream, and includes lymphatic vessels and lymph nodes. It plays a very important role in protecting the body from bacterial invasion.

The system is intimately connected with the blood circulation. When blood leaves the heart and is returned to it through blood vessels, a substantial part of it oozes out of the wall of tiny vessels known as capillaries, to bathe body cells and tissues. This fluid is called *lymph*. It is collected and redirected to the blood-stream by the lymphatic system.

Lymph is similar to plasma, the liquid part of blood, except that it contains less protein. Unlike plasma, however, it does not contain red blood cells. The cells present in lymph are chiefly lymphocytes, of which you have already read a great deal.

Lymph provides oxygen and other nourishment to the cells and eliminates waste matter. In passing from any part of the body, it must traverse regional lymph nodes for filtering.

Although the lymphatic system has no pumping mechanism such as the heart does, lymph is propelled by the contraction of smooth muscle in the walls of the lymphatic vessels and other internal structures, aided by that of muscles on the outside of the body and by the pulsation of large blood vessels. The breathing process also contributes to the effective flow of lymph.

Lymphatic vessels are thin-walled conduits by which lymph is transported from the tissues. They contain paired valves which give them a beaded appearance.

Lymph nodes are small, oval, bean-shaped bodies that vary in size from that of a pinhead to that of an almond. They are widely-distributed complicated filters found studded along the course of the lymphatic vessels, and they are mostly clustered in groups where they drain those particular areas of the body. They represent the most important source of antibodies in humans. In addition to producing lymphocytes, lymph nodes serve as filtration plants.

While filtering bacteria from the lymph stream, these nodes prevent infection from spreading elsewhere. In so doing, however, they themselves become inflamed (lymph adenitis). When there is infection in almost any part of the body, lymph nodes in that region will enlarge and there will be tenderness.

The spleen

The spleen is a dark purplish organ located in the abdomen, just under the left set of ribs. It lies near the stomach, left kidney, pancreas and part of the large intestine. It consists of a network of connective and lymphoid tissues, and contains an abundance of red blood cells.

The functions of the spleen are essentially threefold: blood formation, blood storage and blood filtration. In a human embryo, the spleen is the site of formation of all types of blood cells. In the adult, however, it is a factory that turns out red cells, granulocytes and small platelets which help with blood clotting. The smooth muscle and elastic tissue fibres of which the spleen is composed enable it to contract and discharge these blood cells into the circulation. As a filter, the spleen is instrumental in removing from the circulation bacteria and particulate matter, especially worn-out red blood cells.

Peyer's patches

Peyer's patches (named after the Swiss anatomist, Conrad Peyer) describe groups of lymph nodules embedded mainly in the small intestine, at its junction with the large intestine.

Peyer's patches are another defence mechanism against intestinal invaders, and their content of cells specialized for IgA production is very high indeed.

Tonsils

The tonsils are two almond-shaped structures located one on each side of the opening between mouth and throat. They are composed of lymphoid tissue and are liberally supplied with lymphocytes. They act as a filter to protect the body from bacterial invasion, and aid as well in the formation of WBCs.

Adenoids

Adenoids are lymphatic tissue forming a prominence behind the nostrils.

Appendix

The appendix is a worm-like structure attached to the beginning portion of the large intestine. It contains a substantial amount of lymphoid tissue with functions similar to those of the tonsils.

From the foregoing, you will now probably more fully appreciate how diversified the body's defences really are. They are not confined to a single cell or tissue or organ, nor are they merely the sum of their parts. They are much more than that. They are a superbly organized system with a wide range of resources readily available to deal with innumerable antigenic challenges. The body's defence forces are a fascinating study in intricacy, flexibility and synchronization.

2 HOW THE SYSTEM WORKS

Skin is part of our armour against the invasion of agents foreign to our body. When we are healthy it is usually a remarkably effective shield, permitting no bacterium, virus or other microbe to penetrate it. Other components of the body's first line of defence against interlopers are natural openings such as the mouth, nose, vagina and anus. These orifices are protected by special substances which are inimical to would-be intruders.

Sometimes, however, skin is injured and the broken surface becomes a welcome site of entry for watchful alien organisms. Even when skin remains intact, these foreigners can gain access to the body through the apertures mentioned above, if circumstances are favourable.

A Call to Arms

The following is a simplified scenario of an internal battle against a rhinovirus that has penetrated the body's defences. This is one of about 200 different viruses that cause colds.

Entering the body through the mucous membranes of nose, throat or eyes, the rhinovirus adheres to the surface of its host's cell, penetrates its membrane and injects it with its own genetic material.

Now ensconced within the target cell, the virus's genetic information stimulates production of hundreds of new virus particles, all eager to launch an attack on other cells in the vicinity. They can wreak serious damage if unchecked, but the threatened cells release a powerful chemical called *interferon* which, as the name suggests, literally interferes with the replication of viruses, thus preventing the spread of infection and protecting healthy cells.

While this internal battle is raging, the familiar signs and symptoms of a cold appear: sore throat, stuffy nose, watering eyes, coughing, sneezing, loss of appetite, etc. These represent the body's response to the viral attack.

In the meantime, the body's white blood cells (WBCs) have begun to communicate with one another. The macrophage on sentry duty at the first line of defence initiates what might be considered a cellular conversation. (You will read more about such conversations which take place between cells of the immune and nervous systems in Chapter 4.) This large cell eater (i.e. the macrophage) incorporates a fragment of the enemy's cell – a 'non-self' marker – into its own cell membrane. Subsequently, it presents this marker, as well as its own 'self' marker, to nearby T-cells. This presentation tells the T-cells that the macrophage is a trustworthy part of the defence team but that the rhinovirus is the foe.

T-cells, like other lymphocytes, carry receptors which can recognize small portions of antigens known as *epitopes*. These are the result of a unique sequence of amino acids (protein building blocks). They perceive only one particular epitope. When a lymphocyte meets an antigen, receptor and epitope fit snugly together in lock-and-key fashion. It is estimated that in our lifetime we encounter about a million different antigens. We therefore need a million or so different lymphocytes to protect us from assault by antigens, and the healthy body does a marvellous job of providing these.

The T-cell with the receptor that has discerned this particular virus now multiplies. The newly-formed T-cells secrete chemicals called *lymphokines* which summon additional macrophages to join in the combat. One of the lymphokines, known as *interleukin-2*, is secreted by helper T-cells. It increases the activity of other T-cells.

Some T-cells quickly travel by way of the blood-stream to nearby lymph nodes and other lymphoid tissue to spread news of the invasion. On arriving at their destination, they contact B-cells and killer T-cells (K-cells) which are programmed to react to the rhinovirus. K-cells then promptly depart for the battlefield where infection rages. They fasten their receptors to the enemy cells and chemically destroy them. They then proceed to do likewise to other infected cells.

While these events are taking place, activated B-cells in the lymph nodes are turning out plasma cells which will produce antibodies to the particular virus that has breached the body's security. B-cells will produce antibodies only upon T-cell stimulation, another example of the finely-tuned collaboration and synchronization of all components of the immune system.

Some of these antibodies bind with the viruses and prevent them from latching on to healthy body cells. Others serve to mark the infected cells so that they will be recognized and destroyed by phagocytes. Once activated, these cell eaters sweep across the site of infection engulfing and eliminating the debris which is an inevitable result of battle.

As the WBCs and antibodies are on the point of victory over the enemy virus, suppressor T-cells give them the signal to restrain their efforts. As this occurs, your cold symptoms abate. Your appetite improves and you can again breathe and swallow more easily than when the infecting agent first gained access to your body.

Following this immune battle (and others like it) special lymphocytes called *memory cells* survive and remember, sometimes for decades, the particular virus that assaulted the body. Woe to that specific antigen should it ever reappear! The memory cells will rapidly and vigorously respond to the intrusion, usually destroying the trespasser before it can reproduce and cause disease.

The Inflammatory Response

Whenever there is damage to tissues, either internally or externally, certain changes take place to help the body restore itself to normal function. These are known as the inflammatory response. We can sometimes see evidence of this response when there is a wound to the skin.

Just imagine that you have had an accident and have cut your leg. Here is a simplified version of a sequence of events that takes place.

At the moment of injury, bacteria on the outer skin layer scurry to the inner skin layers through this convenient opening. A macrophage on sentinel duty near the wound will usually engulf the invading organisms. More often, however, the bacteria will replicate and injure nearby body cells. These damaged cells then secrete a variety of chemicals including a powerful one called *histamine*. In response, small blood vessels (capillaries) in the area dilate (widen) allowing an increased flow of blood and causing the wound to redden and feel warm, that is, to become inflamed.

Gaps form between the cells lining the walls of the blood vessels and through them ooze blood serum loaded with proteins and other large molecules. As fluid accumulates in the tissues, swelling becomes apparent. This exerts increased pressure on nerve endings and tenderness and pain ensue. All these symptoms lead to impaired function of the affected limb.

Within minutes of the infection, neutrophils (see Chapter 1) – the 'advance guard' of the body's cell eaters – arrive on the scene. Each neutrophil, in response to chemical signals, squeezes through the cracks in the blood-vessel walls and heads for the bacteria. A fierce struggle follows.

The enemy microbes eject toxins in an attempt to put the neutrophils and surrounding cells out of commission. But a stubborn neutrophil ensnares a microbe, imprisons it and inactivates and destroys it with the help of microbe-killing agents.

The struggle takes its toll, though. The neutrophil dies both from its own secretions and from those released by the microbe. However, reinforcements continually arrive. These consist not only of neutrophils but also of macrophages, the 'big eaters', which can consume hundreds of bacteria before they die.

As the struggle continues, dead tissue, microbes, cells and other debris may ooze from the skin wound as pus.

With the increased blood flow to the infected part come WBCs to combat the infection as well as to clean up residues and help promote healing. Part of the healing process is a substance called *fibrinogen*, which helps repair the damaged tissue. While reparatory work is being done, the body manufactures special protein substances to help close the wound (or if there isn't one, to regenerate healthy tissue to replace diseased parts). New cells take the place of the old and damaged, and capillaries bud forth from those adjacent to carry essential nutrients required for healing.

When regeneration cannot totally reverse the deleterious effects of infection or injury, the body with its wonderful resources tries to find a solution by way of adaptation. One kind of adaptive response is the 'walling off', or isolation, of unhealthy tissue that cannot be made whole. In this way, the spread of disease is arrested. (Such a process is seen, for example, in tuberculosis of the lungs when, although the body's defence forces have been unable to defeat the infection, they can often confine it to a certain area. The result is a cavity surrounded by a sort of fibrous wall which separates it from healthy adjacent tissue.)

The fever, the swelling, redness, pain and impaired function experienced as a consequence of the injury – signs and symptoms of inflammation – are the body's signals that our inner defence forces are doing battle with unfriendly aliens and making ready for reparation of damage.

When macrophages are confronted by some organisms they produce a substance known as *interleukin-1* which triggers fever. Most people, doctors and nurses included, see a rise in body temperature as a call for antipyretics – drugs such as aspirin – to reduce it to 'normal' as fast as possible. Yet there is evidence that fever actually helps fight infection. It may even increase the production of T-cells. Attempts to lower it artificially may give invading germs a decided advantage and according to Andrew Weil, unless a fever is nearing 105°F in adults (40.5°C), trying to reduce it by using medications is probably unwise.

Most of us, I believe, would not allow body temperature to climb this high without doing something about it. Unfortunately, that 'something' is usually a pharmaceutical agent. As long as a fever is mild and does not persist for more than a few days, however, it may actually be working to our advantage in that it seems to increase the efficiency of the body's infection-fighting forces.

Types of Immunity

Immunity (from Latin *immunitas*) is a state of being protected from a disease, especially an infectious one. It is usually induced by exposure to an antigenic substance which stimulates the production of specific antibodies.

Natural immunity
Natural immunity, also referred to as congenital or innate immunity, is the more or less permanent immunity to disease with which an individual is born. It is the body's capacity to eliminate foreign antigens not previously encountered.

Acquired immunity
Acquired immunity, by contrast, is the body's enhanced capacity to rid itself of foreign antigens to which it has been previously exposed. It results from the development within the body of substances that render a person immune. It may be a consequence of having the disease, or of injection with the infectious organism (vaccination).

Vaccination

Vaccination, which was mentioned briefly in Chapter 1, means inoculation with vaccine to establish resistance to a specific infectious disease.

A *vaccine* is a suspension of infectious agents, and there are four classes:

1. those containing living, attenuated (diluted, weakened, less virulent) infectious organisms. The BCG vaccine, given for tuberculosis, and vaccines for smallpox and yellow fever are examples;
2. those containing infectious agents killed by physical or chemical means. Examples are vaccines to protect humans against typhoid fever, rabies and whooping cough;
3. those containing soluble toxins of microorganisms, such as toxoid used to prevent diphtheria and tetanus;
4. substances extracted from infectious agents, such as those responsible for pneumonia.

Vaccines are used to stimulate development of specific defence mechanisms, which result in more or less permanent protection against a disease. They are administered by injection or in a drink.

After the vaccine is introduced, the body's natural anti-disease brigade (antibodies) immediately responds to the foreign agent and fights it off, without the individual actually becoming ill. As long as the antibodies specific to the disease are present, the individual is protected against that disease.

Passive immunity

Passive immunity is a form of acquired immunity produced by actual injection of serum containing the antibodies into the person to be protected.

Cross immunity

Cross immunity refers to immunity produced by inoculation with an agent (e.g. bacterium or virus) that is different from, but closely related to, the agent causing the disease.

According to the British Columbia Medical Association, although routine vaccination saves lives, prevents mental retardation and physical disability, keeps children in school, saves billions of dollars in health care costs and adds years of productivity to the lives of millions of persons, a perfect, risk-free vaccine does not exist. For example, the MMR vaccine, given for protection against measles, mumps and rubella (German measles), can produce side effects such as a brief skin rash, mildly swollen neck glands and aching and swelling of joints. There can be more serious reaction, such as encephalitis (inflammation of the brain), convulsions or deafness, although these are rare. With the oral polio vaccine, about 1 in 5,000,000 persons develops paralysis, and the DPT vaccine, given against diphtheria, pertussis (whooping cough) and tetanus (lockjaw) may produce, in about 1 in 2,000 children, a high fever, convulsions, abnormal screaming episodes or shock.

The British Columbia Medical Association offers these tips on immunization:

– *Check with your doctor* or public health nurses to ensure that the procedure is necessary.
– Keep accurate, up-to-date records about vaccines received.
– *Before immunization*, be sure that the nurse or doctor knows if you or the child to receive the vaccine:

has an illness more serious than a cold;

has an allergy or sensitivity to the antibiotics polymyxin B, neomycin or streptomycin;

has cancer, leukaemia, lymphoma or haemophilia;

has any disease that lowers the body's resistance to infection;

is taking any medication that lowers the body's resistance to infection, such as cortisone or prednisone, either internally or applied to the skin, or cancer chemotherapy drugs;

is on radiation therapy;

has received gamma globulin (a protein formed in the blood) within the preceding three months;

has a history of arthritis or other joint problems;

has a history of seizures, convulsions or other nervous system disorder;

is allergic or sensitive to eggs;

has had a severe reaction to any previous vaccine.

If you are planning on becoming pregnant, you should wait at least three months after receiving any vaccine.

3 EATING FOR PROTECTION

According to Ashley Montagu, genes, chromosomes, or heredity are not to be seen as marks of fate or predestination. Rather, our genetic constitution, being a labile system, is capable of being influenced and changed to varying degrees. Montagu further states that the genetic code for any trait contains a set of specific instructions, and that the manner in which these will be carried out depends upon the nature of their interaction with other sets of instructions as well as with their environments.

Diet and the Immune System

Applying these observations, made by one of today's most respected anthropologists, to the state of the immune system, little persuasion is needed to appreciate that what we take into the body through the diet can and does affect the body's natural defence forces. Similarly, a deficiency of certain essential nutrients will impair the workings of our natural defence system, for it is largely what we eat that supplies the body with the raw material for building the various components of this system. Nutrients from an adequate, wholesome diet are processed by the digestive system and transmitted to every cell, tissue and organ through the blood circulatory system.

Phenylketonuria (PKU)

This is a disease caused by the body's failure to oxidize phenylalanine (an amino acid, or protein building block) to tyrosine (another animo acid), possibly because of a defective enzyme. This is due to a genetic defect, and the routine testing of newborn babies suggests that about 1 in 8,000 have this condition.

PKU must be detected and treated soon after birth in order to prevent brain damage, and many countries routinely test all week-old babies for the presence of phenylketones in the urine or an excess of phenylalanine in the blood to confirm diagnosis.

Treatment is to restrict protein intake to provide only enough phenylalanine for proper growth, but not enough to promote brain damage. As the child grows older, he or she is able to take special foods free from phenylalanine, and tolerance to the amino acid usually increases so that an ordinary diet may be gradually introduced without adverse effects. This, then, is but one example of how diet can influence 'heredity'.

Montagu's remarks are echoed in *Nutrition Against Aging*. In the Foreword, co-author Michael Weiner has stated that as his nutrition studies advanced, he became more certain that our basic genetic inheritance was aided by what he calls rational principles of living. Good nutrition is an essential component of any healthy lifestyle.

According to Adelle Davis, the substantial increase in a number of serious health disorders is a reflection of the ever-mounting consumption of 'nutritionally barren foods'. These include sweets, soft drinks and similar over-refined products.

Regardless of how busy you are and how little time you seem to have, you owe it to yourself and to those in your care to give priority to the wise selection of wholesome foods and to storage and preparation methods that will conserve the nutrients in these foods. While it is very tempting to give preference to cleverly advertised and attractively packaged foods when you are tired and hungry and short of time, succumbing to these temptations too often could eventually have adverse effects on your health and on the well-being of those for whom you are responsible. Ultimately, you will be paying a far greater price, in terms of lowered resistance to disease, than the cost of those enticing, quick-to-fix non-foods.

Immunology research is making it abundantly clear that we can enhance the functioning of our immune system, and in some instances prevent many problems, through the intelligent application of sound nutrition principles. I shall now present some findings of specific effects certain familiar nutrients have on the functioning of our natural defence forces. Although I have highlighted only a few, it is wise to remember that *all nutrients are important and work together* for the good of the system.

Vitamin A (Retinol)

This fat-soluble nutrient is so crucial to the integrity of the skin that it is sometimes called 'the skin vitamin'. It is also important for healthy mucous membranes and for maintaining the disease-fighting properties of tears, sweat and saliva. All these components are part of our first line of defence against invading organisms (see Chapter 1). An early sign of vitamin A deficiency is damage to the lining of the respiratory, digestive and urogenital tracts.

Its role in the immune system

Vitamin A has been shown to have a potent effect on specific immune system functions. It is capable of stimulating both cell-mediated and humoral immunity. In animal studies, a vitamin A deficiency has led to atrophy of the thymus gland and lymphoid tissue. It has also resulted in a decrease of both B- and T-cells, and a reduction of antibody response to the entry into the body of bacteria, viruses and other infectious agents. In addition, an undersupply of vitamin A in the diet has adversely affected the body's inflammatory response (see Chapter 2).

Experiments with human subjects have demonstrated the value of high (mega) doses of vitamin A after surgery. In one study, patients scheduled for surgical operation were divided into groups. One group was given between 300,000 and 450,000 IU (International Units) of vitamin A daily for one week after surgery. The other group was not. Blood samples were taken from all patients one day before, one day after, and seven days after the operation. The group treated with mega doses of the vitamin showed signs of increased T-cell activity seven days following surgery. The untreated group, however, demonstrated the usual signs of suppressed immune system function associated with anaesthesia and surgery.

Dr Benjamin E. Cohen of Houston, Texas, who has done vitamin A studies for many years, has found the nutrient a very useful immune system booster. In experiments with rodents, Dr Cohen demonstrated that vitamin A could counteract the immunosuppressive effects of steroid drugs. (These are often given to transplant patients to help prevent organ rejection.) Unfortunately, these drugs tend to make the subjects more vulnerable to infection. Dr Cohen found that vitamin A lowered the animals' susceptibility to various bacterial infections. Moreover, used in conjunction with a powerful anti-cancer agent, the vitamin caused the agent to be one hundred times more powerful.

Vitamin A has been shown to have a scavenging effect on *free radicals*, substances that are a by-product of protein, carbohydrate and fat metabolism. Free radicals may be considered 'mischievous molecules'. They are believed to play a part in the ageing process as well as in the development of cancer. The former is associated with a declining immune system, and the latter is regarded as the ultimate failure of the body's defence forces.

In the fight against cancer, vitamin A appears to be one of the most protective nutrients. In both human and animal studies, it has proved valuable in preventing altered cells from turning cancerous. In the Philippines, vitamin A has successfully warded off cancer of the mouth in certain susceptible individuals, and a lack of the nutrient has been linked to cancers of the skin, lungs, prostate gland, bladder, colon and cervix.

According to Dr Paul Gerhard Seeger, both the thymus gland and the spleen enlarge slightly in response to an increased intake of vitamin A, and lymphocytes show a corresponding increase in number. This immune system stimulation is of the utmost importance in the war on cancer because, as mentioned earlier, cancer represents the ultimate breakdown of the system.

Food sources of vitamin A
The best food sources of this highly protective nutrient include:
– fresh vegetables, especially the intensely green and yellow ones such as carrots, sweet potatoes, dandelion leaves, turnip greens, parsley, kale, spinach, broccoli and asparagus (one medium size carrot contains about 10,000 IU of vitamin A);
– fresh fruits, especially cantaloupe melons, apricots, papaya, peaches, mangoes and cherries;
– milk and milk products and fish liver oils.

It is prudent to take vitamin A in both the fat-soluble form and the water-soluble form (beta-carotene), the latter being found in dark green vegetables and yellow-orange fruits and vegetables, such as listed above.

Caution Indiscriminate use of vitamin A can produce toxic symptoms such as yellowing and peeling of the skin, fragile bones and tissue damage.

Vitamin B Complex

This group of vitamins affects all components of the immune system. It heightens antibody response to threats from pathogens (substances or microorganisms capable of producing disease). It helps keep the thymus gland active and maintain the germ-killing ability of the fighter cells as well as the efficiency of cellular immune responses.

The B complex are sometimes called 'the nerve vitamins', and it is interesting that during our pre-natal life, structures that would later become our nervous system, skin and adrenal glands shared a common tissue.

Vitamin B$_1$

Vitamin B$_1$ (*thiamin*), sometimes called 'the morale vitamin', enables body cells to obtain energy from nutrients brought to them through the blood circulation.

Vitamin B$_1$ is mildly immunity enhancing, with less marked effects on the system than some of the other vitamins in the complex. A deficiency of the nutrient can, however, result in decreased size of lymphatic organs, fewer B- and T-cells circulating in the blood and lowered host resistance to infection.

Some signs of thiamin deficiency are muscular weakness, fatigue, loss of appetite, shortness of breath, irritability and swelling of tissues.

The richest sources of this nutrient are Brazil nuts, green leafy vegetables, legumes (dried beans, peas, lentils and peanuts), brewer's yeast, potatoes, rolled oats, sunflower seeds, whole grains and yellow cornmeal. Two tablespoons of brewer's yeast contains approximately 3 milligrams of thiamin; one cup of sunflower seeds yields about 2 milligrams.

Vitamin B$_2$

Vitamin B$_2$ (*riboflavin*), along with other B vitamins, is required to preserve the integrity of mucous membranes, part of the body's first line of defence against the entry of injurious organisms.

Vitamin B$_2$ is also involved in antibody production, and a deficiency is linked to weakened antibody response, reduction in the size of lymphatic structures and a decrease in the number of B- and T-cells circulating in the blood.

Good food sources of riboflavin include almonds, asparagus,

blackstrap molasses, brewer's yeast, broccoli, Brussels sprouts, cauliflower, corn, dark green leafy vegetables, legumes, lima beans, milk and milk products, nuts, wheatgerm, whole grains and wild rice.

Vitamin B₃

Vitamin B₃ (*niacin, nicotinic acid, niacinamide, nicotinamide*) is the anti-pellagra principle of the vitamin B complex. Pellagra is a deficiency disease which affects the skin, mucous membrane, stomach and intestines, as well as the nervous system. It is due to a deficiency in the diet or failure of the body to absorb niacin, and is usually associated with a deficiency of a certain amino acid, such as occurs in a high-corn diet. Pellagra may also occur as a sequel to gastrointestinal diseases and alcoholism. The specific treatment is supplementation with niacin.

Niacin has been successfully used to treat some cases of systemic lupus erythematosus ('lupus', or SLE). In a fascinating book entitled *The Sun is My Enemy*, Henrietta Aladjem recounts how Dr L. Popoff and his colleagues, who had been engaged in studies on the therapeutic value of nicotinic acid for many years, saw similarities between pellagra and some forms of lupus, those which the Professor described as the pellagroid types.

Professor Popoff had good results at his clinic when he treated lupus sufferers with anti-malaria drugs combined with nicotinic acid. He had excellent results with those cases that grew worse with the action of sunlight on the body, that is the pellagroid types. (Lupus is an autoimmune disease, in which the body's defence forces literally turn upon the body itself. You can read more about it in Chapter 7.)

Like vitamins A and C, niacin is considered a free-radical scavenger, binding and neutralizing free radicals in a manner not unlike that of the antioxidant vitamin E.

Good food sources of niacin include artichokes, asparagus, brewer's yeast, fish, green leafy vegetables, legumes, nuts, potatoes, seafood, seeds, whole grains and whole grain products.

Vitamin B₅

Vitamin B₅ (*pantothenic acid, calcium pantothenate*) promotes antibody formation and generally enhances immune function. When a vitamin B₅ deficiency was induced in test animals, there was decreased antibody production in response to attack by bacteria and viruses. Vitamin

B_5 deficiency is also implicated in a decrease in size of lymphatic structures.

Vitamin B_5 is regarded as an anti-dermatitis factor, of value in preventing skin inflammations. It is important for healthy skin, our first line of defence against pathogenic invasions.

This nutrient is also important for the normal functioning of the adrenal glands, the secretions of which play a vital role in stress reactions. It has in fact been called 'the anti-stress vitamin'. Stress, as will be appreciated after reading Chapter 5, affects the workings of the immune system. Volunteers in whom pantothenic acid deficiencies were induced became more vulnerable to adrenal gland exhaustion and to various infections than they would normally have been.

Severe allergic reactions have been repeatedly produced in animals deficient in vitamin B_5 by injecting them with foreign substances. In contrast, healthy animals whose diet was adequate in every respect, reacted only mildly or not at all to the same injections.

Good vitamin B_5 sources include avocados, brewer's yeast, broccoli, cabbage, cashew nuts, cauliflower, corn, egg yolk, elderberries, filbert nuts, green vegetables, milk, mushrooms (one cup, cooked, yields about 82 milligrams of pantothenic acid), legumes, pecan nuts, potatoes, salmon, sunflower seeds and unrefined vegetable oils.

Vitamin B_6

Vitamin B_6 (*pyridoxine*) is possibly the most important B vitamin for the maintenance of super natural immune power. An undersupply of this nutrient could cause more serious immune problems than perhaps any other B vitamin deficiency.

As an essential nutrient in the preservation of healthy mucous membranes, pyridoxine is vital for the integrity of the body's first line of defence.

Pyridoxine is important for antibody production, and an undersupply is implicated in diminished response to threats from pathogens. Pyridoxine deficiency also affects cell-mediated immunity and results in fewer circulating T-cells. It brings about atrophy of the thymus gland and may adversely affect the inflammatory response. Pyridoxine also plays a vital role in the metabolism of EFAs (essential fatty acids) which are discussed later in this chapter.

Worthy of note is the fact that pyridoxine and the mineral zinc enhance each other's influence on the functioning of the immune system.

Good sources of this vitamin include apples, asparagus, avocados, bananas, blackstrap molasses, brewer's yeast, buckwheat flour, carrots, eggs, green leafy vegetables such as kale, lettuce and spinach, filbert nuts, fresh fish, peas, prunes, milk, raisins, brown rice, sunflower seeds, tomatoes, wheatgerm, whole grains and whole grain products.

Vitamin B_9

Vitamin B_9 (*folate, folic acid*) has been shown to play a key role in the maturation and differentiation of normal cells. (Differentiation refers to the development of cells in character and form according to their specific function.)

Researcher C.E. Butterworth and his colleagues gave either folic acid or a vitamin C placebo daily for three months to forty-seven women with cervical dysplasia, a condition that is thought to be pre-cancerous. They noted a significant improvement in the group treated with folic acid, compared with the placebo group. The results of this study suggest that folic acid may help prevent pre-cancerous lesions from progressing to cancer, and in some cases even promote a return to normality. (See Potts and Morra, Bibliography.)

Folic acid may also prove useful in regenerating cells adversely affected by drugs used in cancer treatment, such as Methotrexate.

A deficiency of folic acid interferes with the satisfactory formation of WBCs which are the body's disease-fighting cells.

Good food sources of this nutrient include green leafy vegetables, green onions, tempeh (a sort of cheese made from fermented soya beans), wheatgerm and whole grain products.

Vitamin B_{12}

Vitamin B_{12} (*cobalamin, cyanocobalamin*) may have a regulating influence on the immune system according to various studies. One Japanese study, for example, suggests that the vitamin may be important to the proper functioning of both helper and suppressor T-cells. Other studies indicate that a vitamin B_{12} deficiency may cause a decrease of B- and T-cells, impair phagocytosis and diminish antibody response.

Good vitamin B_{12} sources include eggs, milk products, seafood and tempeh.

Antistress Factors

These are vitamin-like substances which have a protective action against the effects of various stressors. Laboratory rats subjected to chemical stressors (e.g. aspirin and cortisone) suffered adverse effects that could not be reversed through supplementation with certain nutrients. When given foods containing the antistress factors, however, the animals were fully protected. These factors also prolonged the survival time of rodents exposed to radiation.

The antistress factors are found in green leafy vegetables, liver, some nutritional yeasts, soy flour from which the oil has not been removed and wheatgerm. Research indicates that ill persons benefit from incorporating as many of these foods as possible into their daily diet.

Vitamin C

Vitamin C (*ascorbate; ascorbic acid*) has long been known to help reduce the severity of minor infections. It is a natural antihistamine, counteracting the action of *histamine*, a chemical substance released when tissues are injured. The runny nose and swollen, inflamed lining of the nasal passages that come with a cold are due to the effects of this chemical. In one experiment, volunteers were asked to inhale histamine. Their levels of airway constriction were measured. The next day, the subjects again received histamine, but this time they were first given 500 milligrams of vitamin C. The result was that the degree of airway constriction (narrowing) was significantly less.

On the first day of a cold, the average concentration of ascorbic acid in the WBCs (white blood cells) drops to about half the level necessary to kill the infecting organisms. To maintain an effective concentration of the vitamin in the WBCs, therefore, vitamin C intake needs to be increased.

Vitamin C has also been used successfully to speed up recovery from more serious infections such as mononucleosis and viral pneumonia. It seems to enhance phagocytosis (the devouring and digestion of germs by phagocytes, see Chapter 1), and to have a beneficial effect on cell-mediated immunity. It also appears to promote the release of anti-viral substances called interferons (see Chapter 2).

Vitamin C may be of substantial value as a supplement to antibiotic and chemotherapeutic agents in the treatment of certain diseases in which the immune system is impaired. In South Africa, a young sister and brother, plagued by frequent infections following drug therapy for an unusual disorder known as chronic granulomatous disease (CGD), finally experienced relief as well as increased weight and growth following vitamin C supplementation.

Blood samples taken from these children following administration of vitamin C showed increase neutrophil activity. Neutrophils, you may recall, are a type of WBC and are the main killer cells responding to bacteria in the body. When vitamin C is undersupplied, the activity of these cells, as well as phagocytosis, can be depressed.

According to Dr Irwin Stone, a pioneer vitamin C researcher, a contributing factor to a vast array of ailments is what he calls 'chronic subclinical scurvy' (CSS). Scurvy is a vitamin C deficiency disease, which can be corrected by increasing the intake of the nutrient through diet or supplementation. Studies have shown that many manifestations of old age, such as dry skin and loss of tissue elasticity, are actually signs of scurvy. Certainly, vitamin C is crucial to the integrity of skin and related tissues, which are an important part of our first line of defence against penetration by potentially noxious agents.

Vitamin C, like vitamin A, is an antioxidant which helps to neutralize free radicals and so prevent carcinogens from forming in the body. (Carcinogens are substances that generate cancer.) In fact, vitamin C is now considered one of the most promising anti-cancer nutrients. Vitamin C deficiency in cancer patients is in fact so striking that it resembles that of scurvy sufferers. Even 300 milligrams of the nutrient administered by mouth or by injection to these patients are so rapidly used up that no trace of it is found in the urine.

Because macrophages play a crucial role in combating malignant tumours, the macrophage-stimulating properties of vitamin C make it useful as a cancer-fighting nutrient. Indeed, this nutrient may provide powerful protection against cervical dysplasia, a condition that predisposes women to cancer of the cervix, according to Dr Sheldon Hendler, author of *The Complete Guide to Anti-Aging Nutrients*. There is also impressive evidence that vitamin C blocks the effects of nitrosamines which are thought to contribute to cancer.

Vitamin C also has an anti-stress function. It lowers the level of *cortisol* in the blood following adrenal gland stimulation. (Cortisol, or hydrocortisone, is one of the corticosteroids secreted by the cortex, or outer portion, of the adrenal glands. It is known to be a powerful immunosuppressant.)

Among the best vitamin C sources are fresh fruits including apricots, blackberries, cantaloupe melons, cherries, elderberries, gooseberries, grapefruit, guavas, honeydew melons, kumquats, lemons, limes, oranges, papayas, rosehips and strawberries; and fresh vegetables including cabbage, dandelion leaves, green and red peppers, kohlrabi, mustard and cress and turnip tops.

Vitamin E

Vitamin E (*tocopherol*) is best known for its antioxidant effects. Like vitamins A and C, it helps protect cells from damage by free radicals. These, you may recall, are produced by oxidation during normal metabolic processes. They can damage cell membranes and the cells' genetic material. They have been implicated in cancerous changes in tissues. Vitamin E may therefore be a very useful protective nutrient in cancer prevention.

When immune battles rage within and macrophages overpower and kill bacteria, free radicals form. The administration of therapeutic doses of vitamin E, along with selenium, helps protect the macrophages from free radicals.

Researchers at the Institute of Food and Nutrition in Warsaw, Poland, found that vitamin E (and vitamin C as well) can decrease the level of free radicals in the blood. One hundred individuals, aged 60 to 100, were given approximately 200 IU of vitamin E or 400 milligrams of vitamin C, or both, every day for one year. The vitamin E alone decreased the free radical level by 26 per cent. The vitamin C decreased it by 13 per cent and vitamins C and E together lowered the level by 25 per cent.

Vitamin E also helps counteract nitrosamines, which are formed by some foods, such as cured and pressed meats.

In animal studies, vitamin E was found to reduce the severity of a number of tumours when applied to the skin or added to food. In other animal experiments, adding vitamin E to the diet significantly boosted the production of antibodies in response to threat from disease-causing agents. When the mineral selenium was given as well, this immune-enhancing effect was even more noticeable. Moreover, when vitamin E intake is increased there is improvement in the bactericidal ability of WBCs, phagocytosis and general resistance to disease. It has also potentiated helper T-cell activity in mice. Like vitamin C, vitamin E may also help lessen the immunosuppressive effect of certain drugs, such as the corticosteroids.

Research has shown that a vitamin E-deficient diet brings about a reduction in the size of lymphatic organs and a decrease in the number of B- and T-cells, as well as weakened inflammatory response and a generally compromised immune system.

Vitamin E is known to strengthen selenium's cancer-fighting antioxidant effects. Alone, the vitamin may prove useful in treating fibrocystic breast disease, a possible precursor of breast cancer.

This remarkable vitamin is considered essential for the optimum functioning of the pituitary, a gland in which it is more concentrated than anywhere else in the body. The health of the pituitary, the 'boss of the repair crew' according to Adelle Davis, is vital to effective stress control. It has been shown that how well animals manage stress depends to a large extent on their ability to produce pituitary (and adrenal) hormones.

Vitamin E may be obtained from almonds and other freshly shelled nuts, broccoli, dark green leafy vegetables, eggs, fresh fruits, legumes, oatmeal, tomatoes, unrefined vegetable oils, wheatgerm, wheatgerm oil and whole grains. (One tablespoon of wheatgerm oil contains about 40 IU vitamin E.)

When oils are refined or hydrogenated, vitamin E is completely lost.

Vitamin E, like other fat-soluble vitamins (vitamins A, D and K) can be toxic if taken in large doses, and some people who take megadoses of this nutrient while on anticoagulants (agents that delay or prevent blood clotting) experience haemorrhage.

EFAs (essential fatty acids)

Essential fatty acids are dietary factors which are sometimes referred to as vitamin F. They are essential because the body must have them to carry out certain vital functions. Because the body cannot make them, though, they have to be furnished by the diet. EFAs are essential, too, because their absence leads to specific deficiency diseases.

There are two series of EFAs: the n6 derived from linoleic acid (LA) and the n3 derived from alpha-linolenic acid, which is the same as linolenic acid, or LNA. The n6 series seems to be more important than the n3, but the latter are now commanding attention in connection with their roles in the proper functioning of the heart, blood vessels and brain.

EFAs are very important for two reasons: they are constituents of *all* membranes and an undersupply therefore results in disturbances in *all* body tissues; they are the building blocks from which a group of short-lived molecules called *prostaglandins* (PGs) are made and as such are PG (prostaglandin) precursors. PGs regulate the activity of the tissues in which they are produced, and there is some evidence that they are involved in the control of T-lymphocytes.

In animal experiments, EFA (essential fatty acid) deficiency has resulted in weakened resistance to certain stresses and to a variety of skin inflammations. LA deficiency has led to impairment of the skin, part of the body's first line of defence against pathogens. Other EFA deficiency symptoms include dried-up tear ducts and salivary glands, the secretions of which are part of the body's disease-fighting forces. Some experts believe that some EFA deficiency symptoms may in fact be related to PG deficiency since EFAs are PG precursors.

In growing animals, total deprivation of EFAs can produce some serious abnormalities, including skin eruptions, increased skin permeability (the skin loses its ability to prevent water loss) and a defective immune system in which there is greater vulnerability to infections.

Like certain vitamins, LA and LNA have no biological activity of their own; if they are to function as EFAs, they require specific transformation within the body. Although the exact functions of each of the fatty acids in the sequence have not been fully determined, it is known that unless LA can be converted to GLA (gamma-linolenic acid, another fatty acid), it has no biological activity as an EFA.

On the whole, the best food sources of EFAs are the oils of certain seeds and nuts, the richest being flax seed oil. Safflower, sunflower and sesame seed oils are rich sources of LA, as are corn and soya bean oils. The oil from the tiny seeds of the evening primrose plant are an excellent source, provided it is a brand that has been clinically well tested.

Human milk and *Efamol* evening primrose oil are the only truly dependable sources of GLA.

Green leafy vegetables are a good source of LNA and soya bean oil provides small amounts. Flax seed oil (and its North American version, linseed oil) is a particularly rich source.

Eicosapentaenoic acid (EA), derived from LNA, is found mainly in marine oils or in oils from migratory fish. Herring, menhaden and salmon oil contain substantial amounts.

Minerals

Iron

Iron is an essential part of immune system enzymes and proteins. It is important for the vitality of T-cells and killer lymphocytes, and for macrophages to maintain their ability to kill bacteria.

A deficiency of this mineral decreases the availability of oxygen to the body's cells, with consequent impairment of the system. Iron deficiency may result in atrophy of lymphoid tissues and a decrease in the number of B- and T-cells circulating in the blood. It may also impair antibody response to pathogen challenge and affect the inflammatory response.

Excessive iron intake, however, can be detrimental as it can have an immunosuppressive effect. Most microbes require iron for reproduction, as do cancer cells, and when infection is present, certain protective body mechanisms exist to deprive these microorganisms of needed iron. An excess of this mineral also interferes with B- and T-cell activity and with the function of the macrophages to fight cancer.

In light of the foregoing, it is wiser to obtain iron from food sources and to be cautious about iron supplementation. Good food sources of iron include artichokes, asparagus, broccoli, blackstrap molasses, Brussels sprouts, cauliflower, eggs, green leafy vegetables, legumes, seaweed, strawberries and wheatgerm.

Selenium

Selenium, according to Soviet researchers, promotes humoral immunity in much the same way that vitamin E does. In fact, these nutrients work very closely together. Laboratory animals given selenium showed increased antibody response to a variety of antigens.

Selenium intensifies the bacteria-killing ability of phagocytes and enhances the tumour-fighting capacity of macrophages and related cells.

Like vitamins C and E, selenium is a powerful antioxidant with free radical scavenging effects. In addition, selenium may be useful in counteracting the immunosuppressive effects of corticosteroid drugs while simultaneously enhancing their anti-inflammatory effects. It is also valuable in helping eliminate from the body heavy metals such as cadmium and mercury, which depress the immune system.

Selenium's cancer-fighting potential is well recognized. Numerous studies show that in populations with low selenium intake, cancer incidence is correspondingly high. In animal experiments, selenium added to drinking water significantly reduced liver, skin, breast and intestinal cancers.

Selenium is highly toxic when taken in excess (more than 200 micrograms daily), and the safest supplement seems to be high-selenium yeast.

Among the best food sources of this trace mineral are apple cider vinegar, asparagus, brewer's yeast, eggs, garlic, mushrooms, seafood, sesame seeds, unrefined cereals, wheatgerm, whole grains and whole grain products.

The refining and processing of foods tend to remove selenium. This is particularly true of items such as white flour, white sugar and refined cereals, where up to 80 per cent of this micro-nutrient is lost.

For more in-depth reading on this important mineral, read *Selenium* by Alan Lewis (see Bibliography).

Zinc

Zinc is one of the most important immune system nutrients. It is crucial to T-cell activity, and zinc-deficient humans manifest a severe depression of cell-mediated immunity. Any effective immune response involves an enormous build-up of WBCs (white blood cells) to fight bacteria, viruses and cancer. Neutrophils, for example, can multiply five times within a few hours after the start of an infection. Lymphocytes can divide and form as many as 500 new cells in four days. If zinc is deficient, this cell proliferation is diminished, with consequent weakening of the immune response.

An undersupply of zinc can lead to atrophy of the thymus gland

and to reduced B- and T-cell bactericidal activity. Zinc deficiency can also adversely affect killer cell activity and the ratio of T-helper to suppressor cells.

Internationally acclaimed immunology expert, Dr R.K. Chandra, treated a group of children suffering from a rare, serious skin disease. The youngsters all had very poor immune responses and very low zinc levels. Shortly after treatment with zinc supplements began, there was remarkable improvement in the children's immune response.

Zinc seems to interact with vitamin A in helping to protect the body against cancer. Epithelial cells, such as those forming the outer layer of skin, may be particularly dependent on zinc and vitamin A. Skin is, of course, an important part of our natural defence against penetration by pathogens.

Zinc is a vital catalyst in the metabolism of EFAs, from which prostaglandins (PGs) are produced (see section on essential fatty acids, p.48). PGs are cell regulators. They are grouped into three series: 1, 2 and 3. Prostaglandins series 1 (PG1) play an important role in the soundness of the immune system, and zinc is crucial to PG1 synthesis. Prostaglandins series 1 have some actions similar to those of thymic hormones (produced by the thymus gland) and seem necessary for the normal functioning of T-lymphocytes.

Zinc-rich foods include brewer's yeast, cheese, eggs, green beans, lima beans, mushrooms, nuts, oysters, pumpkin seeds, seafood, soya beans, sunflower seeds, wheatgerm and whole grain products.

For more information on this very important trace mineral you may wish to read *The Z Factor* by Judy Graham and Dr Michel Odent (see Bibliography).

Amino Acids

Amino acids are protein building blocks. In recent years, however, researchers have demonstrated that the body also uses these constituents to help build infection-fighting cells, regulate emotions and ease pain.

Although all amino acids are essential in the true sense, they are nevertheless classified as either 'essential' (those that the body cannot make and which must come from what you eat) and 'non-essential'. Included in the former category are lysine, phenylalanine (mentioned earlier in this chapter in connection with PKU), histidine, tryptophan and valine, while arginine, glutamine and tyrosine fall into the latter class.

A deficiency of any of the 'essential' amino acids (there are eight altogether) adversely affects certain immune functions, as demonstrated in various studies.

Repeated animal experiments indicate that a good amino acid balance enhances antibody production and strengthens immune cells and organs, thereby reinforcing the body's entire defence system. Tryptophan, phenylalanine and valine seem particularly important for vigorous antibody production, while other amino acids help build strong WBCs, which are a vital part of our natural defence against pathogens and tumours. In preliminary studies, arginine has shown promise as a useful immune booster. Tests done on laboratory rats have indicated that this amino acid inhibits tumour growth, although why it does so is unclear. Scientists speculate, though, that it fortifies the cancer-fighting power of WBCs.

Amino acids help to control *neurotransmitters*, brain chemicals which facilitate transmission of nerve impulses. (Neurotransmitters play a vital role in a wide range of actions and emotions, and you will read more about them and their connection with immunity in Chapter 4.)

Neurotransmitters are made up of amino acids in a certain finely-tuned balance which, if precise, can protect us from disorders such as anxiety and depression. (In Chapter 4, you will also read about how emotions can affect optimum functioning of your immune system.) *Tyrosine*, for example, helps create a key neurotransmitter called *dopamine*, which controls many brain functions, including the maintenance of emotional equilibrium. *Phenylalanine* is crucial for the manufacture of adrenaline, a hormone which is intimately involved in stress reactions. Yet another amino acid, *tryptophan*, has been used to help some individuals counteract certain forms of depression. These people often lack a chemical called *serotonin*, and tryptophan serves to increase serotonin. Moreover, tryptophan is wonderful for promoting a good night's sleep, during which the body replenishes its reserves. *Glutamine* has been used successfully to potentiate the effects of some anti-depression drugs.

It is very important to note that amino acids must be perfectly balanced. In fact many (including arginine and lysine) work together in precise ratios. Taken carelessly in the form of supplements, they can create serious problems by disrupting the body's chemical balance. If at all unsure of dosages, please consult a health professional with a thorough understanding of nutrition and its role in health and disease.

All nutrients work together. Some, however, appear to have a closer collaboration than others. For example, vitamin B_3 (niacin) and vitamin B_6 (pyridoxine) seem to be particularly vital in helping amino acids produce neurotransmitters. They also seem to enhance the action of tryptophan in controlling certain mental symptoms such as depression.

Food sources of amino acids

All good quality proteins will provide you with dietary amino acids. When relying on grains, legumes, nuts and seeds as prime protein sources, do remember that they must be combined in such a way and eaten together at the same meal as to furnish all the 'essential' amino acids. You will find all you need to know about protein complementarity in Frances Moore Lappé's *Diet for a Small Planet* (Ballantine Books, 1971).

Eating Defensively

Having examined various immune-boosting nutrients, I would now like to discuss other aspects of diet that have the potential to impair optimum functioning of your defence resources. I have also included a simple checklist which will be useful when reviewing dietary habits which will promote a strong defence against health-destroying organisms (see p.56). Use this checklist regularly to increase your awareness of errors or omissions in your plan to eat for protection.

Reduce fats

High-fat diets have long been associated with serious health disorders such as cardiovascular disease and cancer. Decrease also your consumption of foods high in cholesterol. Laboratory animals fed high-cholesterol diets seem to be more vulnerable to infection, and some studies indicate that diets high in cholesterol may contribute to diminished cell-mediated and humoral immunity. Macrophages with high cholesterol levels show weakened phagocytic ability.

Be wary of high-protein diets

Too little protein in the diet can lead to serious immune difficulties. Too much protein on the other hand (especially animal protein) can be equally dangerous. Excess protein may cause a deficiency of vitamin B_6 (pyridoxine), a nutrient crucial to the effective functioning of the immune system, as noted earlier in this chapter. High protein intake also interferes with optimum amino acid balance.

Include more complex carbohydrates in your diet

These are 'slowly digested' carbohydrates which consist of natural sugars, starches and dietary fibre. They are found in foods such as brown rice, fresh corn, potatoes, whole grains and whole wheat flour.

Unlike refined sugars, complex carbohydrates burn slowly and safely in the body, acting as a sort of 'time-release' energy source. In contrast with refined foods, complex carbohydrates provide many essential nutrients needed to maintain a healthy immune system. These include vitamins A, C, D and E, the B complex vitamins, minerals and amino acids.

Increase dietary fibre

The fibrous part of plants is known as dietary fibre. It consists of cellulose and hemicelluloses, pectin and lignins. Most of these remain undigested in the body and form bulk.

Among the benefits to the immune system of a diet high in fibre are: more vigorous peristalsis (the wave-like contraction of the intestines which presses their contents onwards), and consequently a shorter transit time, thus lessening opportunity for harmful organisms and substances to damage the mucous membrane lining the intestines; inhibition of growth of bacteria that cause putrefaction and contribute to the formation of carcinogenic substances; promotion of a favourable environment for the flourishing of organisms beneficial to the intestines, such as those that synthesize the B vitamins.

High-fibre foods include berries, black and butter (lima) beans, dates, fresh fruits and vegetables and whole grains.

Decrease caffeine intake

Although there are no conclusive findings that establish a definite link between high caffeine intake and diseases such as cancer, indications are that it is a contributory factor in disorders associated with impaired immunity (see section on SLE in Chapter 7).

Caffeine is one of the *xanthines*, compounds found in coffee, tea, cocoa and cola drinks. They are powerful stimulants, acting on the

nervous, respiratory and cardiovascular systems. They increase the
excretion of water from the body (along with important nutrients),
and can contribute to chronic insomnia, stomach upsets, persistent
anxiety and depression. All these disorders adversely affect the immune
system.

Some common medications (e.g. cold remedies) contain caffeine.
Do read the labels of any medicines you're thinking of buying.

Look out for nutrient antagonists

An antagonist is, literally, that which counteracts the action of
something else. Given below are some of the agents that work against
the potential good of the minerals, vitamins and other nutrients
mentioned in this chapter.

Drugs

Several drugs impair the immune system by destroying essential
nutrients, by increasing a need for them, or by their undesirable effects
on the nervous system. Here are examples: *Aspirin* increases the need
for vitamin C. Stimulants such as the *amphetamines* and *cocaine* impair
the normal functioning of the immune system because they interfere
with sleep and proper nutrition.

Azathioprine (Imuran), a drug used to treat rheumatoid arthritis in
some adult patients, can severely depress the immune system. The
1987 *Compendium of Pharmaceuticals and Specialties* (CPS), published by
the Canadian Pharmaceutical Association, warns that 'chronic
immunosuppression with this purine antimetabolite may increase risk
of neoplasia' (new growths; cancer) and emphasizes that physicians
using this drug should be very familiar with this risk, as well as possible
'hemotologic [blood] toxicities'.

Individuals using *MAO inhibitors* to relieve depression should be well
aware of certain food restrictions. While taking these medications,
you should not eat most cheeses, chicken liver and broad bean pods,
for example; nor should you drink beer or wine. If you do, you could
experience severe headache, heart palpitations, neck pain and perhaps
intracranial haemorrhage (bleeding within the skull).

Smoking

The nicotine in cigarettes, cigars and pipe tobacco affects the lung
macrophages by suppressing their natural functions.

Regular nicotine intake through smoking diminishes the skin's ability to heal itself, and skin integrity is crucial for the protection of internal structures against invasion by disease-causing agents.

Smoking destroys vitamin C and the B complex vitamins and reduces vital oxygen supplies to the tissues. It contributes to premature ageing of the skin.

In addition, smoking damages the cilia, the hairlike processes that line the respiratory passages and help keep potentially harmful material from injuring the lungs.

Alcohol

While an occasional glass of wine or beer or other alcoholic beverage may actually give protection against heart disease, excessive alcohol intake contributes to a variety of health problems. These include lung disease, liver disease and increased susceptibility to infection.

Habitual high alcohol intake eventually interferes with the absorption of essential minerals and vitamins, such as the B vitamins, vitamin C and zinc, nutrients which play important roles in the effective functioning of the immune system. High alcohol intake kills specialized liver macrophages and induces immunosuppression.

Alcohol, moreover, has long been associated with increased cancer risk, perhaps because of the potentially carcinogenic substances in most alcoholic beverages.

Checklist for eating and drinking defensively

1. Reduce your intake of foods high in fats and cholesterol.
2. Curtail your consumption of foods high in animal protein and be wary of high-protein diets.
3. Eat more complex carbohydrates.
4. Increase your intake of dietary fibre.
5. Reduce use of alcoholic beverages.
6. Cut down on beverages containing caffeine.
7. Avoid using drugs of all kinds.
8. Shop wisely. Do not habitually purchase refined, over-processed foods. Buy a wide variety of fresh fruits and vegetables, with increasing emphasis on cruciferous vegetables such as broccoli, Brussels sprouts, cabbage and cauliflower. Buy whole grains, cereals and whole wheat products.
9. Scrutinize labels on bottles and packages for the presence of food

additives. Purchase products with the least amount of these, or with none at all. Buy fewer smoked foods and processed meats such as bacon, which contain potential carcinogens (e.g. nitrates and nitrites).

10.   Refrigerate or otherwise suitably store your food soon after shopping to avoid nutrient losses.

11.   Habitually use food preparation and cooking methods that conserve essential nutrients. For example, don't peel vegetables unnecessarily; don't leave them soaking in water prior to cooking them; don't discard the water in which they have been cooked (incorporate it into sauces, soups and stews). Steam, bake or stir-fry foods in preference to boiling or deep-frying them.

12.   Make mealtimes pleasant and unhurried. Chew food thoroughly. Some harmful organisms are able to bypass the protection normally afforded by the stomach in poorly-chewed pieces of food.

13.   Don't overeat.

4 MIND AGAINST MALADY

In times past when people were physically ill, they sought out a doctor for consultation and treatment. When mentally ill, the expertise of a psychologist or psychiatrist was enlisted, while the therapist of choice for a troubled spirit was usually a minister, priest or other ecclesiastical adviser.

Today, enlightened individuals realize the interdependence of these three aspects of human beings and acknowledge that one of them cannot suffer without involving the other two. Again and again nowadays we see this intimate interrelationship of body, mind and soul when physical ill health is accompanied by or generates psychological symptoms, which in turn lead to spiritual anguish.

Many mainstream doctors who practise orthodox forms of medicine (as opposed to holistic medicine) fear that health professionals who encourage clients to be keenly aware of this mind-body relationship and to 'think positively' may somehow persuade the more naïve to completely relinquish conventional health care and try to cure themselves. They are afraid that by emphasizing the 'will to live' as a potent factor influencing survival, less motivated patients may feel enormously guilty that perhaps they are 'weak characters' who lack self-discipline. These medical practitioners require concrete proof that our thoughts and images are capable of activating physiological processes which are responsible for relaying messages from the brain to cells throughout the body. As Norman Cousins (see Bibliography) has observed, because we live in an age in which we seem to need tangibles to explain effects, we are untrusting of results brought about by our own inner 'intangible' resources which are unseen to the physical eye. And yet there is a wealth of documented evidence to support the powerful influence that mind has over body as well as over microbes.

Psychoneuroimmunology (PNI)

There is now a new breed of specialists who are helping cast light on the mind-body connection. Their speciality is known as PNI (psychoneuroimmunology), which refers to the interaction among three body systems: endocrine, nervous and immune.

PNI researchers investigate the way the brain affects the body's disease-fighting cells. With the most advanced and sophisticated technology at their disposal, they have shown that the brain can transmit signals along nerve pathways to reinforce the body's defences against infection and help them put up a fiercer fight against disease. They have demonstrated, too, that this transmission of nerve signals can be controlled by thoughts and emotions.

Moreover, PNI studies have revealed that not only can neurochemicals (the brain's chemicals) regulate components of the immune system, but also that the immune system can influence the brain. It can send to the brain chemical messages about bacteria and viruses and tumours. It can also, it appears, transmit signals to the brain's emotional and rational centres, which may help explain why irritability sometimes increases and concentration is sometimes impaired during some illnesses.

PNI, although still in its infancy, is already impressive enough to coax many doctors into reviewing their approach to the treatment of disease. Certainly, some medical schools are beginning to integrate PNI into their curricula and research programmes.

The connection between nervous and immune systems is not a recent find. Indeed, around the turn of this century, anatomists discovered that the thymus gland, bone marrow and lymph nodes were supplied with a network of nerve fibres. Later, researchers were able to show that by electrically stimulating parts of an animal's brain, they could improve its infection-fighting capacity. By surgically destroying other parts, they could boost the ability to fight pathogens.

As the science of immunology advanced, researchers lost their initial interest in the relationship between the nervous and immune systems, becoming preoccupied instead with cells of the immune system and the apparent spontaneity with which these cells responded to threats from antigens. But, as scientists know only too well, the idea of an autonomic immune system is contrary to scientific common sense. Why would nature make an exception of this system when other body systems are brain controlled?

The answer to this query came earlier in this decade. It was discovered that neurotransmitters (the brain's chemical messengers) could latch onto immune cells and alter their ability to multiply and kill invading organisms. It was also found that hormones, the secretion of which is regulated by the brain, could influence the immune cells' ability to combat disease. Further, there was evidence that the nerve fibres present in organs of the immune system actually hook up with lymphocytes. Obviously, there is communication between the brain and the immune system, and PNI researchers say that it concerns emotions.

Studies of brain chemicals point to the probability that emotions affect susceptibility to disease. Candace Pert, a leading NIMH (National Institute of Mental Health) neuropharmacologist, made a special study of neuropeptides (small protein-like brain chemicals), and concluded that these are biochemical units of emotion, each somehow contributing to an individual's general mood and feelings. In her study of macrophages, she and her colleagues found that neuropeptides could bind themselves to these infection-fighting cells and alter the speed or direction of their movement. She therefore reasoned that if each neuropeptide had a different effect on macrophage traffic, then the way macrophages fought disease could be influenced by mood. In one study, Pert and colleagues found that when subjects were made to feel helpless, their macrophages moved more sluggishly, most likely due to changes in neuropeptides. Although only a preliminary finding, it suggests a reason why patients who lose hope progress less successfully in the course of an illness than those who remain optimistic. Pert has remarked that the more closely she looks at neuropeptides, the more convinced she is that 'emotions are running the show'.

Feelings aside, there is also the question of reason, which is controlled by the cortex, or outer shell, of the brain, which also regulates the immune system. In his studies of the cortex, French immunologist Gérard Renoux found that the destruction of a mouse's cortex, which does not significantly affect the animal's behaviour, changes both the structure and the activity of its immune cells. Of particular interest was the fact that the damage to the left cortex affected the number of WBCs (white blood cells) in the spleen, and their ability to fight foreign organisms and tumours. Removal of the right cortex resulted in increased aggressiveness of the WBCs.

Renoux therefore concluded that the left side of the cortex stimulates the immune system, the right side suppresses it and the brain controls the whole system in the same way that it regulates behaviour.

Renoux's work has also provided hints of how visualization helps fight cancer. Since imagery is apparently controlled predominantly by the right side of the brain, it is possible that individuals who utilize this brain hemisphere somehow 'distract' it from suppressing immunity. Other researchers suggest that the left brain hemisphere specializes in processing positive emotions such as enthusiasm and optimism. If we accept these observations, then it is not difficult to appreciate how therapies that encourage a sense of self-control and hope could be immeasurably useful in stimulating the brain to reinforce the immune system to combat disease. In one study, conducted by Howard Hall, Psy.D., Ph.D., of Penn State University, selected subjects who practised a specific visualization technique twice daily for one week showed a significant increase of their WBCs. Repeats of this study, and others like it, produced the same results. In another experiment at Michigan State University it was demonstrated that the numbers and function of neutrophils could be altered in response to certain visualization exercises.

As immunology research advances, it is becoming clearer that there is communication between the brain and the immune system and vice versa, and that all body systems are intimately interrelated. In order to maintain homeostasis, in which there is an equilibrium of the internal environment, there has to be feedback from body to brain and from brain to body. Argentine-born scientist Dr Hugo Besedovsky and colleagues implanted electrodes in the brain of a rat and then injected the animal with foreign cells. As the rodent's immune system responded to these antigens, its brain activity increased and the level of some important chemicals dropped. It was crystal clear that the brain knew what the immune system was doing. In subsequent experiments, Besedovsky found evidence that the brain actually uses this information to keep the immune system in balance. When macrophages and lymphocytes encounter foreign microbes, they not only attack them but also transmit chemical signals to the brain by way of the blood-stream. These signals are cues for the brain to activate hormone production, which in turn regulates the activity of immune cells.

Another immunologist, Ed Blalock, has been able to show that immune cells can 'speak' to the brain and that glands can 'converse' with cells through the medium of hormones. His studies have led him to conclude that the immune system can communicate with almost every other body system through a variety of hormones which it manufactures.

Blalock has also remarked on the immune system's specificity (a characteristic that was discussed in Chapter 1). He proposed that the system acts as a sensory organ – like the organs of touch, taste and smell – informing the brain about which microbes are invading and helping it regulate responses accordingly. The immune system, he has commented, may be the 'sixth sense' for which we have been searching.

Yet another immunologist, British-born Nick Hall, in collaboration with psychologists Barry Gruber and Stephen Hersh, has shown that relaxation and certain forms of visualization, such as those used by some cancer patients, actually cause lymphocytes to multiply to fight tumours more effectively.

The foregoing, though only a tiny sampling of the latest research on the connection between the brain and the immune system, should be enough to give insight into how the one influences the other and vice versa. It is certainly thought provoking, and will hopefully whet the curiosity and lead to further probing of the subject. Undoubtedly, PNI is one of the most fascinating and exciting specialities in existence.

Visualization

By learning and practising mind control we can, to some extent, influence hormonal activity which will in turn have a regulating effect on our immune system. It is a wonderful prospect. We can use this skill advantageously to complement any therapy we may be receiving for a particular health condition. We can utilize it to help ourselves stay well. In combination with adequate nutritional support, regular exercise and effective stress management strategies, we can put this skill into practice to give ourselves the best possible chance of attaining and/or maintaining immune fitness.

Before describing specific visualization techniques, here is a story to illustrate how successful imagery can be in altering the course of a health disorder.

Visualization: a case study

Six young migraine sufferers, aged between ten and thirteen, were treated with various medications, including pain-killers, with no success. They were then referred to psychologists who tried to raise the temperature of their hands. This hand-warming technique works on the principle that during anxiety and stress, blood flow to the hands is restricted. With relaxation, the hands become warm and congestion in the head, which contributes to the migraine, is relieved.

Because the boys were overachievers, they found it hard to relax with this technique. They viewed the hand warming as yet another exercise in which to attain excellence, and talked about scoring 90 or 100 per cent. They were trying too hard and were therefore generating additional tension.

Now, almost desperate, the psychologists remembered earlier advice: to make biofeedback imagery concrete and interesting to children. And so they invoked the image of the Jedi Master Obi-Wan Kenobi, a character in the *Star Wars* movies. It was he who had taught Luke Skywalker to use The Force.

The youngsters, who were familiar with the movies and Kenobi's exhortations to relax and use inner strength to achieve goals, had no difficulty in visualizing the appropriate scenes with coaching from their therapists. Actual dialogue from the movies, along with suitable suggestions, was employed: for example, 'Remember a Jedi can feel The Force flowing through him'.

Within three weeks, five of the young migraine sufferers were expert at hand warming and could quickly relax at will. Their migraine had disappeared. The other youngster took six weeks to achieve the same goal. In follow-up examinations over a two-year period, the boys reported no further headaches (see J.C. Horn, Bibliography).

The psychologists' conclusions as to why The Force worked so effectively in these cases are equally applicable to several other approaches used to stimulate self-healing powers. First, treatment is most successful when it increases the individual's sense of self-control, adequacy or self-mastery. Second, treatment is most effective when the client has implicit faith in the therapist and indeed in the treatment. Third, a pleasant, restful image on which to focus for a while is very therapeutic for the whole system. It fosters a state of relaxation which enhances the power of our own inner self-healing forces.

At times, a more aggressive form of imagery is needed, such as that formulated by the Simontons to treat selected cancer sufferers, and which is described in their book entitled *Getting Well Again*. In this type of imagery, the patient is taught to visualize both the cancer cells (the 'bad guys') and the body's self-defence forces (for example, the WBCs – the 'good guys') in a cartoon or other style which is most natural to the afflicted individual.

The sufferer mentally sees these two opposing powers in conflict, and the 'good guys' gaining supremacy. Each person conjures up imagery in keeping with his or her personality and lifestyle. For instance, an outdoors person may visualize the good cells as large, white polar bears and the bad cells as little black seals, with the former pouncing on the latter and devouring them. In fact, not very long ago, I saw a television programme in which a young man, diagnosed with cancer, had utilized similar imagery to help bring him into remission (abatement of symptoms).

Visualization techniques

Here are a few sample visualization techniques to introduce you to the idea of pitting mind against malady. They are simple yet effective in diverting attention from disturbing stimuli and concentrating energies on the positive forces within you. Similar exercises have been taught by health professionals and successfully implemented by clients with a wide variety of problems including cancer. The beauty of these techniques is that they require no gadgets or financial outlay. They are part of the natural armamentarium at our immediate command to use in the war against microbes and other potentially destructive agents. Making use of these and related techniques also provides us with a certain sense of control and helps diminish feelings of helplessness and hopelessness. This, in the light of PNI research, translates into enhanced immunity and an upgrading of the quality of life.

Dr Simonton sees the practice of visualization as a clear mental statement of what you want to happen. By repetition of this statement, you soon come to expect the desired circumstances to materialize. This positive expectation leads you to behave in ways consistent with achieving the longed-for results and actually helps bring them about.

Preparing for visualization

In *The Path to Pain Control*, Meg Bogin draws an interesting parallel between meditation and the way in which artists prepare a canvas. They coat it with a layer of white called the 'ground'. This is the backdrop to the colours that will emerge and against which they will move. For many painters, this is a deeply absorbing, highly creative act.

Think of the meditative processes preceding visualization as preparing the 'ground' of the mind to receive healing energy. Don't rush these preliminaries. They make the body and mind more receptive to the beneficial changes that occur through regular practice of your selected visualization technique.

1. Choose a place where you will not be interrupted, somewhere you feel at ease.
2. Sit or lie comfortably and close your eyes.
3. Unclench your teeth to relax your jaws. Breathe slowly, smoothly and evenly.
4. Make a mental check of your body from toes to head. Let go of tightness wherever you detect it, for example, in the lower back, shoulders, neck and hands.
5. Spend a couple of minutes savouring the feeling of calm that will begin to steal over you.

Now proceed with your visualization technique of choice. Practise every day and/or every night.

A healing breath
1. Check that your jaws are relaxed and that you are breathing slowly and regularly.
2. Through your nostrils inhale slowly, smoothly and steadily without strain. As you inhale, imagine filling your system not only with oxygen but also with a healing force which you may see, for instance, as a gentle ray of light or a soothing jet of warm water. Feel the warmth of this healing force.
3. Exhale slowly and steadily through your nostrils. As you do so, imagine expelling from your body not only stale air but also the germs and poisons contributing to your illness. These may, for example, take the form of a dark cloud of smoke or a muddy stream of water. Your own imagination will fashion a symbol that is meaningful to *you*.

4. Repeat steps 2 and 3, again and again, until you feel ready to resume your activities.
5. Take your time getting up. Avoid any sudden or jerky movements.

Variation on a healing breath
1. Relax your jaws and allow your breath flow smoothly in and out through your nostrils.
2. Rest your hands lightly on the part of your body closest to the affected organ, for example the abdomen or head.
3. As you inhale steadily, visualize a healing force entering your lungs along with your breath. What form this force takes will depend on the type of imagery you employ. It could, for instance, appear as a soothing beam of light or as a sparkling stream of water. Focus on its point of entry into your body, that is, the chest.
4. As you exhale, visualize this healing force leaving your chest, coursing along the arms and entering the affected part of the body through the fingertips. Feel warmth spread to the unhealthy part. Experience a sense of comfort.
5. Repeat steps 3 and 4, with total awareness, again and again, until you feel ready to resume your usual activities.
6. Take your time getting up. Avoid any sudden movement.

A healing meditation
1. Mentally transport yourself to a beautiful spot – somewhere with pleasant associations for you: beside a peaceful lake; in a quiet mountain resort; on a moonlit beach. Spend a few moments appreciating details of the surroundings: the wonderful colours of sea and sky and landscape; the gentle breeze caressing your body; the subtle fragrance of flowers; the taste of salt spray upon your lips.
2. With each slow, smooth, deep inhalation, breathe in the freshness of the surrounding air and the untainted smells of this marvellous place.
3. With each unhurried exhalation, let your body sink ever more deeply into the surface on which you're lying or sitting and completely let go of any residual tensions. As you exhale, too, send away from your mind and body any negative feelings – frustrations, anxieties, resentments – everything unwanted.
4. Repeat steps 2 and 3 several times until you feel very much a part of this exquisitely beautiful spot you've come to revisit in thought.
5. Again inhale: slowly, smoothly and deeply.

6.   As you exhale, mentally say: 'I feel at peace'.
7.   Repeat steps 5 and 6, again and again, always reiterating 'I feel at peace' on the outgoing breath.
8.   When you sense that you are ready to return to your usual abode and activities, do so slowly and awarely, and avoid any sudden or jerky movement.

   Alternatives to 'I feel at peace' are:

> I'm wonderfully relaxed.
> I'm getting better and better.
> I'm growing stronger and stronger.
> I *will* be healed.
> My body is forgiving.
> My faith *shall* make me whole.

These affirmations are suggestions only. Choose and use one that is most meaningful to you and with which you feel totally comfortable.

A healing visualization
1.   Focus your attention on the part you wish to be healed. Visualize the body's scavenger cells, the white blood cells, as little white birds, for example.
2.   Also visualize the enemy agents responsible for your illness (the germs or malignant cells). See them as perhaps little dark worms or insects.
3.   Each time you inhale, picture the little white birds poised to attack the small, dark creatures.
4.   Each time you exhale, imagine the birds devouring and digesting the worms or insects.
5.   Repeat steps 2 and 3 again and again, until the birds have consumed all the worms or insects, and the impulse to end the exercise appears.
6.   Slowly prepare to resume your activities.

   Other suggested forms of imagery for this exercise are:

– Visualize your blood passing through a fine sieve which filters it of impurities. As you inhale, see purified blood bathing the tissues of the affected part. As you exhale, picture the blood leaving the tissues, carrying impurities away, and being filtered through the sieve. Repeat the process.

– Imagine a soft brush dusting away deposits that have settled around your joints in powder form, and which have made them stiff and painful. With each exhalation, see the brush sweeping away this powder.

– Picture gentle, loving hands applying a soothing balm rich in healing ingredients. As the balm is absorbed through the skin, the affected area feels less uncomfortable and begins to improve. With each exhalation, sense this improvement more keenly.

– Hear the dulcet tones of incredibly sweet music. Feel it assuage your anguish and bring you comfort. Experience emotional healing. Let each exhalation enhance a feeling of increasing well-being.

Conclusion

How successful your chosen visualization technique or techniques will be depends on a number of factors. The most important of these are: regularity of practice; implicit belief in the positive results of practice; the suitability of the imagery to the uniqueness of the person you are.

Always in your mind's eye see the desired results as already happening, and make visualization as important a part of your daily life as you do nutrition and exercise. Your self-discipline will not go unrewarded.

5 STRATEGIES FOR STRESS CONTROL

Stress, according to the late Dr Hans Selye, is the non-specific response by the body to any demand made upon it. According to psychologist Richard S. Lazarus, stress occurs when demands tax or exceed one's adjustive resources.

Whereas in the immune system the presence of an antigen is the stimulus bringing about certain reactions, in the nervous system it is a stress-producing agent, or stressor, that is responsible for a number of adjustments known collectively as the stress response. It is initiated in the brain in a small area called the *hypothalamus*. Once stimulated, the hypothalamus activates a tiny gland known as the pituitary (hypophysis), also located in the brain. Although only the size of a pea, this gland regulates all the other endocrine glands, and because of this is sometimes referred to as 'the master gland'.

The pituitary in turn stimulates the adrenal glands which are located one atop each kidney. They then secrete *adrenaline* (epinephrine) from their medullae (sing. *medulla*), or inner part, and *corticosteroids* from their cortex, or outer portion.

You may have felt the effects of adrenaline as it poured into your system during a stressful situation. This state has been described by various terms including 'adrenaline rush' and 'adrenaline high'. You can sometimes feel it as part of the exhilaration following a feat of endurance, such as after running in a race. You can sense it, too, when trying to protect yourself from threat, as in attempting to avoid being hit by a motor vehicle or escape from an attacker.

Adrenaline is what mobilizes your body for 'fight or flight' in any situation you perceive as dangerous or overwhelming, and under its influence a number of body changes occur, some of which you are aware of but some of which you cannot detect. They include:

- increased pulse rate;
- raised blood-pressure;
- faster rate of breathing;

- temporary impairment of digestion;
- shortened blood clotting time;
- fewer neutrophils in the circulation;
- breakdown of proteins from the thymus and lymph glands to form sugar for immediate energy;
- withdrawal of minerals from bones;
- mobilization of fat from storage deposits;
- retention of an abnormal amount of salt in the body.

Whereas you can sometimes sense the effects of increased adrenaline secretion, you are not, as a rule, aware of those resulting from higher levels of the corticosteroids in your blood-stream. These, however, have tremendous impact on your immune system and in time can seriously affect your health.

One of the corticosteroids, called *cortisol*, is especially implicated in many stress-related diseases, which now represent more than 80 per cent of all health disorders. Some of the diseases associated with elevated cortisol levels are Alzheimer's disease, arthritis, cancer, depression, heart disease, high blood-pressure (hypertension), multiple sclerosis (MS), Parkinson's disease, skin diseases and stomach and intestinal ulcers. Some researchers even say that high cortisol levels may be a useful predictor of suicide.

Also known as *hydrocortisone*, cortisol is a powerful immunosuppressant which degrades tissues of the thymus gland and lymph nodes, increases the number of T-suppressor cells and decreases that of helper T-cells. It also interferes with the production of natural killer (NK) cells and of virus-fighting interferon.

Doctors use corticosteroid drugs, such as betamethasone, cortisone and prednisone to treat a variety of conditions including arthritis, skin inflammations, asthma, ulcerative colitis and leukaemia, and to help prevent rejection of tissue and organ transplants. The treatment raises the body's cortisol levels and this not infrequently produces undesirable side effects such as high blood-pressure, mental disturbances and diabetes-like symptoms. These tend to disappear, though, when use of the drugs is discontinued.

There is, however, one cortisol-lowering agent that is far safer than any of the foregoing medications and others like them. It is vitamin C, dealt with at some length in Chapter 3. It inhibits cortisol secretion following adrenal gland stimulation during stress. Its cortisol-lowering properties are thought to be partly responsible for its usefulness in treating viral infections.

Stress and Immunity

There is now persuasive evidence that reducing stress to manageable levels can bolster the body's disease-fighting ability. Researchers Janice K. Kiecolt-Glaser and Ronald Glaser and colleagues at Ohio State University College of Medicine studied forty-five fairly healthy elderly persons living in retirement homes. They divided up the retirees into three groups. The first group was visited three times weekly for one month by students who taught them relaxation techniques as part of a stress-reduction programme. The second group received no relaxation instruction but were visited thrice weekly by college students. (Previous studies had shown the value of relieving loneliness in improving the workings of the immune system.) The third group received neither visitors nor relaxation training.

Studies of blood samples from all the subjects revealed some remarkable facts: people in the first group showed increased activity in their NK-cells and decreased antibodies to herpes simplex virus, both of which indicate enhanced immune system activity. These findings suggested that the long-term practice of daily relaxation could be of substantial immunological value.

NK-cells are thought to be not only part of the cancer surveillance mechanism (please refer to Chapter 1) but also important in controlling infectious disease. Kiecolt-Glaser explained that the enhancement of NK activity through relaxation may therefore be particularly beneficial to older individuals who tend to suffer age-related impairments of their immune system.

In California, psychologist Margaret Kemeny and colleagues have shown how psychosocial factors can affect the workings of the immune system. For six months these researchers did follow-up studies on thirty-six persons, aged between twenty and sixty, with genital herpes. All the subjects had had at least two herpes outbreaks in the previous six months.

Each month the researchers interviewed these individuals about various stressors in their lives, from past events that were still troubling them to future happenings in which they anticipated problems. They were also asked to rate their levels of anxiety, depression and hostility and the degree of satisfaction they experienced in achieving major goals.

Blood samples were taken from nineteen of the test subjects to measure levels of helper and suppressor T-cells, which may be involved in preventing repeated bouts of herpes. The researchers found that it was the depressed individuals (who had lower levels of T-suppressor cells) who suffered more herpes recurrences than the non-depressed subjects. Kemeny therefore reasoned that the decreased level of T-suppressor cells was responsible for the herpes outbreaks and this reasoning was later confirmed.

The brain evidently has a direct effect on the immune system. WBCs which play a key role in immune reactions appear to have receptors for neurotransmitters. When immune responses are weakened by the effect of these brain chemicals, viruses that would normally be destroyed flourish and cancer cells which are usually kept in check may proliferate.

Our thoughts can produce a vast array of physical symptoms. We can experience just as much distress through worrying about a forthcoming event as by worrying about a wild animal about to attack us. In one study at Ohio State University, the level of NK-cell activity fell significantly in medical students on exam day. In another study, college students who seemed under a great deal of stress and who appeared very lonely showed only a third of the NK-cell activity found in other members of their class.

In laboratory experiments with rats, Dr Hans Selye observed and recorded various changes in components of their immune system in response to stress. These included: considerable enlargement of the adrenal cortex; intense shrinking (atrophy) of the thymus, spleen, lymph nodes and all other lymphatic structures. When Dr Selye saw how rapidly the lymphatic organs had disintegrated, he examined the lymphocytes. He was not surprised to discover that their number had diminished. But he was excited to find an even more striking change in the blood picture – one he had not expected: the almost complete disappearance of eosinophils.

Eosinophils, you may remember from reading Chapter 1, seem to be related to immunologic adaptive reactions, especially allergy, because their number markedly increases when an individual suffers from asthma or hay fever or related disorders.

Dr Selye had long before demonstrated that chronic stress suppresses the immune system. For example, lymphocyte function – a reliable indicator of the effectiveness of this system – is substantially depressed in persons who lose a spouse. The mind-body link is further substantiated by research showing that hypnotic suggestion can influence the body's immunity to tuberculosis. In addition, incisions in the hypothalamus, which is directly associated with emotions, will cause immunosuppression. These examples are a paltry sampling of research findings supporting the effects of stress on mood and feelings, which in turn influence the functioning of the body's natural defences against disease.

G.J.V. Nossal has noted that any long debilitating illness – a decided stressor – will make the thymus gland decrease in size. This is why pathologists, who study diseased tissues and organs, used to think that a small thymus was the norm. Consequently, when they saw the thymus of someone who had died suddenly, as in an accident, it struck them as abnormally large.

After years of meticulous research, G.J.V. Nossal, a respected and dedicated immunologist, has remarked that to involve the brain and nervous system in immune phenomena is by no means farfetched. He has voiced sentiments similar to those expressed by Norman Cousins (see Chapter 4). Psychological overtones in certain health disorders are indeed well known. But because we cannot quantitate mental stress and therefore study such concepts objectively, we tend to be sceptical about them.

The findings of the foregoing and other studies clearly indicate that stress so weakens the body's defences that they no longer provide optimum protection against infection and tumours. An individual subjected to unremitting stress therefore becomes very vulnerable to a number of health disorders, including cancer. Researchers have demonstrated that clear links exist between feelings of uncontrollable stress and the normal functioning of the immune system. (I gave examples of this in Chapter 4.) When a sense of helplessness pervades, the body's ability to resist tumour development declines.

In fact, researchers have applied conditioning techniques to effect suppression of the immune response. They injected laboratory mice with a drug that caused stomach pain and suppressed the immune system. At the same time, they gave the animals a saccharin solution to drink. With repetition, in much the same way that Pavlov conditioned his dogs, the researchers were able to produce immunosuppression by giving the mice only the sweetened liquid. These results, which have been duplicated by others, have exciting implications. One is that the human immune response can be enhanced through conditioning to potentiate the effects of drugs and other forms of therapy. The now well-known work of Carl Simonton and colleagues gives us a glimpse of this. It has clearly indicated that it is indeed possible to alter a state of mind to one in which there is a greater sense of control, thereby increasing the chances of tumour rejection or other conquests over disease.

Stressors

As mentioned earlier in this chapter, when a foreign agent invades a healthy body, it activates an immune response. When a stressor confronts an individual, it sets in motion a mechanism known as the stress response. How appropriate or effective this reaction is depends on how the stimulus is perceived. I may react to someone's witty remark by becoming depressed because I see it as adverse criticism. You may delight in it because you regard it as an indication of the other person's brilliance and an acknowledgement of your capacity to appreciate it. Herein, then, lies the power of a stressor – an event, circumstance or other agent causing or leading to stress. How it affects you largely depends on how you see it.

On the whole, challenges that we can clearly control do not harm us and we may even thrive on them. But those that cause us to feel helpless may definitely be dangerous to our health. When, in some primitive societies, witch doctors point a bone in the direction of those who have broken tribal taboos, the transgressors see this gesture as a sign of doom. Accordingly, they fall to the ground, contorted with anguish, shun the company of others and die within days. In not dissimilar fashion, a number of Americans die each year after taking poison in doses too small to cause death under normal circumstances, or after inflicting on themselves small, non-lethal wounds. They die because they are convinced that they will.

Different kinds of stressors

Many stressors take the form of everyday annoyances in our long-term relationship with others: spouse, children, co-workers. Some are short term but more pronounced. All have the potential to damage the integrity of our natural defence system.

Notable stressors include fear, guilt and regret; the agony of uncertainty – when you don't know how something will turn out; conflict – when you are torn between two opposing sets of feelings. These are all negative emotions which, as a reading of this and Chapter 4 should make clear, can impair the smooth running of the body's defence mechanisms and compromise your health.

Another potent stressor is having too many life changes in too short a period of time. Experts predict that this increases our chances of accident or illness and I've seen this prediction come to pass many a time, most recently in the case of a young acquaintance. He has changed his place of residence four times, worked at five different jobs, married and is on the verge of separation, all in the space of six years. He is now undergoing psychiatric treatment for severe depression and is battling as well with a series of minor infections.

A stressor loses its impact upon our system when it ceases to deprive us of our sense of mastery. Another acquaintance told me that although she has been driving a car for many years, she still feels intimidated by road traffic signs that read 'no left-hand turn'. She will therefore drive several blocks out of her way, if necessary, to dodge such signs. Silly as this may strike some people, it is her way of retaining a sense of control by feeling that she does *not* have to bow to the dictates of a mere road sign. My way of dealing with traffic stressors, a strategy I've used successfully for many years, is not drive at all. It has worked amazingly well for me.

The operative work, then, is *control*. Once you can look at a circumstance or event or other potential agent of stress and see it as something over which you do have a measure of control, and which is not going to last forever, then you have already begun to practise effective stress management.

Stress Management Strategies

The first line of defence against potentially harmful forms of stress is information. Reading this book is an example: by equipping yourself with useful information, your furnish yourself with suitable armour for your combat against stress.

The second line of defence against stress is good health. This is not merely the absence of disease; rather it is a state of well-being to which there are many aspects. I have summarized these later in this chapter in a checklist called The VIP Formula (see p.79).

The third line of defence against distress (harmful stress) is to establish a sound emotional support system. This could be a trusted friend or group of friends or even a professional counsellor; one or more individuals to whom you can freely and confidentially express your feelings instead of bottling them up inside. A good support system will also provide encouragement and reinforcement of positive feelings and promote a sense of self-worth and confidence. Again and again, research has shown that suppressing emotion will hurt *you* more than it will ever hurt anyone else.

These, then, are the main stress control strategies as I see them. To complement them, here are miscellaneous tips from various experts:

– To counteract the possible unpleasant effects of the first few seconds of a stressful situation, try Charles Stroebel's Quieting Reflex formula: smile inwardly and also with your mouth and eyes to reduce facial tension. Take a slow, smooth, steady breath and, as you exhale, let go of tightness in your jaw, tongue and shoulders. Mentally tell yourself that you are calm, amused and alert.
– Learn to identify and to anticipate both internal and external sources of stress.
– Learn to recognize symptoms of stress. These include racing heartbeat or palpitations, diarrhoea, headache, anxiety, irritability, tight jaws and backache.
– Regularly practise a relaxation technique you enjoy and find effective, for example, progressive relaxation, visualization, meditation. This provides a break from usual activities and helps to replenish your resources. It helps diminish the impact of stressful stimuli and allows you to recover speedily. It also enables you to be more in touch with

yourself and recognize signs and symptoms of stress.

– Have some fun. Play is very important to well-being. Balance work with a sport or hobby, but be on guard against bringing to your recreation a spirit of competition. Play for pleasure.

– Learn to delegate chores so that you are not overburdened. Learn to say 'no' so that you are not overcommitted. Read Manuel J. Smith's *When I Say No, I Feel Guilty* (Bantam Books, New York, 1975) to help you be more assertive.

– Learn to laugh. Laughter is one of the best medicines. It may even promote healing. Read Norman Cousins's *Anatomy of an Illness* (see Bibliography).

– Practise, practise, practise. Insight is fine but it must be complemented by practice. Practise acting rather than reacting. Don't give others the power to make you react before you are ready to act (back to the Quieting Reflex).

Toe-to-top relaxation

Here is a relaxation technique I've practised for years and still find indispensable.

1. Lie comfortably in a quiet room. Close your eyes. Separate your legs to discourage tension build-up in your thighs. Move your arms away from your sides to discourage tension build-up in your shoulders. Breathe naturally.

2. Pull your toes towards you, pushing the heels away and holding the tightness for a few seconds. Note the tension in feet and legs.

3. Now release the tightness and relax toes, feet and legs. Spend a few moments visualizing the legs growing heavy and sinking into the surface on which you are lying.

4. Focus your attention next on the hips. Tighten your buttock muscles and spend a few moments studying the tension.

5. Now release the tightness in the buttock muscles and let the hips relax. Visualize your bottom resting with all its weight on the surface on which you are lying.

6. With your next *exhalation*, press the back of your waist towards or into the surface on which you are lying. Hold this downward pressure for a few seconds or until your exhalation is complete. Let go of tightness in the small of your back as you continue to breathe normally; relax

your spine and the muscles on each side of the spine.

7.   Tightly squeeze your shoulderblades together and hold the squeeze for a few seconds. Note the tension in the upper back.

8.   Let go of tightness in the upper back and shoulders. Spend a few moments appreciating a growing heaviness in your torso; feel how it is sinking heavily into the surface on which you are lying. Keep breathing naturally.

9.   With your next *exhalation*, tighten your abdominal muscles and note the tightness.

10.   Relax your abdomen as you breathe naturally in and out. Feel the muscles grow soft.

11.   With your next *inhalation*, focus your attention on the way your chest expands. Enjoy the therapeutic stretching of the chest muscles.

12.   Exhaling, relax the chest. Continue breathing slowly, smoothly and evenly. With each exhalation, visualize your body sinking more deeply into the surface on which you are lying.

13.   Turn your thoughts now to the arms and hands. Make tight fists, stiffen your arms and raise them a few centimetres. When next you *exhale*, let the arms collapse heavily onto the surface on which you are lying. Breathe normally and visualize your arms and hands growing warmer and heavier and more relaxed.

14.   Gently roll your head from side to side a few times.

15.   Re-position your head for comfort. Let go of tightness in your neck. With each exhalation, visualize any remaining neck tension disappearing with the outgoing breath.

16.   *Exhaling*, stick your tongue out through wide open mouth; open your eyes wide, as if staring; note the tension in your face.

17.   Inhale and close your eyes and mouth. Breathe naturally and visualize, with each exhalation, all the little lines of fatigue and tension fading away from your face. Visualize a serenity spreading over your facial features.

18.   Now spend the remainder of your period of toe-to-top relaxation contemplating your breathing. With each inward breath, visualize filling your system with peace and positive feelings. With each outward breath, visualize sending away forever everything disturbing and harmful.

Resuming activity

When you sense that the time has come for you to end your relaxation, spend at least a couple of minutes in a slow, leisurely stretching of your limbs and in other gentle body movements to prepare you for a return to your various activities. Never get up suddenly. Always take your time.

The VIP Formula (Formula for Vigorous Immune Potential)

The VIP Formula which I have devised is a sort of checklist. Make a copy of it. Put it where you will see it. Refer to it periodically to alert you to points you may have been neglecting.

– Ensure adequate nutrition and fluid intake. Restrict use of alcoholic beverages and those containing caffeine. Avoid using drugs of any kind. Don't smoke. Review Chapter 3 periodically.
– Ensure regular elimination without reliance on commercial laxatives. An adequate diet and regular exercise are helpful. Review Chapters 3 and 6 from time to time.
– Exercise regularly. Choose forms of exercise that are suitable for *you*, which you enjoy and which you will therefore do consistently. Review Chapter 6 periodically.
– Avoid unnecessary exposure to the sun. It could damage your skin, part of your body's first line of defence against invasion by harmful agents.
– Practise relaxation daily. Select a technique which you enjoy, find effective and with which you are totally comfortable. Review Chapters 4 and 5 now and then. You may also wish to look for suitable techniques in books on stress management, holistic health or yoga, or participate in a class where you will learn such exercises.
– Try to obtain regular, good-quality sleep without dependence on medications. Exercising and relaxing reguarly will contribute to this.
– Establish and maintain a sound emotional support system. Those who are a part of this network should respect the various components of your preferred lifestyle. Periodically review Chapter 5.
– Consciously cultivate positive feelings and attitudes to enhance your sense of self-worth. Do something nice for *you* from time to time. Review Chapter 5.
– Maintain a balance between socialization and solitude (as opposed to loneliness). Daily relaxation, for instance, provides you with a period

of withdrawal from social demands. Avoid socializing with those who deplete your energies and depress you.

– Faithfully practise stress management strategies that work for you. Study Chapter 5 periodically.

6 EXERCISING FOR IMMUNE FITNESS

According to psychoanalyst Erich Fromm, if you want to master any art your must either devote your whole life to it or it must be somehow an integral part of your lifestyle. Your person then becomes an instrument in the practice of that art and must be kept fit to perform the specific functions it is intended to carry out. Your body and mind, through which you practise the art of healthful living, should therefore be kept in peak condition if they are truly to be sources of super, natural immune power. They have to be kept in a state of optimum fitness.

What then is fitness? It is not simply the absence of disease. Essentially, it is an individual's general ability to adapt to his or her environment.

There is more to fitness than physical capability. Nicholas Kounovsky, in *The Joy of Feeling Fit*, has suggested that an important aspect of fitness is what he has called 'a state of enchanting well-being'. I believe that this is what the French refer to as '*joie de vivre*', the joy of living.

Another way of describing fitness is 'a balance of the mental, physical, social and emotional components of the human organism', which is the way I like to think of it.

The main ingredients of bodily fitness may be considered as follows:

(a) General work capacity, which in turn depends on the efficiency of the heart, blood vessels and lungs (cardio-respiratory, or CR, fitness), sometimes referred to as 'aerobic' fitness. Activities such as brisk walking, bicycling, running, rope skipping and swimming are examples of forms of exercise that contribute to CR fitness.
(b) Muscular strength, or the force a group of muscles can exert against a movable object (isotonic contraction) or an immovable one (isometric contraction).
(c) Muscular endurance, or the ability of muscle groups to function efficiently over a period of time.
(d) Joint flexibility, or the widest range of movement of a joint without

strain. This largely depends on the condition of the muscles controlling the movement of the joint.

Several factors determine or limit a person's actual fitness. Among these are general medical health, nutritional state, weight, emotional state, postural habits, physical activity, ability to relax and quality of sleep.

Exercise and the Immune System

Most of what is known about the relationship between exercise and the immune system is the result of studies on obese people. There is evidence, for example, that in persons who are exceedingly overweight, neutrophils show a decreased capacity to destroy bacteria. There are also indications that raised cholesterol levels adversely affect phagocytosis, weaken antibody formation and reduce the production of white blood cells.

Since obese individuals often have abnormal blood fat levels, it is not unreasonable to expect that exercise, which reduces body and blood fats, would be of value in strengthening the immune system. In fact, one of the first recommendations doctors make to such persons is that they engage in suitable, regular exercise to reduce weight and improve health.

Exercise helps to maintain healthy blood and lymph circulation, by which essential nutrients are transported to all cells. It is also by means of blood and lymph that antibodies are borne to sites of infection and disease.

Exercise helps to maintain good body tone and reduce the rate of cell breakdown, which not infrequently heralds ageing and with it the possible onset of autoimmune disease (see Chapter 7).

Researchers from Purdue University and the University of Arizona, studying the combined effects of supplemental vitamins C and E, found that brisk exercise potentiated the immune-boosting ability of these nutrients. More remarkable, though, was the fact that those subjects who exercised but did not take the vitamin supplements still had above normal levels of infection-fighting T-cells in their blood. (See Shealey, Bibliography.)

The May/June 1986 *Health News Digest* reports that athletic women are less prone to cancer than non-athletic women. They comment that this is probably because they tend to be leaner than less active females and also because they produce less oestrogen. Both factors have been associated with cancer.

As a stress reliever, exercise is unsurpassed by any other single activity, except perhaps the regular practice of a relaxation technique. Stress reduction influences the mental state, shifting it towards optimism and away from pessimism. In Chapter 4, you read of the far-reaching effects of mind over malady and of emotions on the functioning of the immune system.

Benefits of the selected exercises

The exercises offered in this chapter have been thoughtfully chosen for the following reasons:

- They can be used as warm-ups as well as an actual exercise routine.
- They are excellent for promoting and maintaining flexibility.
- They discourage the build-up of tension and are therefore helpful in relieving stress.
- Because they encourage concentration and conscious breathing, they are superb for promoting a 'fine tuning-in' to oneself, in contrast with those forms of exercise that are done automatically, sometimes to the accompaniment of loud music. This approach respects the body-mind interrelationship, an appreciation of which is so vital in maintaining immune fitness.
- They are in accord with the 'new' approach now being taken by enlightened exercise instructors and practitioners. This approach is based on Eastern models and offers a combination of CR, isometric and isotonic conditioning and flexibility training. The Daily Dozen sequence (p.85), for instance, practised about twelve times at a fairly fast pace, will give some CR benefits.
- They are highly beneficial to the lymphatic system (see Chapter 1) because:

by contracting muscles they exert gentle pressure on underlying blood vessels, which in turn provide a therapeutic massage to lymphatic vessels;

the non-violent stretching action provided by all the movements temporarily removes 'kinks' from lymphatic vessels and promotes a smoother flow of lymph;

the semi-inverted posture gives the valves inside the lymph vessels a temporary rest, thus easing their work load;

they improve the tone of muscles and underlying blood and lymphatic vessels.

Before practising the exercises
– Always *check with your doctor* before embarking on any new exercise programme.
– Exercise regularly, preferably every day (or at least every other day), for about twenty minutes. You can limit aerobic (CR) exercises to three times a week.
– Be comfortable and wear loose-fitting clothing which will permit ease of breathing and movement.
– Don't exercise on a full stomach.
– Warm up before exercising to avoid strains and pulls on muscles and joints and their attachments.
– If you have to interrupt your exercise schedule for a day or more, start up again gradually. Don't over-exert yourself to 'make up for lost time'.

After exercising
Be sure to cool down adequately after exercising to help the circulation return to normal without the experience of ill effects such as dizziness and nausea.

The toe-to-top relaxation technique described in Chapter 5 is suggested for this purpose.

Warm-ups
Warm-ups are an important part of any effective exercise programme. They help to reduce stiffness, increase body temperature and improve blood and lymph circulation. They are useful in preventing muscular strain once the exercises themselves are in progress.

The Daily Dozen exercise series which follow serve a dual purpose. Done in slow motion, several times in succession, they may be used as warm-ups. Done one by one, with full focus on leisurely stretching in synchronization with the appropriate breathing, they may be employed as a set of exercises to bring about the benefits mentioned earlier.

For a more aerobic effect, to improve CR fitness, the series may be practised at a faster pace. It is because of its versatility and far-reaching benefits that The Daily Dozen sequence has been included in the exercise programme offered on the following pages. Yoga practitioners will be familiar with these exercises as The Sun Salutations.

It is best to practise on a firm, padded surface such as a carpeted floor or grassy area. I shall refer to this surface from now on as the 'mat'.

The Daily Dozen

1 Stand erect, with your arms relaxed at your sides and your feet slightly apart. Distribute your body weight equally between your feet (Fig. 1). Breathe in and out naturally.

Figure 1

2.   *Inhale* and reach upwards. Look up and *carefully* bend backwards as far as comfortable. Tighten your knees. Also tighten your buttock muscles to help protect your back (Fig. 2).

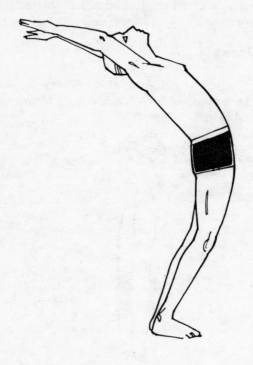

Figure 2

3.   *Exhaling,* bend forward at the hip joints rather than at the waist, and place your hands on the mat beside your feet (Fig. 3). You may need to bend your knees slightly to begin with, but as you become more flexible, you will be able to execute this step with knees straight.

Figure 3

4. *Inhale* and look up. Taking the weight of your body on your hands, step back with your *left* foot (toes point forward) (Fig. 4).

Figure 4

5.   Suspending your breath briefly (neither inhaling nor exhaling), also step backwards with your right foot (Fig. 5). The weight of your body is now borne by your hands and feet, and your body is level from the back of the head to the heels.

Figure 5

6.   Exhale and lower your knees to the mat. Also lower your chin (or forehead – whichever is more comfortable) and chest to the mat (Fig. 6).

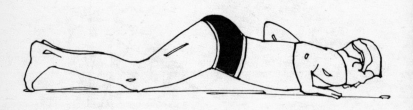

Figure 6

7. *Inhaling*, relax your feet so that your toes point backwards. Lower your body to the mat and *slowly and carefully* arch your back. Keep your head up and hands pressed to the mat (Fig. 7).

Figure 7

8. *Exhale* and point your toes forwards; push against the mat with your hands to help raise your hips. Arms are straight, or almost straight, and head hangs down. Aim your heels towards the mat but don't strain (Fig. 8).

Figure 8

9.   *Inhaling*, look up, rock forwards onto your toes and step between your hands with your *left* foot (the same foot with which you stepped backwards in number 4 of these instructions) (Fig. 9).

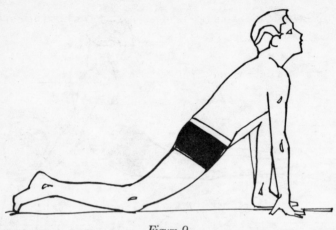

Figure 9

10.   *Exhaling*, step between your hands with your right foot and bend forwards (as described in number 3 of these instructions) (Fig. 10).

Figure 10

11.   *Inhaling, carefully* come up to a standing position and move smoothly into the backward bend described in number 2 of these instructions (Fig. 11).

12.   *Exhaling*, resume your beginning position, as described in number 1 of these instructions (Fig. 12).

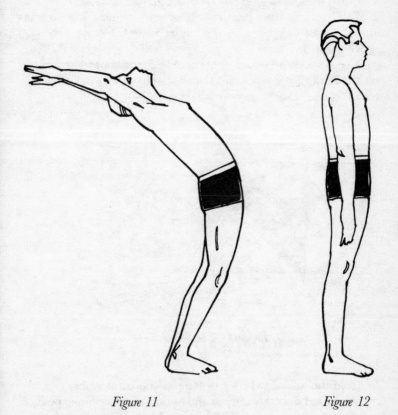

Figure 11   *Figure 12*

Breathe normally. Repeat the sequence (steps 2 to 12) as many times as desired, alternating left foot with right in steps 4 and 9.

The Spinal Twist

1.   Sit naturally erect on your mat. Stretch your legs out in front of you. Relax your arms at your sides. Breathe as normally as you can throughout the exercise.

2.   Bend your *right* leg and step over your outstretched left leg with your *right* foot. Position this foot so that it is near the knee, but not much higher, or it may be difficult to complete the twist.

3.   Raise your arms and smoothly turn your body as far as you can to the *right*, without straining. Look over your *right* shoulder. Press your *left* elbow against your bent *right* knee and maintain this contact throughout the exercise. If you can, hold on to your outstretched left leg with your left hand.

4.   Keep looking over your right shoulder. Bend your right arm and rest the back of the right hand against your lower back (Fig. 13). Remember to breathe as normally as possible.

Figure 13 The Spinal Twist

5.   Hold this spinal twist for as long as you comfortably can.

6.   Slowly and smoothly untwist and resume your beginning position (step 1).

7.   Repeat steps 2 to 6, substituting the word 'left' for 'right' and vice versa in the instructions.

The Triangle

1.   Stand tall, with legs as far apart as comfortable and toes pointing forwards to provide a wide, stable base. Relax your arms at your sides and breathe normally.
2.   Inhale smoothly and deeply as you raise your arms sideways until they are at shoulder level. Palms are turned downward.
3.   Exhaling, bend to the *right*, sliding the right hand down the right leg. If you can, continue the sideward bend and bring the *left arm* over the side of the head (keep the left shoulder back and the arm in line with the ear) (Fig. 14).

Figure 14 The Triangle

4.   Hold this position as long as you comfortably can, breathing as normally as possible.
5.   Slowly and smoothly resume your beginning position (step 1), synchronizing breathing with movement.
6.   Relax your arms.
7.   Repeat steps 2 to 5, bending to the *left* this time.
8.   Sit or lie down and rest.

The Shoulderstand

1.   Lie on your back with your arms beside you, palms turned down and legs stretched out in front.
2.   Bend your knees and position your feet comfortably close to your bottom.
3.   Lift one leg and point the foot straight upwards; do the same with the other leg.
4.   Pressing your palms and elbows firmly against the mat, kick backwards to raise the hips. Keep the upper arms and elbows in firm contact with the mat but support the raised hips with your hands, thumbs in front. You may end the exercise here or you may proceed to step 5. In either case, hold the completed position for as long as you are comfortable in it. Breathe normally throughout.
5.   Carefully move your hands towards the upper back until your body is in a more vertical position, and your chin touches your chest (Fig. 15).

Figure 15 The Shoulderstand

Maintain this position for as long as you are comfortable in it, breathing as normally as possible.

To come out of position
Tip your feet backwards slightly and rest your arms beside you on the mat. Keep your chin up and your head pressed to the mat as you *slowly and carefully* lower your hips. Bend your knees and lower your legs, one at a time, to the mat. Relax for a minute or two.

7 THE IMMUNITY CONNECTION

One of the characteristics of a properly functioning immune system is its ability to recognize a foreign antigen that has entered the body and to protect it from being harmed by that agent. Sometimes, though, the system malfunctions and when it does autoimmune disease results.

Autoimmune Diseases

Autoimmune diseases represent an immunologic attack on the body's own tissues, in which the body begins producing *autoantigens* (its own antigens) and responds to these by forming *autoantibodies* (antibodies to self).

Autoimmunity is characterized by the inappropriate activity of immune regulatory activity. Examples of this are: B-lymphocytes that begin to synthesize autoantibodies and T-lymphocytes that infiltrate tissues and destroy them.

The body's defences against foreign agents do not function equally effectively in all people, and the potential for autoimmunity is present in everyone.

Factors contributing to the onset of autoimmune disease include nutritional state, age, sex, race, the use of certain drugs, radiation, alcohol intake, heredity, fatigue and stress. Autoimmune disease can also occur in response to infections, especially those of long standing, as a sequel to conditions affecting a specific organ, such as inflammation of the thyroid gland, as well as in disorders affecting several body systems as seen, for instance, in systemic lupus erythematosus which will be discussed later.

Autoimmune disease is prevented when immune regulatory mechanisms are working well. Chiefly responsible for this are the interactions between various sub-populations of T-lymphocytes. When there is an imbalance resulting either in abnormal production of helper T-cells or deficiency of suppressor T-cells autoimmunity could occur. But a defect in any part of the immune system could be responsible.

In various immune-related disorders, the WBCs (white blood cells) are either absent or insufficient. These protector cells may be inhibited by a wide range of factors, some of which have just been mentioned.

The role of genetic factors in autoimmune disease is still largely unknown. Much better known is the role of emotional factors. A person with lupus, for example, may have a genetic makeup that makes her susceptible to the disorder. But it generally takes something to trigger the onset of the disorder. This can be unnecessary exposure to sun or using certain medications or stress. In fact, lupus often appears following a period of intense stress, such as after the loss of a significant relationship. I'm painfully reminded of this fact by the case of my own, younger, sister who was diagnosed with lupus after she and her husband separated despite many years of marriage.

Some drugs that may produce symptoms of autoimmune disease are diphenylhydantoin, isoniazid, hydralazine and procainamide, used to treat epilepsy, tuberculosis, hypertension (high blood-pressure) and irregularities of the heart respectively. The symptoms usually disappear, however, when the offending drug is discontinued.

Arthritis (from Greek *arthron*, joint, and *itis*, inflammation) is literally inflammation of a joint. It is usually accompanied by pain and changes in tissue structure.

This widespread condition may result from or be associated with a variety of disorders, including infection, traumas and degenerative diseases.

There are several types of arthritis, and there is no lack of informative literature on the subject. I shall deal here only with rheumatoid arthritis, which afflicts millions of people, striking about twice as many women as men.

Rheumatoid arthritis
Rheumatoid arthritis (RA) begins as an inflammation of the synovial membrane, which lines the capsule of joints and which lubricates them. Although the exact cause of the inflammation is uncertain, many medical researchers believe that it is a consequence of an attack on the joints by the body's immune system. In RA victims, suppressor T-cell deficiencies may exist. Experts also believe that diet and stress play a part in initiating the inflammatory processes of RA, and it is decidedly possible that all three factors are contributory.

In addition to its effect on joints, RA can produce generalized symptoms such as fatigue, lack of energy and loss of appetite. It tends to become chronic and to wax and wane. It is frequently disabling.

Writing about RA in his book *Evening Primrose Oil*, Richard Passwater explains that the inflammation of the synovial membrane in RA is brought about by the two series prostaglandins produced by arachidonic acid (AA) (please refer to the section on essential fatty acids (EFAs) in Chapter 3, p.47). Dr Passwater further points out that the inflammation can be reduced by slowing down the release of stored AA or retarding production of prostaglandin E2 (PGE2).

Many doctors prescribe drugs such as corticosteroids and indomethacin to relieve the pain of RA and reduce inflammation by slowing down AA release from storage. These medications, however, have a serious drawback: they block production of a desirable prostaglandin, PGE1 (also discussed in Chapter 3).

A preferable way of controlling AA release from storage is to provide a dietary source of PGE1. As Dr Passwater notes, it is always wiser to utilize natural compounds to regulate the body rather than to use synthetic drugs if the same degree of control can be achieved. Although some RA sufferers may need drug therapy in addition to improved nutritional support, others respond very well indeed to dietary adjustments alone.

In several well conducted studies, evening primrose oil (EPO) proved useful in controlling RA in a number of patients. For EPO to be effective, though, the diet must be adequate in all respects, particularly in vitamins B_5 (pantothenic acid), B_6 (pyridoxine), C and E.

According to Dr Richard A. Kunin, correlations between nutrient deficiencies and inflammation of the joints are too many and too great to be dismissed, and he has made several dietary recommendations in his book entitled *Mega-Nutrition* (see Bibliography). These include care in ensuring an adequate intake of vitamins A, B_3 (niacin), B_6 and C and the minerals magnesium and zinc. He also suggests supplementation with silica (a form of silicon) to enhance the replacement of calcium, which is lost through arthritic inflammations.

In an article appearing in *Alive Canadian Journal of Health & Nutrition*, issue number 71, Baz Edmeades refers to silica as 'nature's recalcifier'. In research conducted at the University of Rabat in Morocco, improving the diet of older patients with joint disorders through silica supplementation resulted in a lessening of pain and an increase in mobility in a high percentage of cases.

Oats are among the relatively few foods that do have a high silicon content; but they must be rolled or steel cut, rather than the instant kind.

In choosing a silicon supplement, you should insist on an *aqueous extract* of spring horsetail. Mineral silica and ground horsetail herb powder should *not* be used since they are abrasive to the stomach and intestines.

Multiple sclerosis

Multiple sclerosis, or MS, is the most common nervous system disease affecting young adults. It occurs slightly more frequently in women than in men. In some countries it is known as *disseminated sclerosis*.

MS is so called because of the many (multiple) scars (sclerosis) appearing in a number of places within the nervous system. It is often classified as an autoimmune disease, in which the body literally wages war against itself. Although the exact cause of this condition is still undetermined, it *is* known that the *myelin sheath* is affected. This is the term given to the coating around nerve fibres. It may be useful to think of myelin as the insulation on an electrical cord. If this is frayed or otherwise worn, electrical currents may be short circuited. Similarly, if the myelin sheath is defective – as it is in MS – messages from the brain to the muscles may be slowed down or not even get through.

MS varies greatly from person to person and in its severity and course. In yoga classes I've conducted for MS sufferers, there were students who were almost symptom free and whose coordination, balance and range of motion were amazing. For some, the disease follows a path in which exacerbations alternate with remissions; that is, there are periods in which symptoms flare up and others when they abate. Many persons have one or two attacks and then may not be significantly troubled during the rest of their lives. Still others may experience a slowly progressive course with no remissions.

Among the factors that contribute to exacerbations are emotional upsets, infections, over-exertion and fatigue, injuries, surgery and pregnancy.

Since it is now well known that a body kept in the best possible condition has the best chance of recovering from an illness, it makes good sense to give this top priority. MS organizations emphasize that the body's immune system functions best when the individual with MS is doing well emotionally.

Adelle Davis has written that in people with whom she worked, MS was invariably brought on by very severe stress during periods when pantothenic acid was deficient in their diets. In experimental animals, a lack of pantothenic acid results in actual loss of the myelin sheath (as occurs in MS).

Stress greatly increases the need for this nutrient, as well as that of other B vitamins and vitamin E. If these are undersupplied, nerve degeneration occurs in both animals and humans. However, a number of individuals have recovered completely from this nervous system disorder when dietary improvements were made soon after diagnosis.

MS organizations also emphasize the importance of those factors which are included in The VIP Formula (outlined in Chapter 5, p.79).

Author Judy Graham, who has MS, has written about the value of evening primrose oil (EPO) in her book with the same name (see Bibliography). She points out how it works on the T-suppressor lymphocytes which keep parts of the immune system under control and make sure that the body's defences attack foreign agents rather than its own tissues. She also remarks on the anti-viral properties of EPO, as well as its regulating effect on the release of neurotransmitters and on prostaglandin balance. You may also be interested in reading Graham's other book entitled *Multiple Sclerosis – A Self-help Guide to Its Management* (Thorsons).

Autopsy studies have revealed a marked decrease in the lecithin content of the brain and myelin sheath of MS victims and abnormality of the little there was. Normally, these body tissues are high in lecithin.

MS is most common in countries where the diet is high in saturated fats. This invariably means that the lecithin content of the blood is decreased. When MS sufferers were put on low-fat diets, they experienced fewer difficult periods in the course of the disorder than they would otherwise have, and these periods were of shorter duration. When three or more tablespoons of lecithin were added to the diet, even greater improvement was noted.

Adelle Davis has remarked in *Let's Eat Right to Keep Fit*, that lecithin can be made in the intestinal wall provided that choline and inositol (two B vitamins) and EFAs are supplied. (Good food sources of choline are: oats, organ meats, soya beans and wheatgerm; of inositol: barley, cantaloupe melons, grapefruit, blackstrap molasses, oats, oranges, organ meats, peanuts, wheatgerm and whole wheat products.) Davis has also pointed out, in *Let's Get Well*, that any nutrient lack which prevents lecithin production can cause MS to worsen. Notable are magnesium, vitamin E, vitamin B_6 and other B vitamins, and MS sufferers would do well to ensure an adequate intake of these nutrients. (Food sources of magnesium include blackstrap molasses, dark green leafy vegetables, freshly shelled nuts, peas, brown rice, soya beans and whole grain products.)

Good dietary sources of lecithin include eggs, liver, nuts, soya bean oil and wheat, as well as unrefined foods containing oil.

(For sources of other nutrients mentioned in this section, please refer to Chapter 3.)

Systemic Lupus Erythematosus

Systemic Lupus Erythematosus (lupus, or SLE) is a complex syndrome that can affect many tissues and organs, such as the heart and blood vessels, lungs, kidneys, brain and nervous system, muscles, joints, skin and collagen. Symptoms can come and go; they include fever, arthritis and signs of heart and lung involvement.

SLE can be very difficult to diagnose because, as Henrietta Aladjem writes in *The Sun Is My Enemy* (see Bibliography), it is like a chameleon – always changing. Because the various symptoms of SLE closely resemble those of other diseases, they are sometimes mistaken for another illness. Also, because the symptoms come and go, some doctors tend to believe that patients are imagining their ailments.

The main diagnostic finding in SLE is the presence of the LE cell, a polymorphonuclear neutrophil which has eaten the nucleus of another white blood cell (WBC). A low WBC count is also an important feature of SLE. With newer diagnostic techniques, mainly the LE cell test, milder forms of SLE have been recognized.

SLE appears most frequently in women of childbearing age and seems to be on the increase among normally dynamic women.

Although there may be a genetic predisposition to SLE, it usually takes something to 'trigger' its onset. Most notable of these 'triggering factors' is emotional stress such as bereavement, excessive exposure to sunlight and illness.

Numerous medications are used to treat SLE and these include the cortisone group of drugs, ACTH, anti-malarial drugs, immunosuppressive drugs and aspirin. All can produce harmful side effects.

Drugs to avoid, unless specifically prescribed by a doctor who is knowledgeable in drug therapy for SLE patients, are penicillin, sulfa drugs, pronestyl (a drug for treating certain heart conditions), hydralazine and apresoline (for high blood-pressure), some drugs used for controlling seizures, birth control pills and caffeine. In the laboratory, it has been found that caffeine inhibits the ability of the body's cells to repair their DNA (deoxyribonucleic acid, which carries the hereditary information for each cell and specifies its function). One of the factors contributing to SLE is the inability of cells to repair their DNA properly, and laboratory studies suggest that SLE patients would be wise to avoid drinks containing caffeine, such as coffee, tea and colas (do read labels).

Some doctors advise women with SLE against pregnancy for fear of kidney involvement. This is subject to individual discussion. Many persons with SLE consider adoption rather than take health risks. A former co-worker of mine adopted twin girls from Central America.

If you have SLE or know someone who does, here are useful suggestions based on recommendations by The National Lupus Erythematosus Foundation Inc., Van Nuys, California. They are very much in accord with The VIP Formula outlined in Chapter 5.

– Never fail to take prescribed medications; be familiar with their side effects.
– Stick to an adequate, wholesome diet. Avoid beverages containing caffeine.
– Exercise *moderately* and regularly. Simple yoga exercises are suitable.
– Avoid fatigue. Get plenty of sleep and practise a relaxation technique daily.
– Cultivate a positive outlook and maintain an active mental life. Get involved with something in which you are keenly interested and find pleasantly stimulating.
– Avoid unnecessary exposure to the sun. Wear protective clothing

and use a suitable sunscreen lotion. (I have given detailed information on the effects of sun on skin and on suitable protection from the sun's ultraviolet rays in *Silky, Smooth and Strong*.)

Hypersensitivity

An intact immune system is essential for the successful defence against microorganisms. Inappropriate or excessive activation of the system can be harmful. Such responses are technically referred to as *hypersensitivity reactions*. We generally speak of them as allergies.

Hypersensitivity may be an inherited trait. Susceptible persons react within minutes of exposure to the offending agents. These include pollen, dust, hair, fur, feathers, scales or dandruff and sometimes specific foods such as eggs, chocolate, milk, wheat, tomatoes, citrus fruits, oatmeal and potatoes. It is thought that antibodies of the IgE class are then formed to these antigens.

Hypersensitivity is caused by the entry of foreign substances into the blood-stream. These substances can gain access by injection, as with drugs, vaccines and serums; through the skin, as do some cosmetics, insect venoms and poison oak or ivy; through mucous membranes of the nasal passages, for example pollens, dust and dandruff; from the intestinal tract as do foods, bacteria, moulds, histamine and drugs.

Signs and symptoms of hypersensitivity include *eosinophilia*, in which there is an accumulation in the blood of an unusual number of eosinophils (see Chapter 1), urticaria, hives, eczema, rash, asthma, hay fever, migraine, digestive disturbances and even mental disturbances.

Anaphylaxis

Early in this century, researchers attempting to protect dogs against a sea anemone toxin by repeated immunizations with small doses of the toxin observed that some animals developed fatal shock after receiving a dose much lower than the toxic dose for an unimmunized animal. Thus, they coined the word *anaphylaxis*, which means the opposite of protection, to describe this reaction.

Symptoms of anaphylactic shock occur suddenly and include irritability, difficulty breathing, blue colouration of the skin and mucous membranes and sometimes convulsions and unconsciousness. Death can occur if emergency treatment is not given. Milder symptoms include a slight fever and redness and itching of the skin.

Serum sickness

In the early 1900s, researchers were also investigating the protective value of serum from animals immunized with diphtheria and tetanus toxins. Although most humans responded favourably, some developed fever, rash, enlarged lymph nodes and painful joints within a week or two of receiving animal serum. These symptoms were collectively called *serum sickness*.

Allergy

Allergy (from Greek *allos*, other and *ergon*, work) describes an altered reaction of body tissues to a specific substance (allergen) which, in non-sensitive persons, will in similar amounts produce no adverse effect. It is essentially an antibody-antigen reaction although in some cases the antibody cannot be demonstrated. The reaction may be due to the release of histamine or histamine-like substances from injured cells.

Well-known allergic conditions include asthma, ear and eye allergies and hay fever.

The early nineteenth-century studies made it possible to distinguish between the protective potential of immune responses and those that were harmful. Healthy individuals do not respond abnormally when exposed to allergens; they are not adversely affected. It therefore appears that emphasis must be placed on building health rather than on avoiding potentially harmful substances which, in many cases, cannot even be identified.

Dr Hans Selye long ago pointed out that allergic symptoms are often nothing more than the body's response to stress. When animals' adrenal glands are removed to prevent cortisone from reaching the blood (thus simulating adrenal exhaustion in humans), the allergic reaction to an injection of a foreign substance is exceedingly severe; sometimes fatal. Identical injections have hardly any untoward effects on healthy animals.

Stresses such as an inadequate diet, emotional upsets, insufficient sleep, infections or the use of certain drugs usually precede the appearance of allergies. The added stress of a toxic allergen can be devastating.

Although high stress levels increase practically all dietary requirements, allergy sufferers have been found to be pitifully deficient of every essential nutrient except carbohydrates. When the missing factors are supplied, however, the allergies often disappear.

In a study done on thirty-two allergic children suffering from bronchial asthma and allergic eczema, when the subjects were fed sufficient protein, no refined carbohydrates, adequate essential fatty acids (EFAs) and daily supplements of vitamins A, C, D, E and the B complex, all recovered within two months. (See Davis, *Let's Get Well*, Bibliography.)

Pantothenic acid (vitamin B₅)

Allergies have been repeatedly produced in animals by injecting them with numerous foreign substances. The allergic reaction is particularly severe or even fatal when pantothenic acid is deficient. (You can read more about this highly protective vitamin in Chapter 3.)

It would seem that in allergies, the lack of no other nutrient has an effect comparable with that of a pantothenic acid deficiency. Because cortisone cannot be produced without pantothenic acid, injections of raw egg white, for instance, cause marked hay fever-like symptoms in animals undersupplied with this vitamin. If, however, the diet is adequate in every respect, or if cortisone is given, injected animals show few or no hypersensitive reactions.

There is a striking similarity between the symptoms allergy sufferers report and those of subjects deficient in pantothenic acid. These include lethargy, poor appetite, digestive upsets, headache, irritability, anxiety, depression, sleepiness, recurring infection of the lungs and air passages as well as eosinophilia (abnormally large numbers of eosinophils in the blood and lymph). Correcting the pantothenic acid deficiency often brings welcome relief.

Food allergies

It is well to bear in mind, however, that all nutrients work together. It is also worth remembering that the improper digestion of foods can produce food allergies. Partially digested food particles that enter the blood can act as irritants. When proteins are undigested, for example, the amino acid *histidine* can be changed by certain intestinal bacteria into histamine. This substance is found in abnormally large quantities in the blood of many allergic persons. The importance of chewing food thoroughly thus becomes evident.

Pantothenic acid, vitamin B_6 (pyridoxine) and vitamin C have an antihistamine action, and an undersupply of any of these nutrients can lead to eosinophilia (explained earlier in this chapter), which is a characteristic feature of allergies.

Allergies and cell permeability

An adequate diet of wholesome food, which provides all the essential nutrients, makes for healthy body cells. Such cells are not easily penetrated by harmful substances. If their *permeability* is increased, however, nutrients can leak from them and toxic materials pass into them. Nutrient deficiencies can cause such increased cell permeability.

A vitamin C deficiency makes cells more permeable by promoting the breakdown of connective tissue. An EFA (essential fatty acid) deficiency will also lead to increased cell permeability, permitting ready access of harmful substances. If EFAs are damaged by oxygen because of an undersupply of vitamin E, the same results occur.

Vitamin A is very useful in decreasing cell permeability in both the skin and mucous membranes. When large doses of vitamins A and E were given daily for a short period to adults, their cells showed a marked and rapid increase in ability to prevent penetration by foreign substances.

Persons with allergies have abnormally small amounts of vitamin C in their blood. A major function of this vitamin is as a detoxifying agent, and for decades it has been known to prevent the harmful effects of allergic reactions and anaphylactic shock caused by drugs. Apart from its detoxifying action, vitamin C potentiates the action of cortisone, acts as an antihistamine and decreases the permeability of cells.

Prescription for allergies

Dr Richard Kunin has remarked that there is no doubt about the value of nutrients in the treatment of allergic disorders. He recommends strengthening what he calls the 'anti-inflammatory system' by the proper use of pantothenic acid, vitamins A, C and E and other nutrients mentioned in this book. In addition, he suggests an adequate intake of dietary fibre and the use of lactobacillus acidophilus tablets or culture to lessen food allergies by increasing bowel transit time.

Since nutrition is only one aspect of health maintenance, however, the prescription for allergies must of necessity include an effective stress management programme, and a review of Chapter 5 is therefore suggested.

Immune Deficiency

When I mentioned to friends that I was writing a book on the immune system, the first thing they asked about was AIDS. This is a typical reaction nowadays, and any mention of immune deficiency immediately calls to mind this serious and much publicized health hazard.

Immune deficiency, or defects in immunity, can be inherited as well as acquired. Because of the nature and scope of this book, I shall limit myself to a brief discussion of only one example of each type.

In all immune deficiency disorders, the lymphocytes or the antibodies produced by the B-cells or both are either insufficient or absent. In fact, it is decidedly possible that both types of cells may have originated from common stem cells.

Defects may also result from imbalance among the various cells that regulate immune functioning. Causes of the foregoing include faulty genes, diets deficient in essential nutrients, emotional stress, hormonal imbalances, injuries, surgery, radiation and drugs.

Severe Combined Immunodeficiency (SCID)

This is a syndrome consisting of different genetic diseases, characterized by a deficiency of lymphocytes in the blood (lymphopenia), defective development of tissue (hypoplasia) in all lymphoid organs, and impaired cellular and humoral immunity. Deficiencies in the number of T-cells and the functions of B- and T-cells are also consistently seen.

Infants with this disorder usually die within the first two years of life from multiple severe infections. Although bone marrow transplants offer some hope to youngsters so afflicted, they do not always 'take'.

Acquired Immune Deficiency Syndrome (AIDS)

Acquired Immune Deficiency Syndrome (AIDS), as the name suggests, is an acquired rather than an inherited disease. It is an infection caused by a virus of the retrovirus family, HTLV-III (human

T-lymphotropic virus type III). It severely damages the immune system, making the body vulnerable to many other illnesses. People afflicted with AIDS become very sick and many die from secondary illnesses such as pneumonia and cancer. Two of the most common of these are PCP (Pneumocystis carinii pneumonia) and KS (Kaposi's sarcoma), a rare form of skin cancer which damages the lining of blood vessels.

The infections seen in AIDS patients were previously known only in individuals born with certain immune system defects, in those whose immunity had been impaired by chemotherapeutic agents used to treat cancer or who were given immunosuppressants to help them resist rejection of organ transplants. AIDS, it appeared, killed its victims by destroying their immune system.

According to Jeffrey Laurence, Assistant Professor of Medicine at the Cornell University Medical Center, and Assistant Attending Physician at New York Hospital, the total collapse of the immune defences seen in AIDS victims stems largely from a single defect: a reduction in the number and a change in the function of the T4 lymphocytes, one of the many distinct kinds of cells that make up the immune system. Characteristic of this dreaded disease is the altered ratio of T-helper to T-suppressor cells (the norm is about 1.8 helpers: 1 suppressor cell).

Signs and symptoms
In the early stages of infection, a person with AIDS usually looks and feels fairly well. This is a 'carrier' state which may last for months or even years. A carrier can, however, pass the virus to others.

AIDS symptoms include:

- thrush (white spots or a thick grey-white coating in the mouth or throat or on the tongue);
- swollen lymph nodes in the neck or in the armpits or groins;
- bruising or unexplained bleeding from any body orifice;
- marked weight loss;
- extreme fatigue;
- recurring fevers and night sweats;
- a chronic harsh, dry cough;
- joint pains;

– persistent diarrhoea or the presence of blood in the stools;
– skin eruptions, sores or discolorations (e.g. slowly enlarging purplish nodules);
– blurred vision or chronic headaches.

These are also symptoms of other diseases. If you experience them, it does not necessarily mean that you have AIDS. If, however, they persist for more than a couple of weeks and you are at risk for AIDS (more on this later), you should *see a doctor.*

A simple blood test can detect the presence of AIDS antibodies in the blood, although it does not confirm diagnosis. The test is fairly accurate, though, after a person has had the infection for about six months.

ARC (*AIDS-related condition*)

Many individuals have been infected with the virus causing AIDS (also called HIV, or Human Immunodeficiency Virus) and show at least two of the symptoms related to AIDS for more than three months, but do not have one of the accompanying diseases that confirm a diagnosis of AIDS. These persons are said to have ARC, and some of them will go on to develop AIDS.

At risk

AIDS is basically a sexually-transmitted disease. The virus is present in the semen or vaginal fluid of infected persons and can be transmitted during sexual intercourse. Homosexual and bisexual males are at greatest risk, as well as female partners of males at risk.

The AIDS virus is also present in the blood of infected individuals and poses a special risk for those who inject themselves with drugs, especially if they share needles or syringes.

Similar risks exist with other skin-penetrating practices. It is unsafe to use inadequately sterilized ear-piercing equipment or tattooing or acupuncture needles. It is also potentially dangerous to share a razor or toothbrush used by an infected person.

The AIDS virus has been isolated in the laboratory from the tears and saliva of infected individuals.

An infected woman could transmit the virus to her baby either during pregnancy, at the time of birth or through breastfeeding.

Haemophiliacs, who depend on transfusions of blood products, could also be at risk, as well as women artificially inseminated with sperm from infected donors.

Cure for AIDS

There is, at present, no known cure for AIDS, although Michael A. Weiner (see Bibliography) has described at some length a promising regimen of treatment being carried out by Dr Robert F. Cathcart III, in Los Altos, California. It is essentially the oral and intravenous administration of large doses of vitamin C, and Dr Weiner has described the treatment protocol at length.

AIDS prevention

- Be responsible.
- Fewer sexual partners, fewer risks. To be absolutely safe, either abstain from sexual intercourse or stick with one partner who does not indulge in high-risk practices (see section entitled At Risk). Your partner should also be *known* to be free of infection. Take the time to get to know your partner; discuss your concerns about AIDS and other sexually-transmitted diseases before becoming sexually involved.
- The use of condoms reduces risk. They offer considerable protection, provided they are suitable and used correctly and consistently. Condoms used along with spermicides containing nonoxynol-9 are even safer. Synthetic (latex) condoms are better than natural (animal skin) condoms. Vaseline and other oil-based lubricants reduce the effectiveness of condoms. Read labels.
- Do not indulge in oral sex with a partner of dubious health.
- Do not engage in practices where body fluids are exchanged (e.g. 'French kissing') with a partner of whose health status you are unsure.
- Do not indulge in anal sex – it is highly dangerous. The rectal wall is only one cell layer thick.
- Never share or re-use syringes or needles.
- Try to avoid receiving blood transfusions, especially if travelling abroad. Blood for transfusion is not checked for the AIDS virus in some countries. In some parts of the world, too, medical equipment, such as scalpels and needles, may not be properly sterilized.
- Do not share razors or toothbrushes.
- Do not allow blood, semen or urine to contaminate any skin break such as a cut or wound. Carefully wash any part of your body that may have come in contact with secretions or excreta from a suspected

AIDS carrier. The AIDS virus is very sensitive to soap and water.
– Avoid using alcohol or drugs before sexual intercourse. These
substances remove inhibitions and prevent the exercise of caution in
protecting oneself.
– Do not ignore AIDS symptoms. Seek medical help promptly.
– Keep your resistance up. The better your physical, mental and
emotional health, the better you are able to withstand *any* virus. Review
the points covered in The VIP Formula in Chapter 5.

Cancer

Tumour cells, according to *Medical Microbiology* (Samuel Baron, MD,
ed.), differ from normal cells in their ability to proliferate (reproduce
rapidly) in an abnormal fashion and to metastasize (to transfer
themselves from one part of the body to another through the blood
vessels or lymph channels).

A further and important difference between cancerous and normal
cells is the new antigens on the surface of tumour cells. These are
recognized by the immune system and elicit a specific immune response
capable of destroying the tumour. In health, the immune system can
distinguish normal ('self') cells from abnormal ('altered self') cells and
can effectively reject the latter as they arise. When the system is
suppressed, however, by drugs or infections or other harmful agents,
this protective mechanism can fail and cancer may result. Indeed,
proponents of the cancer surveillance theory contend that immuno-
suppressed animals are more vulnerable to tumour development by
cancer-provoking viruses than normal animals, and in humans there
is a higher incidence of cancer in those whose immune system is
suppressed than in the general population.

Cancer cells may nullify the functions of certain parts of the immune
system, such as the helper T-cells, and they may unduly stimulate
others such as the suppressor T-cells. These aberrations may lead not
only to uncontrolled tumour growth, but also to greater susceptibility
to all kinds of infections.

Cancer seems to 'run' in some families and if this is true of yours,
you would be wise to be particularly careful in avoiding known
carcinogens (cancer-causing agents) such as smoking, undue exposure
to the sun, unnecessary food additives, etc. Also take care to avoid

any other agents that can depress your immune system, such as certain drugs and a combination of smoking and high alcohol intake. You would be prudent, too, to provide your body's natural defences with the best possible nutritional and psychological reinforcements, as outlined in this book.

The mind factor

Sceptics dismiss as nonsense the idea that mental processes could be involved either in the appearance of certain cancers or in their outcome. It is not worthwhile even to attempt a defence of this narrow-minded attitude. There is too much persuasive literature written by reputable health professionals to support a respectable case on behalf of the link between mind, emotions and cancer.

Based on my own contact with cancer patients and knowledge of their personal histories, I have come to believe that such a connection is no myth at all. I was reminded of this while writing the manuscript for this book. A friend of mine died of ovarian cancer shortly after her forty-fifth birthday. In the previous six months, she told me a great deal about her life as a growing girl and also as a married woman. The more I heard, the more I became convinced of the powerful influence emotions can exert on health. Two other friends, both in their thirties, are currently battling with cancer. The lives and circumstances of both have many components in common with my deceased friend, including the fact that none of these three individuals was ever encouraged to express her feelings. Are the experts right? Can emotions kill? Is there indeed a cancer-prone personality?

The cancer-prone personality

One profile of such a personality has been sketched by Dr Lawrence LeShan, a psychologist who has worked with many cancer patients. Dr LeShan has found that the lives of these individuals have certain points in common, including:

– difficult interpersonal relationships during early life, with feelings of neglect, alienation and despair predominating;
– an all-consuming preoccupation with a meaningful relationship or career, around which life centred;
– deep depression following the loss of this relationship or vocation, and recurrence of the anguish experienced in childhood;

- putting up a happy exterior and appearing in control while suppressing negative feelings such as hurt, anger, resentment, hostility, unhappiness, helplessness and hopelessness.

It is not the stresses themselves that bring about disease-producing changes in the body, but the ability of these persons to handle them maturely and effectively. Our capacity for managing stress in a healthful way affects natural killer (NK) cell activity, a key factor in resisting cancer. As has been impressively demonstrated by Carl Simonton and colleagues, we can enlist mental forces to strengthen other therapeutic agents in the fight against cancer. (Please review Chapters 4 and 5.)

Cancer alert
Many forms of cancer give early warning signs. Here are major ones:

- unusual discharge or bleeding from any internal or external body site;
- change in bowel or bladder habits;
- increasing or persisting cough or hoarseness;
- changes in the size, shape or appearance of a wart or mole;
- indigestion or difficulty in swallowing;
- a lump or thickening in any part of the body, especially the breast;
- a sore that doesn't heal;
- unexplained weight loss.

The appearance of any of these signs should be brought to a doctor's attention without delay.

Strategies for cancer prevention
The following guidelines, used in conjunction with The VIP Formula outlined in Chapter 5, should prove useful in helping ward off cancer and keep your body's natural defence forces in tip-top condition.

- Be a non-smoker: 80 per cent of all lung cancers could be prevented by not smoking.
- Adhere to a low-fat diet.
- Stick to a high-fibre diet.
- Eat generously of complex carbohydrates (rather than refined carbohydrates), provided by foods such as potatoes, fresh corn, brown rice and whole wheat products.

– Ensure that your diet is adequate in all respects. Take particular care to provide enough essential fatty acids (EFAs), vitamins A, C and E, the B vitamins and the minerals selenium and zinc.

– Avoid obesity. Achieve and maintain your ideal weight.

– Protect yourself from unnecessary exposure to the sun.

– Avoid contact with known cancer-producing substances at work, at home and in the community (e.g. cigarette smoke, automobile exhaust, pesticides and radiation).

– Have regular medical and dental checkups.

– Women: have a regular Pap (smear) test, which detects changes in the neck of the womb, indicating a precancerous or cancerous condition. Also do monthly breast self-examinations.

– Investigate any lump or sore that does not heal, or any change in your normal state of health.

– Limit your intake of alcohol to the equivalent of a glass of wine (or less) a day.

– Eat more dark green and deep yellow vegetables which are rich in beta-carotene (a form of vitamin A), a highly protective nutrient. Also increase your consumption of vitamin C-rich vegetables and fruits. Vitamin C is believed to counteract the formation of cancer-causing substances known as *nitrosamines*. Frequently include cruciferous vegetables in your diet. These belong to a family of plants, the flowers of which have four leaves arranged in the pattern of a cross. They include broccoli, Brussels sprouts, cabbage, cauliflower and kohlrabi. Tests indicate that these vegetables may contribute to building immunity to some forms of cancer.

– Reduce consumption of smoked foods and those cured with salt and nitrite. These include hams, some sausages and some fish. They contain carcinogens which are chemically similar to the tars in tobacco smoke. Nitrite has long been used for meat preservation to destroy organisms that cause food poisoning (botulism) and to improve the colour and flavour of the product.

Also reduce consumption of barbecued foods. In the process of barbecuing, particles called PAH (polycyclic aromatic hydrocarbons) are produced. These are thought to be cancer causing.

8 NOTABLE IMMUNE BOOSTERS

When a nation is threatened by an enemy, it reinforces its defences to prevent invasion and takeover. Likewise, when the human body is menaced by stressors with the potential to overpower its natural protective forces, the need for fortification arises. Drugs, chemicals, surgery, emotional difficulties and infections are only a few examples of agents of stress which undermine immunity to illness. In a weakened state, the body then requires essential nutrients in larger amounts than it does under normal circumstances. If these requirements are not met, the body becomes prey to attack by pathogens which hover around us, poised to strike the moment we are off guard.

The following are selected products now on the market which show exciting possibilities as super natural immune boosters. Used in conjunction with a wholesome diet, as part of an immune enhancing lifestyle, these products may be considered useful during those times when life's demands tax to the limit or overwhelm our natural resources for dealing with them.

Coenzyme Q10

Coenzyme Q is a naturally occurring molecule. It is also known as *ubiquinone* (from the word 'ubiquitous', which means 'everywhere'). It is found in virtually every cell in the body.

Both animals and humans have a variety of molecular formulations ranging from coenzyme Q6 to coenzyme Q10. Only coenzyme Q10 (which will be referred to as CoQ10 from now on) is found in humans and is the form used by the body for functions requiring energy. The animal form of the enzyme can, however, be raised to the Q10 status when taken into the body as part of the diet.

CoQ10 is a vital catalyst in the generation of energy needed by all the body's cells, and since immunity requires a constant supply of first-grade energy, CoQ10 must be available to all cells at all times. Because of the crucial part CoQ10 plays in creating as much as 95 per cent of the total energy needs of the body, it would be worthwhile taking a look at the source of this energy and how CoQ10 fits in.

The mitochondria

All body systems are made up of cells. Each cell may be considered a unit of life. All systems run on energy and the cells of which they are composed also run on energy. Within each cell is a sort of minature engine that converts the nutrients received from food eaten into the energy needed to carry out vital functions. This 'miniature engine' is the *mitochondrion* (plural, *mitochondria*). The word comes from the Greek *mitos*, thread, and *chondros*, cartilage, and indeed mitochondria appear under the microscope as slender filaments or rods.

Mitochondria are often referred to as the powerhouses of cells because, just as a powerhouse burns fuel to produce electricity, the mitochondria burn glucose to produce ATP molecules, the chemical energy needed by cells. In the process, mitochondria use up energy and give off carbon dioxide and water. The oxygen you inhale enters first the cells and then the mitochondria. The carbon dioxide you exhale is released by the mitochondria. Because an exchange of gases is involved, mitochondria are said to carry on *cellular respiration*.

Each mitochondrion is composed of an inner and outer membrane. The inner one is thrown into transverse folds that project into the fluid-containing interior. These are the *cristae* (sing. *crista*). The respiratory enzymes that contribute to the production of energy are located in a sort of assembly-line manner along these membranous projections. Each crista contains a complete set of enzymes. Thus, structure is admirably suited to function, making the mitochondrion a remarkably effective machine.

The number of mitochondria found in any given cell varies from hundreds to thousands, depending on the amount of energy needed by that cell to carry out specific functions. Various enzymes within the mitochondrion's fluid interior make possible the complex reactions whereby the food we eat is broken down to release energy. Other enzymes, located along the cristae within the mitochondrion, help to capture and hold this energy and store it for a time in the chemical bonds of a compound called *adenosine triophosphate* (ATP). ATP may be regarded as the 'common currency' of energy for most cellular processes. This energy-rich compound then moves out of the mitochondrion, ready to power the various metabolic operations taking place throughout the cell.

Every cell needs a certain amount of ATP energy to synthesize molecules, but many require ATP for specialized functions. Muscle cells, for instance, need it to be able to contract, and nerve cells require it for the conduction of nerve impulses.

Although ATP serves as the energy current for all cells, its quantity is in fact limited. It must therefore be constantly produced to provide a continuous supply of energy. Food provided by a wholesome diet furnishes the raw material for ATP, with the help of CoQ10.

The CoQ10 connection

CoQ10 is an integral part of the mitochondria. As mentioned earlier, it is the vital catalyst in the generation of energy needed by all living cells. It may be useful to think of a single human cell as an automobile engine. The mitochondria would be the cylinders where petrol is ignited and explodes to produce the force to move the pistons. This energy is then relayed to other parts of the automobile to turn the wheels and set the vehicle in motion. In the human machine, energy is created by complicated processes that involve a chain of chemical reactions known as the electron transport system of intracelluar respiration. CoQ10 is one of the most important chemicals in this chain. Without it, there would be no spark or ignition or energy. Without sufficient CoQ10, the cellular machine would misfire. If CoQ10 deficiency is severe enough, the mitochondria may even cease to function and there would be no energy. Energy is life. CoQ10 is the vital component in the production of that energy. CoQ10 is essential to life.

CoQ10 is most abundant in organs and structures that need the largest energy supplies, for example, the powerful heart muscle which is constantly pumping, and components of the immune system which are continuously at work to protect the body against invasion by disease-causing organisms.

CoQ10 and the immune system

Breakthrough experiments done in the late 1960s by Dr Emile G. Bliznakov and associates demonstrated that supplementation with CoQ10 increases the phagocytic activity of macrophages and the bactericidal ability of WBCs (white blood cells). CoQ10 supplementation also increased the number of killer cells in response to experimentally induced infection.

In antibody studies, it was found that mice treated with CoQ10 responded with a significantly higher level of antibody production than those which were not.

Further experiments revealed the ability of CoQ10 to reduce the number and size of chemically-induced tumours in mice and to increase the number of survivors. A potent carcinogenic substance (dibenzpyrene) was injected into the test animals to produce tumours that closely resemble those occurring in humans. Fifty-five days after the cancer-causing substance was injected, 85 per cent of the animals not treated with CoQ10 had developed tumours. By day 69, *all* the untreated mice had succumbed. By contrast, only 25 per cent of the rodents treated with CoQ10 had developed tumours at day 55, and even by day 300, only 77 per cent had displayed tumour growth. Moreover, not only did fewer mice in the CoQ10-treated group develop tumours, but those growths that did develop were substantially smaller. Even more remarkable was the fact that by day 132, *all* the untreated mice were dead, whereas 80 per cent of the CoQ10-treated animals were still alive by day 300.

CoQ10 has been shown to prolong the survival rate of mice infected with a number of disease-causing agents (e.g. E. coli and Candida albicans). Two out of ten mice treated with CoQ10 survived a massive E. coli infection that killed all the animals not so treated.

In human studies done by Dr Karl Folkers and fellow researchers at the Institute for Biomedical Research at the University of Texas, subjects treated with CoQ10 showed increased levels of IgG (see Chapter 1). Eight patients with various diseases including cancer were given 60 mg (milligrams) of CoQ10 daily in the form of three 20 mg capsules each for several months. The rise in their IgG levels was remarkable. This, the researchers concluded, could indicate either a lessening of existing immunodeficiency or indeed improved immuno-competence.

It now appears certain that immune function declines with advancing age. In studies on older mice, atrophy of the thymus gland and a marked CoQ10 deficiency were demonstrated, as well as unmistakable depression of the entire immune system. When supplemental CoQ10 was administered, however, this depression was somewhat reversed. This implies that supplementation with CoQ10 may be useful in helping prevent, perhaps even reverse, age-related immunosuppression.

Based on various studies on the effect of supplemental CoQ10 on the immune system, it would appear that the effects of the enzyme do not stem from increased production of new immune cells but rather from an increase in the defence potential of already existing cells. This would prevent immune system organs, such as the spleen, from being overloaded with an excess of immune cells. Herein, then, lies the critical difference between the action of CoQ10 and that of certain other immune system stimulants. It is what makes it so effective and so safe.

CoQ10 supplementation

Because of its crucial role in energy production, CoQ10 must be adequate at all times. A deficiency could lead to or aggravate a number of health disorders. Chief among the reasons why CoQ10 supplementation may be needed are:

– faulty CoQ10 synthesis due to nutritional deficiencies;
– a genetic or an acquired defect in CoQ10 synthesis;
– increased tissue demands arising from specific health disorders;
– the ageing process;
– stress.

CoQ10 is not a drug. It performs in much the same way as an antioxidant. It acts as a free-radical scavenger. Free radicals can damage the protective membranes of cells and mitochondria. CoQ10 taken orally can confront free radicals at the mitochondria level and neutralize them before they can endanger vital biochemical processes. It is therefore possible to correct a deficiency through the use of supplements which are now available.

CoQ10 has been used for over a decade in Japan. Millions take it regularly, usually in dosages of 10 mg three times a day. It is generally well tolerated, with no serious side effects reported, even after long-term use.

CoQ10 is safe: in toxological tests involving thousands of human subjects, no CoQ10 toxicity has been observed. It is a completely natural substance. The only side effects reported were mild cases of epigastric (literally, above the stomach) discomfort, loss of appetite, nausea and diarrhoea.

Because the synthesis of new CoQ10-dependent enzymes is slow, do not expect a response from taking the supplement until at least eight weeks after the start of supplementation.

Contraindications
Please *note well* that CoQ10 should *not* be used during pregnancy and lactation. It should also *not* be used in cases of known hypersensitivity.

Organic Germanium

Germanium (Ge) is a trace element that occurs naturally in the earth's crust to the extent of about 0.0007 per cent. It belongs to the dioxide compounds, which are known to stimulate the production of red blood cells. Indeed, it was used successfully in America in the 1920s to treat anaemia. Ge is also found in relatively high concentrations in plants with special therapeutic properties. These include aloe, chlorella, comfrey, garlic, ginseng and watercress. Other plants have significant quantities of Ge, but they are not as familiar to most people as the plants just mentioned. These include shelf fungus (a variety of Reishi mushroom and a traditional Russian anti-cancer remedy), pearl barley, boxthorn seed, waternut and wisteria knob.

In 1950, a Japanese chemist named Dr Kazuhiko Asai discovered Ge in fossilized plants. A few years later, following up on Russian reports that the element had anti-cancer activity, he found that certain healing plants and medicinal herbs, such as those just mentioned, were enriched with Ge. He concluded that the Ge content was partly responsible for their therapeutic value.

By 1967, Dr Asai had synthesized a new Ge compound. He found that this manufactured substance, carboxyethyl sesquioxide of germanium, had remarkable healing powers. Testing it first on himself, he was able to cure his chronic arthritis in weeks, and was understandably excited at the implications. Because the product contained carbon in its molecular architecture, it was given the name *organic germanium*.

Since then, organic germanium has become virtually a household term in Japan, and it continues to be the subject of many studies and trials. You can find some of the results in Dr Asai's book entitled *Miracle*

Cure: Organic Germanium (see Bibliography). In it, you can also read many physicians' case histories which support the efficacy of this amazing element.

Organic germanium – roles

In Chapter 3, I pointed out that diet can indeed play an important part in the development or correction of even genetically-determined health disorders. Certainly, diet can be used to raise nutritional status and so reduce vulnerability to disease. Evidence indicates that organic germanium is useful in helping do just this.

Germanium seems to play a role as an oxygen catalyst, an antioxidant, an electro-stimulant and an immune system booster. Doctors describing cellular injury conclude that lack of oxygen is probably the most common cause of cell damage and consequent disease. One example of diminished oxygen supply to cells is when atherosclerotic plaques clog blood vessels and restrict blood flow. Another is cell death that occurs in myocardial infarction (heart attack). Yet another instance of oxygen depletion is the effects that environmental pollutants such as cadmium, lead and mercury have on the body. These effects probably result from the reactions of free radicals (see Chapter 3).

Free radicals have an intimate relationship with oxygen. They may reduce available oxygen supplies with consequent damage to cells and the potential for disease. Organic germanium shows much promise in relieving oxygen shortage.

Like vitamins A, C and E and the minerals selenium and zinc, organic germanium acts as an antioxidant, a fact that may contribute to its non-toxicity. According to Betty Kamen, antioxidants are compounds that oppose the enemy. We need them for guard duty: to control oxidative reactions that burn food and create energy. We need oxygen for the conversion of potential energy (from nutrients in food eaten) to usable energy for living. This process is called *oxidation*: the combining of a food substance with oxygen to release the stored chemical energy. Nutrients provide the fuel for this process, but oxygen is the spark. Without an adequate supply, various disorders can arise. Here are examples, with their consequences.

– Over-acidity, due to the intake of too much coffee and commercial soft drinks as well as fatty red meats. The resulting high acid levels reduce oxygen available to body tissues.

– Shortness of breath even after minimal exercise. This indicates an undersupply of oxygen to the tissues.

– Common yeast infections (e.g. Candida albicans). The infecting organisms produce a substance that injures the cells. This leads to impaired immunity.

– Frequent use of drugs of all kinds. These require oxygen for their metabolism and so steal from supplies needed by body cells.

– Oxygen-depleted indoor environments and an oxygen-deficient lifestyle in which there is not enough oxygen available for active muscle tissue and optimum cellular health.

– Cancer. Cancer cells have lost the ability to utilize oxygen.

Studies and trials

Science is finally confirming what Dr Asai had known for years: that organic germanium is a splendid immune-boosting agent. In animal studies, organic germanium consistently inhibited tumour development and significantly increased survival time. In other experiments, animals were inoculated with cancer cells and then treated with oral organic germanium. The results suggested that germanium works by beneficially influencing immune responses rather than direct attack on cancer cells. It strengthens host resistance to disease by making host tissues healthier and better able to withstand viral infections and tumour growth. Moreover, germanium demonstrated marked analgesic (pain-relieving) effects, as well as retarding the spread of metastases. Conventional chemotherapeutic agents, by contrast, kill cancer cells directly and often in the process destroy non-cancerous host tissue as well.

The ability of organic germanium to stimulate interferon production in humans and in animals is very well documented. This puts it in the class of select immunity-stimulating agents which includes vitamins C and E and CoQ10. Many of the immunity-enhancing effects of organic germanium are a result of its ability to stimulate interferon production. In volunteers and patients with cancer or rheumatoid arthritis, organic germanium effected normal functioning of B- and T-lymphocytes, NK-cell proliferation and antibody-forming cells. Particularly noteworthy is the ability of organic germanium to stimulate

NK-cell activity. (You may recall that NK-cells are regarded as key components in the body's natural defences against the spread of cancer cells – see Chapter 1.)

In aged animals, organic germanium has significantly boosted immune response, a response that seems to weaken with age.

At an International AIDS Treatment Conference held in Japan in 1987, organic germanium was one of the six substances authorized for use in intensive clinical testing. It was chosen mainly because of its antiviral action.

From these and other studies, it appears that organic germanium works in an indirect way to stimulate the immune system. The system will then produce substances such as interferon, which will help combat disease-producing organisms. It will also, it seems, enhance the efficiency of NK cells. Because it helps regulate functions indirectly, organic germanium may be considered an *adaptogen*, and as such is non-toxic.

Organic germanium has an oxygen-sparing effect: it helps lower the requirement for oxygen although it is not a substitute for it. Oxygen deficiency is probably the most common cause of cell injury and resulting tissue damage. Organic germanium offers oxygen-starved or damaged cells a chance to repair themselves. Organic germanium is, as well, a detoxifier. It assists the body in the excretion of pollutants. It does this by binding harmful substances, such as cadmium and mercury, and holding on to them tightly enough for them to be eliminated from the body. This is referred to as a *chelating* effect.

To support life, there must be a continuous flow of electricity and sufficient oxygen to draw the current. Organic germanium helps the body discharge unwanted electric current, thereby allowing needed current to flow freely to maintain electric balance. It is therefore sometimes referred to as a 'catalytic electro-nutrient'.

Dosages and side effects

Organic germanium is not a drug. It is an adaptogen. It helps the body help itself. No prescription is necessary to obtain it, and it is not habit forming.

Various studies indicate that organic germanium has no toxic properties at conventional levels and almost no toxicity even at high dosages. Moreover, it does not accumulate; it clears from the system in twenty to thirty hours.

Reported side effects include mild skin eruptions, which clear up in a short time. Some people have also reported increased urination and softer stools but no diarrhoea.

Note well: It is important to be aware of the fact that there is also an *inorganic germanium* (germanium dioxide), and that this *can be toxic*. Be sure that the germanium you buy is verified by the manufacturer as organic germanium (Carboxyethyl sesquioxide of germanium).

Superdioxide Dismutase

Superdioxide dismutase (SOD) is an enzyme which is found in all body cells. It is also known as *erythrocuprein* (from Greek *erythro*, red, and Latin *cuprum*, copper).

According to Kurt W. Donsbach, Ph.D., the enzyme's *modus operandi* is to fight the devastating effects of superdioxides, which are among the most harmful of free radicals. These are unstable oxygen molecules that behave at the cellular level much like high-powered bullets. Normally, the body is able to keep superdioxides under control by slowing them down with antioxidants like vitamins C and E and the mineral selenium. In addition, the body controls these radicals by combining them with other superdioxide radicals. This encourages *dismutation* (deactivation) by means of a family of enzymes called *superdioxide dismutases*. This altering of free radicals prevents what may otherwise be irreparable damage, which results in rapid ageing and tissue degeneration.

SOD roles
SOD is produced by cells in almost all body tissues, but research indicates that the older we become the less SOD is manufactured. On the other hand, free radical activity does not slow down to match this ageing process. Rather, it may even increase, a fact thought by many scientists to be a cause of ageing itself. Free radicals attach themselves to collagen, the body's supportive tissue, and undermine it. Skin, our first line of defence against invasion by enemy organisms (see Chapter 1), begins to wrinkle and sag. SOD helps prevent this deterioration or at least considerably slows it down. In so doing, it

enhances immunity, which tends to weaken as we age.

Superdioxide free radicals also appear to increase the risk of cancer. SOD may therefore play a protective role against this dread disease. Certainly, SOD has been found to lessen the toxic effects of radiation, a known cause of cancer. Some call it 'the radiation antidote'. It helps to relieve inflamed conditions that arise from radiation treatment of the abdomen for some types of cancer. Some patients, for example, develop radiation cystitis (bladder inflammation). SOD may prove to be a boon to the many hundreds of such sufferers.

Trials with an injectable form of SOD (Orgotein) have indicated that this substance may be of value in treating arthritis. In Denmark, Dr Knud Lund-Olesen gave SOD injections to more than 200 arthritis sufferers and claimed that it proved effective as well as safe in all the patients to whom he gave it.

SOD sources
SOD occurs in all plants that grow in oxygen. The greener the plant, the more SOD it contains. It is the chlorophyl, the 'green' in all vegetation, that releases oxygen. The best natural SOD sources, then, are the 'super greens' such as broccoli, collards, comfrey, kale and spinach.

The most biologically active forms of SOD contain the minerals copper and zinc. This is the type generally sold in health food stores. SOD should also be combined with *catalase* (a dismuting enzyme) if it is to provide optimum protection. Always *check the label* on any container of SOD you plan to purchase. It usually comes in 50-100 mcg (microgram) tablets.

Whether you wish to retard ageing, to relieve arthritis, to help prevent cancer or to protect your body from the damaging effects of pollution or radiation, SOD may be just the supplement to give your body's immune system a needed boost.

GLOSSARY

Accessory cells	Lymphoid cells that cooperate with T- and B-cells in the immune response.
Acquired immunity	*See* Immunity.
Adenosine triphosphate	A compound containing adenine, ribose, and three phosphates, two of which are high-energy phosphates. The 'common currency' of energy for most cellular processes.
Adrenal glands	Two endocrine glands located above the kidneys.
Adrenaline (epinephrine)	A hormone secreted by the medullae of the adrenal glands.
Agranulocyte	A non-granular leucocyte.
Allergen	Any substance that produces an allergic reaction.
Amino acid	The end product of protein digestion; protein building block.
Anaesthesia	Loss of sensation.
Analgesia	Loss of sensitivity to pain.
Antagonist	Something that counteracts the action of something else.
Antibody (immunoglobulin, or Ig)	A specific substance produced by a person or animal in response to the presence of an antigen.
Antigen	Any substance which, when introduced into the blood or tissues, stimulates the formation of antibodies.
Antigenic	Refers to antigen.
Antigenic determinant	Same as epitope.
Antihistamine	Any agent that counteracts the effect of histamine.
Antioxidant	A substance that slows down the destructive

effects of oxygen or other substances.

Antiviral — Acting against a virus.

ATP — *See* Adenosine triphosphate.

Atrophy — A wasting, or decrease in size, of a part of the body.

Autoimmunity — Immunologic attack against the body's own tissues.

Autonomic — Self-governing.

Bacillus (plural, *bacilli*) — A rod-shaped microorganism.

Bacteria (sing. *bacterium*) — A general name given to minute vegetable organisms which live on organic matter.

Bactericidal — Capable of killing bacteria, e.g. disinfectants, sunlight, great heat.

Beta-carotene — An orange plant pigment. It is stored by the body and converted into vitamin A as required.

Capillary — Literally, hair-like. Minute vessels connecting an artery and a vein. Also found in the lymphatic system.

Carcinogen — Any substance or agent that produces or incites cancer.

Carcinogenic — Refers to carcinogens.

Carcinoma — A malignant epithelial tumour.

Cardiovascular — Refers to the heart and blood vessels.

Catalyst — A substance that speeds up the rate of a chemical reaction without itself being permanently altered in the reaction.

Cell-mediated immunity — Immunity brought about predominantly by T-lymphocytes and macrophages. Same as cellular immunity.

Clone — Set of cells having the same genetic constitution.

Collagen — A fibrous insoluble protein found in connective tissue including skin.

Complement — A series of enzymatic proteins in normal

serum which, in the presence of a specific sensitizer, destroys bacteria and other cells.

Cortex · The outer layer of an organ.

Cortisol · A hormone from the cortex of the adrenal glands. Also known as hydrocortisone.

Cortisone · A hormone from the cortex of the adrenal glands. It can also be prepared synthetically. Closely related to cortisol.

Differentiation · Acquirement of form or character according to specific function, which may differ from that of surrounding cells.

DNA (deoxyribo-nucleic acid) · The nucleic acid that transmits information from parent to offspring. The chemical basis of heredity. The carrier of genetic information for almost all organisms.

EFAs · Essential fatty acids.

Effector · Producing an effect when stimulated.

Embryo · The young of any organism in an early stage of development; in humans between the second and eighth weeks inclusive.

Endocrine gland · A gland whose secretion (hormone) flows directly into the blood-stream and is circulated to all parts of the body.

Enzyme · A complex protein that is capable of bringing about chemical changes in other substances without being changed itself.

Eosinophilia · Accumulation of an unusual number of eosinophils (a type of white blood cell) in the blood.

Epithelial · Refers to epithelium.

Epithelium · The layer of cells forming the epidermis, or outer layer, of the skin.

Epitope · Area of an antigen that determines the specificity of antigen-antibody binding.

Eruption · A breaking out and becoming visible, e.g. a skin rash.

Essential fatty acids (EFAs) — Fatty acids required by the body for vital functions, which the body cannot make and which must be supplied by food.

Flora — Literally, plant life (as distinguished from animal life), occurring or adapted for living in a specific environment (e.g. intestinal or skin flora).

Flora (normal) — Population of microorganisms that live on or in the body and do not represent a hazard to healthy individuals.

Fungicide — Agent that can destroy bacteria or fungi.

Fungus (plural, *fungi*) — A vegetable cellular organism that subsists on organic matter.

Gastrointestinal — Refers to the stomach and intestines.

Granulocytes — White blood cells with a granular protoplasm.

Haemorrhage — Abnormal internal or external discharge of blood; bleeding.

Helper T-cell — A T-cell that stimulates T-cell growth, B-cell antibody production and macrophage activation.

Histamine — A chemical substance produced when tissues are injured.

Holistic medicine — A system of practising medicine in which all the needs of the patient (i.e. physical, emotional, social, etc.) are considered and cared for.

Hormone — A chemical substance generated in one organ and carried by the blood to another in which it excites activity. A secretion of endocrine glands.

Host — The organism from which a parasite obtains its nourishment.

Humoral immunity — Immunity mediated by antibodies.

Humour — Literally, a liquid. Refers to body fluids.

Hypersensitivity — Abnormal sensitivity to any kind of stimulus.

Hypothalamus	An area of the forebrain which influences various metabolic activities, as well as emotional expression.
Immune	Protected, or exempt, from a disease.
Immune response	Reaction of the body to foreign substances, or those interpreted as foreign.
Immune surveillance	*See* Surveillance.
Immune system	The body's natural defences against disease.
Immunity	State of being immune to, or protected from, a disease, especially an infectious disease.
Immunization	Process of rendering an individual immune.
Immunocompetence	Ability or capacity to develop an immune response following exposure to an antigen.
Immuno-compromised	Having the immune response weakened, as by administration of certain drugs, radiation, some diseases or malnutrition.
Immunoglobulin (Ig)	Same as antibody.
Immunology	The study of immunity to diseases.
Inflammation	A series of changes in tissues indicating their reaction to injury.
Ingestion	The process of taking material into the gastrointestinal tract, or the process by which a cell takes in foreign particles.
Inoculation	Injection of a microorganism, serum or toxic material into the body to improve its powers of resistance to disease.
Interferon	Protein(s) formed when cells are exposed to viruses. Non-infected cells exposed to interferon are protected against viral infection.
Interleukins	Literally, 'acting between leucocytes'. Soluble substances produced by leucocytes, which stimulate growth or activity of other leucocytes.
Keratin	An extremely tough protein substance in skin, hair and nails.
Keratinocytes	Skin cells that synthesize keratin.

Killer cells (killer T-cells)	T-cells that specifically target and destroy virus-infected and cancer cells.
Lesion	An injury, wound or diseased area of the body.
Leucocytes	White blood cells.
Leukotrienes	Bioactive molecules synthesized from cell membrane lipids in response to specific allergens, and which mediate hypersensitivity reactions.
Lipids	Fat-like substances.
Lymph	The fluid from blood which has passed through capillary walls to supply nutrients to tissue cells.
Lymphatic system	A system of vessels and glands involved in transporting lymph from the tissues to the blood-stream.
Lymph nodes	Small bean-like structures found at intervals along the course of lymphatic vessels.
Lymphocytes	White blood cells developed in lymph glands and lymphatic tissue.
Lymphoid	Relating to lymph.
Lymphokines	Soluble mediators produced by lymphocytes, which influence the functions of other cells.
Lyse	Dissolution to bring about lysis.
Lysis	Destruction of a blood cell by a lysin (a specific antibody acting destructively upon cells and tissues).
Macrophage	A cell capable of engulfing foreign particles.
Malignant	A word applied to any disease of a virulent or fatal nature.
MAO inhibitors	A group of drugs used to treat depression.
Mediate	To accomplish by indirect means.
Memory cells	T- and B-cells that recognize and react against a specific antigen to which the immune system has been exposed.
Metabolism	The sum of all the chemical changes that take place within an organism.

Metastasize	Refers to the transfer of a disease from one part of the body to another through the bloodstream.
Microbe	A microorganism, such as a bacterium, fungus or virus.
Microorganism	A minute living body not perceptible to the naked eye, e.g. a bacterium.
Microphage	A small phagocyte.
Mitochondrion (plural, *mitochondria*)	The ATP-producing component of the cell. The cell's powerhouse.
Mucin	The chief constituent of mucus.
Mucous	Pertaining to or secreting mucus.
Mucus	The secretion of mucous membranes.
Natural killer (NK) cells	Lymphocytes that can destroy virus-infected or tumour cells without prior sensitization.
Neoplasia	The development of new tissues or neoplasms.
Neoplasm	A new and abnormal formation of tissue, e.g. a tumour.
Neurotransmitter	A chemical messenger which conveys electrical impulses from one nerve cell (neuron) to another.
Nitrosamines	Potentially cancer-causing substances formed from nitrites (a food preservative).
Oestrogen	An endocrine secretion which stimulates the female generative organs to reproductive function.
Opsonins	Antibodies that bind to microorganisms to facilitate phagocytosis.
Opsonization	Action of opsonins to facilitate phagocytosis.
Oral	Pertaining to the mouth.
Orally	By mouth.
Orifice	Any opening in the body.
Oxidize	To combine with oxygen.
Pathogen	Infectious agent able to damage a host organism.

pH   Potential of hydrogen. In chemistry, the degrees of acidity or alkalinity of a substance are expressed in pH values.

Phagocytes   White blood cells capable of destroying and disposing of invading microbes.

Phagocytosis   The engulfing of particles by phagocytes.

Physiological   Refers to body function.

Pituitary gland   An endocrine gland located in the base of the brain. Also called the hypophysis.

Placebo   An inactive substance given to satisfy the demand for medication.

Plasma cells   Antibody-secreting cells derived from B-lymphocytes.

Platelets   Cells that play a part in blood clotting.

Polys (polymorpho-   Phagocytic blood cells.
nuclear cells)

Potentiate   To increase the effectiveness of (e.g. a drug).

Precursor   A parent substance from which another substance is made chemically; forerunner.

Prognosis   A forecast of the course and duration of a disease.

Proliferate   Multiply rapidly, as may occur in a malignant growth.

Prostaglandins (PGs)   Highly reactive short-lived molecules. Their main action is that of local messengers which regulate the activity of the tissues in which they are formed.

Receptor cells   Group of cells that receive stimuli.

Remission   Lessening of severity or abatement of symptoms.

Replicate   Duplicate or repeat.

Respiratory   Pertains to respiration, or breathing.

Sensitize   Make susceptible to a particular substance (e.g. an antigen).

Serotonin   A chemical involved in nervous system mechanisms.

Serum	The watery portion of blood after it has clotted.
SLE (systemic lupus erythematosus)	A chronic autoimmune disease, that is, one in which the body produces disordered immunological response against itself.
Spleen	A lymphoid organ located in the abdomen, below the stomach. It is responsible for the formation, storage and filtration of blood.
Stressor	Anything that causes stress.
Supplement	Something added to supply a need or to reinforce.
Suppressor T-cells	T-cells that inhibit the progression of the immune response to specific antigens.
Surveillance (immune surveillance; immuno-surveillance; cancer surveillance)	The monitoring function of the immune system in recognizing and rejecting newly formed small clones of malignant cells.
Syndrome	A group of signs and symptoms that characterize a particular disease or abnormal condition.
Synthesize	Combine elements or parts to form a whole.
Target cells	Cells selectively affected by a particular agent (e.g. a drug or hormone).
Thymic	Refers to the thymus gland.
Thymocytes	Lymphocytes arising in the thymus gland.
Thymus gland	An endocrine gland located in the chest, above the heart; composed of dense lymphoid tissue.
Thyroid gland	A two-lobed endocrine gland situated in front of the windpipe.
T-lymphocyte (T-cell)	Thymus-derived lymphocyte responsible for cell-mediated immunity or for immune regulation.
Toxin	A poisonous substance of animal or plant origin.
Vaccination	Inoculation with any vaccine to establish resistance to a specific infectious disease.

Vaccine	A suspension of infectious agents given to help establish resistance to an infectious disease.
Viral	Pertaining to or caused by a virus.
Virus	A minute organism not visible with ordinary light microscopy, but which can be seen by use of electron microscopy.
WBCs (white blood cells; leucocytes)	White blood cells which act as scavengers and so help combat infection.

BIBLIOGRAPHY

Aladjem, Henrietta. *The Sun Is My Enemy. One Woman's Victory Over a Mysterious and Dreaded Disease*. Englewood Cliffs, New Jersey: Prentice-Hall, 1972

Alive Canadian Journal of Health & Nutrition. 'Eternity Enzyme. SOD may increase your span of years'. Burnaby, B.C., Canada: Issue 33, p.42

Asai, Kazuhiko, Ph.D. *Miracle Cure: Organic Germanium*. Tokyo and New York: Japan Publications Inc., 1980

Baron, Samuel, MD (Ed.). *Medical Microbiology* (2nd ed.). Menlo Park, California: Addison-Wesley Publishing Company, 1986

B.C. Centre for Disease Control, Ministry of Health. *AIDS. Be Responsible For Life*.

Berger, Stuart M., MD. *Dr Berger's Immune Power Diet* (Signet Book ed.). New York: New American Library, 1985

Bliznakov, Emile, G., MD, and Hunt, Gerald L. *The Miracle Nutrient: Coenzyme Q_{10}*. Wellingborough, England: Thorsons Publishers Ltd., 1988

Bogin, Meg. *The Path to Pain Control*. Boston: Houghton Mifflin Company, 1982

British Columbia Medical Association, Canada. *Immunization Risks and Benefits*.

Calder, Ritchie. *The Wonderful World of Medicine*. Garden City, New York: Garden City Books, 1958

Canadian Cancer Society. 'Food Choices for Cancer Prevention'

Canadian Pharmaceutical Association. *Compendium of Pharmaceuticals and Specialties* (22nd ed.). Ottawa, Canada, 1987

Chaffee, Ellen E., RN, MN, M.Litt., and Lytle, Ivan M., Ph.D. *Basic Physiology and Anatomy* (4th ed.). Philadelphia: J.B. Lippincott Company, 1980

Coffey-Lewis, Lou. *Be Restored to Health*. New York: Ballantine Books, 1982

Cousins, Norman. *Anatomy of an Illness*. London: Bantam Books, 1987

— *Human Options*. New York: Berkley Books, 1983

David, John, MD. 'Organs and Cells of the Immune System' *Scientific American*, Vol. IX, No. 12, December 1986

— 'Immune Response Mechanisms' *Scientific American*, Vol. IX, No. 12, December 1986

Davis, Adelle. *Let's Eat Right To Keep Fit*. London: Unwin Paperbacks, 1979

— *Let's Get Well*. London: Allen & Unwin, 1966

Diagram Group, The. *Man's Body*. New York: Paddington Press Ltd, 1976

Donsbach, Kurt W., Ph.D., D.Sc., N.D., D.C., and Brennan, Richard O., D.O. *Superdioxide Dismutase*. Huntington Beach, California: The International Institute of Natural Health Sciences Inc., 1982

Dorland's Illustrated Medical Dictionary (26th ed.). Philadelphia: W.B. Saunders Company, 1974

Ebersole, Priscilla, RN, MS, and Hess, Patricia, RN, Ph.D. *Toward Healthy Aging* (2nd ed.). St Louis: The C.V. Mosby Company, 1985

Edelhart, Mike, with Lindenmann, Dr Jean. *Interferon*. New York: Ballantine Books, 1982

Edelson, Richard L., and Fink, Joseph. 'The Immunologic Function of Skin' *Scientific American*, Vol. 252, No. 6, pp. 46-53, June 1985

Edmeades, Baz. 'Nature's Recalcifier' *Alive Canadian Journal of Health & Nutrition*, No. 71, pp. 21-22

Faelten, Sharon. 'Selenium, The Small But Mighty Health Force' *Prevention*. September 1980, pp. 79-85

Feltman, John. 'Zinc – The Do-Everything Mineral' *Prevention*, November 1979, pp. 69-74

Freedman, Samuel O., MD, FRSC, and Gold, Phil, MD, Ph.D. (eds). *Clinical Immunology* (2nd ed.). New York: Harper & Row, 1976

Friedlander, Mark P., Jr, & Phillips, Terry M., PhD. *Winning the War Within*. Emmaus, Pennsylvania: Rodale Press, 1986

Fromm, Erich. *The Art of Loving*. New York: Harper & Row, 1970

Gottlieb, Bill. 'Here's Natural Relief for Colds and Sinus' *Prevention*, January 1980, pp. 55-59

Graham, Judy. *Evening Primrose Oil*. Wellingborough, England: Thorsons Publishers Ltd, 1984

— and Odent, Dr Michel. *The Z Factor*. Wellingborough, England: Thorsons Publishers Ltd, 1986

Greig, James D. *AIDS. What Every Responsible Canadian Should Know*. Canadian Public Health Association, 1987

Grossbart, Ted A., Ph.D., and Sherman, Carl, Ph.D. *Skin Deep. A Mind/Body Program for Healthy Skin*. New York: William Morrow and Company Inc., 1986

Guyton, Arthur C., MD. *Textbook of Medical Physiology* (7th ed.). Philadelphia: W.B. Saunders Company, 1986

Hanssen, Maurice. *E for Additives*. Wellingborough, England: Thorsons Publishers Ltd, 1984

Health League News Digest, May/June 1986. Toronto: Health League of Canada

Hendler, Sheldon, MD. *The Complete Guide to Anti-Aging Nutrients*. New York:

Simon and Schuster, 1985

Horn, Jack C. 'Fighting migraines with The Force' *Psychology Today*, November 1985, p. 74

Horrobin, David F. (ed.). *Clinical Uses of Essential Fatty Acids*. Montreal: Eden Press, 1982

Kamen, Betty, Ph.D. *Germanium: A New Approach to Immunity*. Larkspur, California: Nutrition Encounter Inc., 1987

Kee, Joyce LeFever, MSN, RN. *Laboratory and Diagnostic Tests with Nursing Implications* (2nd ed.) Norwalk, Connecticut: Appleton & Lange, 1987

Kenton, Leslie, and Kenton, Susannah. *Raw Energy*. London: Century Publishing, 1984

Kidd, Parris M., Ph.D. 'Ge-132: Research Breakthrough from the Orient.' Vancouver, Canada: Sisu Enterprises Ltd, 1986

Kolata, Gina. 'Immune Boosters' *Discover*, September 1987, pp. 68-74

Kounovsky, Nicholas. *The Joy of Feeling Fit*. New York: Avon Books, 1974

Kunin, Richard A., MD. *Mega-Nutrition*. St Louis: McGraw-Hill, 1980

Larson, Leonard A., and Michelman, Herbert. *International Guide to Fitness and Health*. New York: Crown Publishers Inc., 1973

Laurence, Jeffrey. 'The Immune System in AIDS' *Scientific American*, December 1985, Vol. 235, No. 6, pp. 84-93

Lazarus, Richard S. *Patterns of Adjustment* (3rd ed.). New York: McGraw-Hill Book Company, 1976

Lee, William H., R.Ph., Ph.D. *Coenzyme Q-10. Is It Our New Fountain of Youth?* New Canaan, Connecticut: Keats Publishing Inc., 1987

LeShan, Lawrence. *You Can Fight For Your Life*. New York: M. Evans & Co., 1977

Lewis, Alan. *Selenium*. Wellingborough, England: Thorsons Publishers Ltd, 1983.

Mader, Sylvia S. *Inquiry Into Life* (4th ed.). Dubuque, Iowa: Wm. C. Brown, 1985

Maleskey, Gale. 'Zinc: The Whole-Body Mineral' *Prevention*, May 1985, pp. 65-70

— 'The New Power of the Imagination, *Prevention*, June 1985, pp. 107-111

— 'A Doctor's Guide to Anti-Aging Nutrients' *Prevention*, August 1985, pp. 24-30

McConnell, Edwina A., RN, MS. 'Leukocyte Studies. What the Counts Can Tell You' *Nursing 86*, March, pp. 42-43

Maness, Bill. 'What You Don't Know About Exercise' *Reader's Digest*, April 1976, p.72

Meade, Jeff. 'Amino Acids: The New Health Story' *Prevention*, June 1986, pp. 97-100

Mervyn, Len, Ph.D. *Minerals and Your Health*. London: Unwin Paperbacks, 1981

Mizel, Steven B., and Jaret, Peter. *In Self-Defense*. New York: Harcourt Brace Jovanovich, 1985

Montagu, Ashley. 'Chromosomes and Crime' *Psychology Today*, 1968, 2, 44-49

National Geographic Society, The. *The Incredible Machine*. Washington, D.C., 1986

National Lupus Erythematosus Foundation Inc., The. *Lupus*. Van Nuys, California

Nossal, G.J.V. *Antibodies and Immunity* (2nd ed.). New York: Basic Books Inc., 1978

Passwater, Richard A., Ph.D. *Evening Primrose Oil*. New Canaan, Connecticut: Keats Publishing Inc., 1981

Pearce, Evelyn C., SRN, RFN, SCM, MCSP. *Anatomy and Physiology for Nurses* (13th ed.). London: Faber and Faber Ltd, 1956

Pelletier, Kenneth R. *Healthy People in Unhealthy Places. Stress and Fitness at Work*. New York: Dell Publishing Co. Inc., 1985

Potts, Eve, and Morra, Marion. *Understanding Your Immune System*. New York: Avon Books, 1986

Rodale, Heidi. 'Vitamins for Your Inner Youth' *Prevention*, April 1987, pp. 27-31

Schulick, Paul. *The Immune System Health Guide Book*. Brattleboro, Vermont: Herbal Formula Research, 1986

Seeger, Paul Gerhard, MD. 'Protecting Yourself Against Cancer' *Alive Canadian Journal of Health & Nutrition*, No. 77, pp. 22-26

Sell, Stewart, MD. *Immunology Immunopathology and Immunity*. Maidenhead, England and Hagerstown, Maryland: Harper & Row, 1972

Selye, Hans, MD. *The Stress of Life* (Rev. ed.). New York: McGraw-Hill Book Company, 1978

Shaw, George Bernard. *The Doctor's Dilemma*. Harmondsworth: Penguin Books, 1982

Shaw, Linda. 'Vitamins That Perk Up A Sagging Defense' *Prevention*, April 1980, pp. 151-154

Shealey, Tom. 'Infection Protection: 21 Ways to Avoid Trouble' *Prevention*, February 1986, p. 79

Simonton, O. Carl MD, Matthews-Simonton, Stephanie, and Creighton, James. *Getting Well Again*. London: Bantam Books, 1980

Stark, Elizabeth. 'Stress, depression and herpes' *Psychology Today*, December 1985, Vol. 19, No. 12, p. 12

Steele, Russell W., MD. *Immunology for the Practicing Physician*. Norwalk, Connecticut: Appleton-Century-Crofts, 1983

Stroebel, Charles F., MD. *QR The Quieting Reflex*. New York: Berkley Books, 1983

Thomas, Clayton L., MD, MPH (Ed.). *Taber's Cyclopedic Medical Dictionary* (13th ed.). Philadelphia: F.A. Davis Company, 1977

Tritter, Robert J. 'Less stress, better immunity' *Health League News Digest*, November/December 1985, Vol. 4, No. 6

Uhlaner, Jonathan. 'Selenium, a Mineral Made to Fight Cancer' *Prevention*, February 1980, pp. 128-132

U.S. Department of Health, Education and Welfare, Public Health Service, National Institutes of Health. DHEW Publication No. (NIH) 73-529

Wade, Carlson. 'Anti-Aging Antioxidants' *Alive Canadian Journal of Health & Nutrition*, No. 62, pp. 29-30

— *Carlson Wade's Nutrition and Your Immune System*. New Canaan, Connecticut: Keats Publishing Inc., 1986

Wechsler, Rob. 'A New Prescription: Mind Over Malady' *Discover*, February 1987, pp. 51-61

Weil, Andrew, MD. *Health and Healing*. Boston: Houghton Mifflin Company, 1983

Weiner, Michael A., PhD., and Goss, Kathleen, M.A. *Nutrition Against Aging*. New York: Bantam Books, 1983

— *Maximum Immunity. You Can Fortify Your Body's Natural Defenses Against Disease*. Bath: Gateway Books, 1987

Weller, Stella. *Silky, Smooth and Strong: Natural Care for Your Hair, Skin and Nails*. Wellingborough, England: Thorsons Publishing Group Ltd, 1988

Yudkin, John, MD. *The Penguin Encyclopaedia of Nutrition*. Harmondsworth, England: Penguin Books, 1985

INDEX

acquired immune deficiency
    syndrome, see AIDS
acquired immunity, 33
adaptogen, 122
additives, food, 110
adenoids, 24, 28
adenosine triphosphate (ATP),
    115, 116
adrenal glands, 42, 45, 46, 69,
    72, 103
adrenaline, 52, 69, 70
aerobic fitness, 81, 83, 84, 85
affirmations, 67
ageing, 82, 117, 118, 122, 123,
    124
agranulocytes, 16
AIDS, 19, 106-110, 122
AIDS-related condition (ARC),
    108
Aladjem, Henrietta, 41, 100
alcohol, 56, 79, 95, 111, 113
alcoholism, 17
allergens, 103
allergies, and antibodies, 22;
    and eosinophils, 72; and
    immunization, 35; and
    vitamin B$_5$, 42, 104;
    explained, 102, 103-104;
    food, 104-105
alpha-linolenic acid, see
    linolenic acid
Alzheimer's disease, 70
amino acids, 30, 36, 51-3, 54
anaphylaxis, 102-103, 105
antagonists, mineral and
    vitamin, 55
antibiotics, 17, 35, 44-5
antibodies, AIDS, 107; and
    allergies, 102; and amino
    acids, 52; and B-cells, 30;
    and cholesterol, 82; and
    CoQ10, 117; and immune
    deficiency, 106; and iron
    deficiency, 49; and lymph
    nodes, 27; and memory
    cells, 30; and organic
    germanium, 121; and
    selenium, 49; and the
    thymus gland, 25; and

vaccines, 34; and vitamin B$_2$,
    40; and vitamin B$_5$, 41; and
    vitamin B$_6$, 42; and vitamin
    B$_{12}$, 43; and vitamin E, 46;
    classes of, 21, 22
anticoagulants, 47
antigens, 11, 20, 23, 30, 33, 59
antihistamine, 44, 105
anti-malaria drugs, 41
antioxidants, 45, 46, 118, 120,
    123
antipyretics, 33
antistress factors, 44
anxiety, 52, 55, 63, 72, 76, 104
appendix, 24, 28
arachidonic acid, 97; see also
    essential fatty acids
arthritis, 35, 70, 96, 100, 119,
    124; see also rheumatoid
    arthritis
Asai, Kazuhiko, 119, 121
ascorbate, see vitamin C
assertiveness, 77
asthma, 70, 73, 102, 104
ATP, see adenosine
    triphosphate
autoantibodies, 95
autoantigens, 95
autoimmune diseases, 82,
    95-102

backache, 76
barbecuing, 113
barriers to infection, 12, 14, 15,
    29
basophils, 16, 18
B-cells, and antibodies, 30;
    and autoimmune disease,
    95; and immune deficiency,
    106; and iron deficiency, 49;
    and organic germanium,
    121; and vitamin A, 38; and
    vitamin B$_1$, 40; and vitamin
    B$_{12}$, 43; and vitamin E, 47;
    and zinc, 51; explained, 18,
    20
bereavement, 73
Besedovsky, Hugo, 61

beta-carotene, 39, 113
biofeedback, 63
Blalock, Ed, 61, 62
Bliznakov, Emile G., 116
blood-pressure, high, 69, 70
blood transfusions, 108, 109
Bogin, Meg, 64
bone marrow, 16, 17, 20, 24,
    59
bone marrow transplants, see
    transplants
breastfeeding, and AIDS, 108
breast self-examination, 113
breathing, and relaxation, 77,
    78
breathing exercises, 65, 66, 67,
    68
brewer's yeast, 40, 43, 50
Butterworth, C.E., 43
B vitamins, see vitamin B
    complex

caffeine, 54, 56, 79, 101
calcium, 97
calcium pantothenate, see
    vitamin B$_5$
cancer, 110-113; and alcohol,
    56; and amino acids, 52;
    and caffeine, 54; and
    CoQ10, 117; and cortisol,
    70; and drugs, 55; and
    exercise, 83; and fats, 53;
    and hereditary, 110; and
    immunization, 35; and iron,
    49; and nervous system, 72;
    and NK-cells, 122; and
    organic germanium, 121;
    and selenium, 50; and SOD,
    124; and visualization, 61,
    64; and vitamin A, 39; and
    vitamin B$_9$, 43; and vitamin
    C, 45; and vitamin E, 46;
    and zinc, 51; of breast, 47;
    of cervix, 45; of skin, 107;
    prevention of, 112, 113; signs
    of, 112; surveillance, 71, 110
cancer-prone personality,
    111-112
carbohydrates, 54; see also

complex carbohydrates
carcinogens, 45, 110, 113, 117
cardio-respiratory fitness, 81, 83, 84, 85
cardiovascular disease, *see* heart disease
catalase, 124
Cathcart, Robert F., 109
cell-mediated immunity, 18, 50, 53; *see also* immunity
cells, of immune system, 16
Chandra, R.K., 51
checklist, dietary, 56, 57
chemotherapy, 17, 35, 45, 107, 121
chewing, value of, 57
chlorophyl, 124
cholesterol, 53, 56, 82
choline, 100
chronic granulomatous disease (CGD), 45
chronic subclinical scurvy, 45
cilia, 14
cobalamin, *see* vitamin B$_{12}$
coenzyme Q10, 114-19, 121
Cohen, Benjamin E., 38
collagen, 100, 123
common cold, 29
complement, 22
complex carbohydrates, 54, 56, 112
condoms, 109
connective tissue, 105
convulsions, 35
cooking methods, 57
cooling-down exercises, 77-8, 84
copper, 124
CoQ10, *see* coenzyme Q10
cortex, of brain, 60, 61
corticosteroids, 47, 50, 70, 97
cortisol, 45, 46, 70, 71
cortisone, 35, 103, 104, 105
cough reflex, 14
Cousins, Norman, 59, 73, 77
cowpox, 20
cross immunity, 34; *see also* immunity
cruciferous vegetables, 113
cyanocobalamin, *see* vitamin B$_{12}$
cystitis, 124

daily dozen exercise series, 84, 85-91
Davis, Adelle, 37, 47, 99, 100
depression, 52, 53, 55, 70, 72,

104, 111
diabetes, 17, 70
diarrhoea, 76, 108
diet, 36; high-fat, 53; high-protein, 53, 54, 56; low-fat, 99, 112
dietary fibre, 54, 56, 105, 112
diphtheria, 21, 34
disseminated sclerosis, *see* multiple sclerosis
DNA, 101
Donsbach, Kurt W., 123
drugs, 55, 56, 96, 101, 106, 121
dysplasia, cervical, 43, 45

eczema, 102, 104
Edelson, Richard L., 12, 13
Efamol, 49
EFAs, *see* essential fatty acids
Ehrlich, Paul, 22
eicosapentaenoic acid (EA), 49
electron transport system, 116
elimination, 79
emotional support, 76, 79
emotions, and autoimmune disease, 96; and brain control, 61; and cancer, 111; and disease, 60. and immunosuppression, 73; and multiple sclerosis, 98, 99; suppression of, 76
endocrine glands, 69
endocrine system, 59
enzymes, 14, 49, 115, 123
eosinophilia, 102, 104, 105
eosinophils, 16, 18, 73
epilepsy, 96
epinephrine, *see* adrenaline
epitopes, 30
essential fatty acids (EFAs), 47-9; and allergies, 104; and cancer prevention, 113; and cell permeability, 105; and lecithin, 100; and rheumatoid arthritis, 97; and vitamin B$_6$, 42; and zinc, 51; deficiency symptoms, 48; sources of, 48
evening primrose oil, 48, 97, 99
exercise, 79, 82, 84, 101
exercises, 85-94; relaxation, 77-8; *see also* visualization
faith, 63, 68
fast foods, 37
fats, 53, 99

fat-soluble vitamins, 47
fever, 33
fibre, *see* dietary fibre
fibrinogen, 32
fibrocystic breast disease, 47
fitness, 81, 82
flexibility, 81, 83
folate, *see* vitamin B$_9$
folic acid, *see* vitamin B$_9$
Folkers, Karl, 117
food allergies, *see* allergies
food, storage of, 57
free radicals, and CoQ10, 110; and organic germanium, 120; and superdioxide dismutase, 123, 124; and vitamin A, 38, 39; and vitamin B$_3$, 41; and vitamin C, 45; and vitamin E, 46
Fromme, Erich, 81

gammaglobulin, 35
gamma-linolenic acid (GLA), 48, 49
germanium, 119; *see also* organic germanium
germanium dioxide, 123
German measles, 35
glandular fever, *see* mononucleosis
Glaser, Ronald, 71
glutamine, 52
Graham, Judy, 99
granulocytes, 16, 24, 27
Gruber, Barry, 62

haemophilia, 35
Hall, Howard, 61
Hall, Nick, 62
hand warming, 63
hay fever, 103
headache, 63, 104
healing, self, 63, 67, 68
health, defined, 76
heart disease, 53, 56, 70
helper T-cells, 19; and AIDS, 107; and autoimmune disease, 95; and cancer, 110; and cortisol, 70; and emotions, 72; and interleukin-2, 30; and vitamin B$_{12}$, 43; and vitamin E, 47; and zinc, 51
Hendler, Sheldon, 45
heredity, 36; and allergies, 102; and autoimmune disease, 95, 96; and cancer, 110; and

CoQ10, 118; and immune deficiency, 106; and nutrition, 37; and systemic lupus, 100
herpes, 71, 72
Hersh, Stephen, 62
high blood-pressure, 96
histamine, 22, 31, 44, 102-104
HIV, 108
Hodgkin's disease, 15
holistic medicine, 58
homeostasis, 61
hope, 60, 61
hopelessness, 112
hormones, 47, 60, 61, 62
Horn, J.C., 63
horsetail, 98
host, 23
HTLV III, 106-107
humoral immunity, 20, 38, 49, 53; see also immunity
hydrochloric acid, 14
hydrocortisone, see cortisol
hypersensitivity, 19, 102-106, 119; see also allergies
hypertension, see high blood-pressure
hypnosis, 73
hypophysis, see pituitary gland
hypothalamus, 69, 73

imagery, see visualization
immune system, 15-28; and CoQ10, 116; and EFA deficiency, 48; and exercise, 82-3; and loneliness, 71; and PNI, 59; and stress, 72, 73; and zinc, 50; as sensory organ, 62; deficiency, 106-113; suppression of, 74
immunity, 15; and ageing, 117; and selenium, 49; cell-mediated, 18; humoral, 20; natural, 23; passive, 21; types of, 33
immunization, 20, 35
immunocompetence, 26
immunoglobulins (Ig), see antibodies
inflammatory response, 31-3, 38, 42, 49
inoculation, 20, 34
inositol, 100
insomnia, 55
interferon, 29, 44, 70, 121, 122
interleukin-1, 33
interleukin-2, 30

iron, 49

Jenner, Edward, 20

Kamen, Betty, 120
Kaposi's sarcoma (KS), 107
Kemeny, Margaret, 71, 72
keratin, 13
keratinocytes, 13
Kiecolt-Glaser, Janet, K., 71
killer cells, 19, 20, 30, 49, 51, 116
Kolata, Gina, 24
Kounovsky, Nicholas, 81
Kunin, Richard, 97, 105
Kupffer cells, 15

lactation, 119
lactobacillus acidophilus, 105
laughter, 77
Laurence, Jeffrey, 107
laxatives, 79
Lazarus, Richard S., 69
LE cell, 100
lecithin, 99, 100
LeShan, Lawrence, 111
leucocytes (WBCs), 16-20, 29-32 passim; and amino acids, 52; and autoimmunity, 96; and cholesterol, 82; and CoQ10, 116; and cortex of brain, 60; and emotions, 72; and skin, 12-13; and systemic lupus, 100; and tonsils, 28; and visualization, 61; and vitamin B9, 43; and vitamin E, 47; and zinc, 50
leucocytosis, 17
leucopenia, 17
leukaemia, 18, 35, 70
linoleic acid (LA), 48
linolenic acid (LNA), 49
lockjaw, see tetanus
loneliness, 71
Lund-Olesen, Knud, 124
lupus, see systemic lupus erythematosus
lymphatic system, 26-7; and exercise, 83, 84
lymphocytes, 17, 18-20; and AIDS, 107; and bone marrow, 24; and epitopes, 30; and hormone production, 61; and immune deficiency, 106; and lymph nodes, 27; and nerve fibres,

60; and stress, 72, 73; and the thymus gland, 25, 26; and the tonsils, 28; and vitamin A, 39; and zinc, 50
lymphokines, 19, 30
lymphoma, 35

macrophages, 14, 32; and alcohol, 56; and cellular conversation, 30; and cholesterol, 53; and CoQ10, 116; and free radicals, 46; and helper T-cells, 19; and hormone production, 61; and inflammation, 31; and inflammation, 31; and interleukin-1, 33; and iron, 49; and lymphocytes, 18; and mood, 60; and selenium, 50; and smoking, 55; and vitamin C, 45
magnesium, 97, 100
MAO inhibitors, 55
measles, 35
meditation, 65, 66, 67, 76
memory cells, 20, 23, 31
memory, immunologic, 23
mental disorders, 70
microglia, 15
microphages, 14
migraine, 63, 102
Miller, J.F.A.P., 25
mind-body link, 58; and cancer, 111, 112; and exercise, 83; and lymphocyte function, 73; and PNI, 59; and visualization, 61, 62; and white blood cell activity, 72
minerals, 49-51, 54, 70
mitochondria, 115, 116, 118
MMR vaccine, 35
monocytes, 17, 18, 24
mononucleosis, 17, 44
Montagu, Ashley, 36, 37
mucin, 14
mucus, 12, 14
multiple sclerosis (MS), 70, 98
mumps, 35
mushrooms, 42, 50
myelin sheath, 98, 99

National Institutes of Health, 12
natural immunity, 33
natural killer (NK) cells, 19, 20; and cancer, 112; and cortisol, 70; and organic

germanium, 121, 122; and stress, 71, 72
nervous system, 59
neurochemicals, 59
neuropeptides, 60
neurotransmitters, 52, 53, 60, 72, 99
neutrophils, 16, 18; and infection, 32; and obesity, 82; and stress, 70; and visualization, 61; and vitamin C, 45; and zinc, 50
niacin, see vitamin B_3
nicotinamide, see vitamin B_3
nicotine, 55, 56
nicotinic acid, see vitamin B_3
nitrates, 57
nitrites, 57
nitrosamines, 45, 46, 113
non-self substances, 15, 23
Nossal, G.J.V., 24, 25, 73

oats, 98, 100
obesity, 82, 113
oestrogen, 83
opsonin, 15
organic germanium, 119-123
organ rejection, 38
overweight, 82
oxidation, 120
oxygen, 120, 122, 124
oxygen depletion, 120, 121, 122

pain, 51
palpitations, heart, 76
pantothenic acid, see vitamin B_5
Pap test, 113
Parkinson's disease, 70
passive immunity, 34
Passwater, Richard, 97
pathogens, 40, 52, 59
pellagra, 41
peristalsis, 54
permeability, cell, 105
Pert, Candace, 60
pertussis, see whooping cough
Peyer's patches, 24, 27
phagocytes, 14, 31, 50
phagocytosis, 14, 15; and cholesterol, 82; and CoQ10, 116; and vitamin B_{12}, 43; and vitamin C, 44, 45; and vitamin E, 47
phenylalanine, 36, 52
phenylketonuria (PKU), 36, 51
pituitary gland, 47, 69
plasma cells, 20, 23, 25, 30

platelets, 24, 27
pneumonia, 34
pneumocystis carinii pneumonia (PCP), 107
PNI, see psychoneuroimmunology
polio, 35
polys, 16
prednisone, 35
pregnancy, 35, 98, 101, 108, 119
processed meats, 57
prostaglandins (PGs), 48, 51, 97, 99
protein, 49, 53, 54, 56
protein complementarity, 53
psychoneuroimmunology (PNI), 58, 59, 62, 64
pyridoxine, see vitamin B_6

quieting reflex, 76

rabies, 34
radiation, 35, 44, 106, 113, 124
red blood cells, 24, 27
relaxation, 71, 76, 77-8, 79, 83, 101
Renoux, Gérard, 60, 61
reticuloendothelial system (RES), see tissue macrophage system
retinol, see vitamin A
rheumatoid arthritis, 24, 55, 96-121; see also arthritis
riboflavin, see vitamin B_2
rubella, see German measles

scurvy, 45
Seeger, Paul Gerhard, 39
seizures, 35
selenium, 46, 47, 49-50, 113, 120, 123
self substances, 15, 23
self-worth, 79
Selye, Hans, 69, 72, 73, 103
serotonin, 52
serum sickness, 103
severe combined immunodeficiency (SCID), 107
sexually transmitted disease, see AIDS
Shaw, George Bernard, 14, 15
shopping strategies, 56, 57
shoulderstand exercise, 94
silica, 97
silicon, 97, 98

Simonton, Carl, 64, 74, 112
skin, and AIDS, 108; and cortisol, 70; and essential fatty acids, 48; and free radicals, 123; and smoking, 56; and sun, 79, 102; and systemic lupus, 100; and the thymus gland, 26; and vitamin A, 37; and vitamin B_5, 42; and vitamin C, 45; and vitamin E, 46; and zinc, 51; care, 13, 14, 79, 102; facts about, 12; protective role of, 12, 29
SLE, see Systemic lupus erythematosus
sleep, 52, 55, 79, 103
smallpox, 20, 34
smear test, 113
smoked foods, 113
smoking, 14, 55, 56, 79, 110, 111, 112
socializing, 79, 80
solitude, 79
spermicides, 109
spinal twist exercise, 92
spleen, 24, 27, 39, 72, 118
stem cells, 18, 106
steroids, 38
Stone, Irwin, 45
stress, 69-77; and alcohol, 95; and allergies, 103, 106; and amino acids, 52; and blood flow, 63; and cancer, 112; and CoQ10, 118; and dietary requirements, 104; and disease, 70; and exercise, 83; and immune deficiency, 106; and immunity, 71-4; and multiple sclerosis, 99; and rheumatoid arthritis, 96; and systemic lupus, 96, 101; and vitamin B_5, 42; and vitamin C, 45; and vitamin E, 47; defined, 69; management, 76-80; symptoms of, 76
stressors, 44, 69, 74-5, 114
Stroebel, Charles, 76
suicide, 70
sun, and cancer, 100, 113; and skin, 41, 79, 102; and systemic lupus, 96, 101; sun salutation exercises, 85-91
sunflower seeds, 40, 42, 43, 51

superdioxide dismutase (SOD), 123-24
superdioxides, 123
suppressor T-cells, 19, 31; and AIDS, 107; and autoimmune disease, 95; and cancer, 110; and cortisol, 70; and emotions, 72; and multiple sclerosis, 99; and rheumatoid arthritis, 96; and vitamin B$_{12}$, 43; and zinc, 51
surgery, 38
surveillance, immune, 23, 24, 71
systemic lupus erythematosus, 19, 41, 95, 100-102

T-cells, 18-20; and autoimmune disease, 95; and exercise, 82; and fever, 33; and immune deficiency, 106; and iron, 49; and lymphokines, 30; and organic germanium, 121; and prostaglandins, 48; and the thymus gland, 25, 26; and vitamin A, 38; and vitamin B$_1$, 40; and vitamin B$_6$, 42; and vitamin B$_{12}$, 43; and vitamin E, 47; and zinc, 50, 51; in skin, 12, 13
tension, 63
tetanus, 34, 35
thiamin, see vitamin B$_1$
thymocytes, 25
thymus gland, 13, 18, 24, 25-6; and cortisol, 70; and nervous system, 59; and stress, 70, 72, 73; and vitamin A, 38, 39; and vitamin B complex, 40; and vitamin B$_6$, 42; and zinc, 50, 51
thyroid gland, 95
Tien-Sun, Tung, 23
tissue macrophage system, 15
T-lymphocytes, see T-cells
tocopherol, see vitamin E
tonsils, 24, 28
transplants, organ and tissue,

70, 106, 107
triangle exercise, 93
tryptophan, 51, 52, 53
T-suppressor cells, see suppressor T-cells
tuberculosis, 18, 32, 34, 73, 96
tumour cells, 110
tumours, and amino acids, 52; and CoQ10, 117; and organic germanium, 121; and immune surveillance, 23, 24; and stress, 73; and T-cells, 18; and visualization, 62; and vitamin C, 45; and vitamin E, 46; rejection of, 74; see also cancer
typhoid fever, 34
tyrosine, 52

ubiquinone, 114
ulcerative colitis, 70
ulcers, peptic, 70

vaccination, 20, 33, 34
vaccines, 20, 34
VIP formula, 79-80, 99, 101, 110, 112
viruses, 29
visualization, 61, 62-8, 76, 77, 78
vitamin A (retinol), 37-9; and allergies, 104; and cell permeability, 105; and cancer prevention, 113; and free radicals, 41; and joint inflammation, 97; and zinc, 51; as antioxidant, 45, 46, 120; in complex carbohydrates, 54
vitamin B complex, 40-43, 54, 56, 99, 100, 104, 113
vitamin B$_1$ (thiamin), 40
vitamin B$_2$ (riboflavin), 40, 41
vitamin B$_3$ (niacin), 41, 53, 97
vitamin B$_5$ (pantothenic acid), 41, 42, 99, 104, 105
vitamin B$_6$ (pyridoxine), 42, 43, 53, 54, 97, 100, 105
vitamin B$_9$ (folic acid), 43
vitamin B$_{12}$ (cobalamin), 43

vitamin C (ascorbic acid), 44-6; and AIDS, 109; and allergies, 104, 105; and cancer, 45, 113; and cervical dysplasia, 43; and cortisol, 70, 71; and drugs, 55; and evening primrose oil, 97; and exercise, 82; and free radicals, 41; and immunosuppression, 47; and organic germanium, 121; and smoking, 56; and stress, 45; as an antihistamine, 105; as an antioxidant, 46, 50, 120, 123; in complex carbohydrates, 54
vitamin D, 54, 104
vitamin E, 46-7; and allergies, 105; and cancer prevention, 113; and evening primrose oil, 97; and exercise, 82; and multiple sclerosis, 99, 100; and organic germanium, 121; and selenium, 49; as an antioxidant, 41, 50, 120, 123; in complex carbohydrates, 54
vitamin F, see essential fatty acids
von Behring, E.A., 21

walling off, 32
warm-up exercises, 83, 84
WBCs, see leucocytes
weight loss, 107, 112
Weil, Andrew, 33
Weiner, Michael, 37, 109
wheatgerm oil, 47
white blood cells, see leucocytes
whooping cough, 18, 34, 35
will to live, 58

xanthines, 54, 55

yeast infections, 121
yellow fever, 34

zinc, 42, 50-51, 56, 97, 113, 120, 124

A DATE TO DIE FOR

A HOPGOOD HALL MYSTERY

E.V. HUNTER

Boldwood

First published in Great Britain in 2023 by Boldwood Books Ltd. This paperback edition published in 2024.

1

A CIP catalogue record for this book is available from the British Library.

Paperback ISBN 978-1-83561-887-5

Large Print ISBN 978-1-80483-567-8

Hardback ISBN 978-1-80483-566-1

Ebook ISBN 978-1-80483-564-7

Kindle ISBN 978-1-80483-565-4

Audio CD ISBN 978-1-80483-572-2

MP3 CD ISBN 978-1-80483-569-2

Digital audio download ISBN 978-1-80483-563-0

Boldwood Books Ltd
23 Bowerdean Street
London SW6 3TN
www.boldwoodbooks.com

PROLOGUE

'Don't even think about pulling the rug now. You're in too deep.'

'I don't respond well to threats,' he snarled.

'This is no threat, and we both know it.' She jerked at the sound of a fox barking. Typical townie, he thought. 'You owe me.'

'And I've paid.'

'Not nearly enough.'

She smirked, fully aware that she held the upper hand, and something inside of him snapped. A red mist of anger caused spots to dance before his eyes, blurring his vision. Without conscious thought for the consequences, he reached for her and grabbed her by the throat. She fought him with everything she had, pummelling his chest with her fists and desperately trying to kick out as he ruthlessly crushed her windpipe. He watched dispassionately as her face contorted and his anger slowly abated.

A rational corner of his brain warned him to stop. He was no murderer. It wasn't as if she could report the attack without drawing attention to her own nefarious activities. Oh yes, he knew what she used to be, and sometimes still was. What would that scandalous snippet of gossip do for her fledging business in a village this size? Why hadn't he thought of that before? There was no need to kill her. He could simply fight fire with fire.

He released his hold on her neck and she fell forward, chest heaving, wheezing and coughing, hands resting on her bent knees.

'You bastard!'

She recovered faster than he'd expected and launched herself at him. He instinctively put out a hand to ward her off, shoving her backwards with considerable force. She fell with a sickening thud and cried out as her head struck the ground. There was blood. Too much blood. She groaned, then stopped moving. He felt for a pulse and didn't find one.

That's what happened when you went soft, he reflected. He'd been willing to let her live but she'd brought her fate on herself. His thoughts now turned to survival. He couldn't leave her here but had plenty of time to cover his tracks. There was no need to panic.

Calm and methodical, he threw her over his shoulder. Strapped to the back of his quad bike, she lolled like a rag doll. He rode to a more isolated spot and dug a shallow grave. Then, once the body was wrapped in an old blanket, he tossed it uncer-emoniously into its final resting place, glad to be rid of the threat she posed once and for all. He filled the earth back in, sweating from his efforts, and scattered leaves and branches over the disturbed soil.

'Rest in peace,' he said sardonically, before remounting his bike and returning home to a stiff drink and a warm bed.

1

Alexi's heels echoed on the boarded floor of her loft as she made a final check for rogue possessions. The space felt devoid of character as it awaited someone else's imprint. Outside, a spring drizzle turned London monochrome, reflecting her own grey mood. She looked at her reflection, ghosted in the picture window against a backdrop of rain. She shuddered at the defiant image that glared back at her and turned away. At the flat's front door, she paused to say mental goodbyes to her old life.

'Okay, Cosmo, let's hit the road.'

Her black cat rubbed his head against her calf and stalked through the door ahead of her.

In the underground car park, Alexi stowed her case in the boot of her Mini and placed her computer bag behind the passenger seat, into which Cosmo had already installed himself. Alexi pulled the seatbelt across and fastened his leash to it. The police could be funny about unrestrained pets in vehicles, unenlightened as they were when it came to Cosmo's idiosyncrasies. There were cats, and then there was Cosmo, whose oddities she was still getting to grips with herself, and the last thing she needed was an altercation with the law.

Alexi climbed into the driver's seat, stowed her handbag, and turned the key in the ignition. Apprehension, anger, and relief fought for supremacy as she pulled out into the flow of traffic on the Battersea Road and watched her old home grow smaller in her rear view mirror.

Twenty minutes later, they were on the Westway heading towards the M4, music blasting on the radio, the windscreen wipers on intermittent to counteract the light drizzle that continued to mirror Alexi's mood. She automatically lifted her foot off the accelerator when she saw a warning sign for a speed camera. Always in a hurry, Alexi put her foot down once she was clear of the danger zone, only to lift it again almost immediately.

'You know what, Cosmo,' she said, 'we don't actually have to be anywhere. For the first time in living memory, I don't have a deadline.'

Cosmo's ears twitched.

Alexi felt a flash of optimism filter through her anger and insecurity. When had she last not had at least one assignment to keep her dashing from pillar to post? When had she last taken time for herself, rather than channelling every second into her career?

She'd made it, too, or at least thought she had. She had won the respect of some of her fiercest critics through hard work and persistence. But now it had all come crashing down in a spectac- ular ball of flames, and she was left with... well, with Cosmo and two bags of possessions. Not much to show for all that ambition.

Perhaps it was time to reassess.

She sighed, the sound of her mobile pulling her from her reverie. She moved to pick up the call without screening it. As a journalist, she never allowed her phone to go unanswered. Then she remembered that she no longer *was* a journalist – at least not a gainfully employed one – and checked to see who wanted her.

'Patrick,' she muttered, pressing the reject button.

She was well and truly over the two-faced schemer. *He* still had his cushy number on the *Sunday Sentinel*, with plum additional duties – *her* duties. He claimed to love her, but he'd known what changes were in the offing weeks before the announcement and hadn't warned her. That didn't add up to love in Alexi's book. She blew air through her lips and bashed the heel of her hand hard against the steering wheel. Cosmo opened an eye.

'I should have known there was something wrong when you kept trying to bite his ankles,' she told her cat.

Cosmo shot her an *I-told-you-so* look and went back to sleep.

Alexi hummed along with the radio as other cars sped past her, feeling calmer with every mile she put between herself and London. Driving slowly was cathartic. Who knew? The motorway rolled out through open countryside she'd never had time to look at before, and she decided to leave the busy road a couple of junctions short of her destination. The drizzle had stopped and a weak sun threatened to break through. The Berkshire fields undulated gently as she drove through small villages. She slowed to the speed limit on the road into Lambourn, a pretty town lying within a fold of the chalk downs. A large sign welcomed her and asked her to drive carefully. The area was dotted with large houses and stables, the fields fenced with post-and-rail; barely a leaf out of place. She could almost smell the money. A few leggy horses grazed in one of the fields but most of them appeared unoccupied, as did the roads. It was peaceful, pristine, and eerily quiet.

'I hope you like fresh air and horses, Cosmo,' she said as the cat finally stirred, sat up, and took notice. 'And remember what we talked about. No terrorising Cheryl's dog.'

Cosmo arched his back and sent her an appraising look through piercing hazel eyes.

* * *

Alexi followed the directions issued by the disembodied voice from the satnav, feeling guilty that she needed guidance to her best friend's door; a door she hadn't passed through since Cheryl's wedding ten years before. She'd been too busy building a career but in her hour of need, her neglected friend had welcomed her with open arms.

It was humbling.

She drove to Upper Lambourn, past a pub called the Malt Shovel, curious about the origins of its name. Turning left, she took a right through brick gateposts that she still remembered, a discreet plaque advising her that she had reached:

Hopgood Hall
Boutique Hotel.

The gardens on either side of the gravel drive looked pristine. What Alexi knew about gardening could be written on the back of a postage stamp but even she recognised a display of late daffodils and tulips. After the drizzle of London, a chilly breeze had sprung up, blowing away the blanket of cloud and showing the rural setting in its best light.

The old manor house had a façade of honey-coloured stone, wisteria climbing against it, its pendulous purple flowers giving off a heady perfume. Alexi breathed the scent deeply into her lungs. Hers was the only car in the visitors' parking area, she noticed, but before she could decide if that was a bad omen, the front door burst open and Cheryl flew down the steps, messy blonde curls dancing around her face.

'You're here!' she cried, launching herself into Alexi's arms and almost knocking her from her feet. 'And you look fantastic, damn you.'

'You don't look so bad yourself,' Alexi replied, wondering how she had let something as inconsequential as work get in the way of their friendship. The warmth of her reception caused the years to fall away and she knew she had done the right thing in coming here to lick her wounds. 'Thanks for the invite.'

'Where else would you go in your hour of need?'

Alexi's reunion with her old friend was interrupted by a series of indignant meows from inside Alexi's Mini.

'I'd best let him out before he frightens the horses,' Alexi said.

Cheryl peered into the car, only to be hissed at. It didn't seem to faze her. 'Wow, I've never seen such a huge cat.'

'I did warn you.' Since being adopted by Cosmo, Alexi had heard him described as anything from a panther to a racoon, or various combinations thereof. 'Are you absolutely sure he's welcome? I wish I could say the bad mood was a big act, but it isn't.'

'I'm sure we'll get along just fine.'

Alexi shrugged, crossed the fingers of one hand behind her back, and released Cosmo's leash with the other. Her cat indulged in another slow stretch, his eyes fixed speculatively upon Cheryl. Alexi tensed when Cheryl reached out a hand and waited for the explosion that didn't come. Instead, Cosmo submitted to Cheryl's ministrations and then regally stalked off into a nearby clump of bushes.

'My god, he remembered his manners. That's a first.'

They watched his rigid tail disappear deeper into the bushes.

Alexi grabbed her handbag and linked her arm through Cheryl's. 'I want to hear all your news. How long is it since we last had a chance to catch up face-to-face?'

Cheryl screwed up her nose. 'When I came to London and stayed with you, more than two years ago. Come on, Drew just put the kettle on. Although the sun's no doubt over the yardarm somewhere, and if your arrival doesn't count as an excuse to break out the bubbly, then I don't know what does. Oh!' Cheryl clapped her free hand over her mouth. 'There I go again, letting my tongue run away with me. I guess you're not in a celebratory mood.'

'I'm *always* in the mood for bubbly.'

'Attagirl!'

They made their way into a large, homely kitchen at the back of the house in which a bear of a man was setting out tea things with remarkable delicacy. He saw Alexi, gave a whoop of delight, and swept her clean off her feet.

'Thank god you're here,' he said. 'Cheryl's been listening to the traffic news all day, convinced that every time there was mention of an accident, you had to be involved in it.'

'Well, you have always been a bit of a reckless driver,' Cheryl protested.

'I got more responsible.'

Cheryl stifled a disbelieving laugh. 'So come on, tell us about it. What happened to you?' she asked, her smile fading. 'You've been working so hard. I don't really understand why it all fell apart.'

'Let the poor woman get some tea down her before you interrogate her, love,' Drew said mildly.

Cheryl shrugged. 'I didn't think a lot of that Patrick guy. You're worth way more than someone that self-centred.'

'Yeah, well... oh no!'

A strangled howl from the back garden had Alexi leaping from her seat, already guessing the source of the noise. Cosmo was on the lawn, squaring up to a little terrier.

'Cosmo, what did I tell you?' Alexi demanded, joining him outside and placing her hands on her hips.

Cosmo backed down and fixed Alexi with an innocent look. With his tail rigid, he approached a trembling Toby and rubbed his head against the dog's body.

'I'll be damned,' Drew said, shaking his head.

Cheryl grinned. 'It seems they've worked the pecking order out,' she said. 'Come on in for that tea, Lexi, then we can legitimately crack open a bottle or six.'

Alexi didn't move. Instead she stared at the ugly row of prefabricated chalets occupying a big chunk of the manor's large garden. They were on the far side, away from the windows in the main house, which is why she hadn't seen them before.

'What happened?' she asked.

'Come on in and we'll tell you,' Cheryl said, grimacing.

Cosmo preceded them through the door and meowed for food. Toby followed behind and barked in support.

Drew guffawed. 'They're a bloody double act already.'

Grinning, Alexi reached into her bag and found a pouch of dried cat food she'd had the presence of mind to keep close at hand. Cheryl took it from her and decanted the contents into a plastic bowl.

'Right,' Alexi said, as they sat around the scarred pine kitchen table drinking Earl Grey. 'Spill.'

'We just couldn't get the bookings to keep the hotel afloat.' It was Drew who answered her. 'It's all seasonal here. We rely on well-off people who want to rub shoulders with the elite of the racing world. Problem is, if the weather's crap, they abandon that idea and sod off to sunnier climes.'

'Plus there're a lot of cheaper hotels springing up in the area,' Cheryl added.

'Don't you get owners and other high-end horsy types?'

Drew shrugged. 'Owners either stay with their trainers or just come in for the day.'

'We get a lot of their business in the bar and restaurant,' Cheryl said in a cheerful tone that sounded strained.

'We have a prima donna chef who knows his own worth and causes almost as many problems as he solves,' Drew said. 'But at least he draws the punters in. Trainers who want to impress potential owners, stuff like that.'

'But the... er... annexe?' Alexi asked, bewildered. 'How does that fit with your posh image?'

'Something had to be done. No way was I going to let Drew lose his family home,' Cheryl said defensively.

Cheryl and Drew had met in a pub during Alexi and Cheryl's final year at university. The two of them had hit it off immediately and were married the day after Cheryl graduated with a degree in hotel management. Drew had taken out a bank loan to buy out his siblings' shares of the family home, with plans to turn it into an upmarket hotel.

'You've been holding out on me,' she said, frowning at her friend.

'Pride goeth before a fall,' Cheryl replied, her chin supported in her hands. 'I wasn't about to admit to my hotshot journalist friend that we'd messed up.'

'Oh, Cheryl.' Alexi leaned forward to give her a hug. 'I might have been able to help. I could have got our travel section to give you a good write-up, stuff like that. I did mention the place several times but readers don't look for travel tips in the stuff I write... wrote.'

'Sorry, hon.' Cheryl squeezed Alexi's hand. 'Take no notice of me. I'm on edge all the time nowadays.'

'You haven't told her?' Drew asked.

'Told me what?' One look at their soppy grins and Alexi realised what ought to have been immediately apparent when she saw Cheryl's expanding waistline. She slopped tea over the table as she jumped up and hugged them both. 'About time too. Congratulations!'

'Thanks,' Cheryl said.

'When's the baby due?'

'Another four months yet,' Cheryl replied, grimacing.

'A late-summer baby then. Do we know what you're having?'

'No,' Drew replied. 'We're being old-fashioned and prefer a surprise.'

'I plan to make up for being a crap friend by spoiling the baby rotten.'

'You'll have to join the queue,' Cheryl warned, nodding at her husband who was still sporting a goofy grin. 'Anyway, we hope you'll agree to be a godmother.'

'With pleasure, although what spiritual guidance I can offer is debatable.'

'You have good morals, which is all that counts nowadays,' Cheryl said.

'Those... er, whatever they are in the garden.' Alexi reminded them. 'You still haven't told me what that's all about.'

'We let them to grooms and trainee jockeys from a local yard,' Drew admitted. 'I know we were full of lofty ideals when we started out.' He shrugged. 'But this is the real world and needs must.'

'We would have gone under without them,' Cheryl added starkly.

'Most trainers either have staff accommodation on site or

make arrangements locally.' Drew rubbed his chin. 'But last winter, one major trainer had a fire on his premises—'

'Graham Fuller,' Alexi said. 'I remember there was a lot of speculation about that.'

'Right. There were suspicious circumstances,' Drew said. 'Fuller was on bad terms with another trainer. The other guy accused him of poaching one of his top owners, and the row escalated.'

'Didn't Fuller cry arson?' Alexi asked, her interest piqued.

'I think my friend senses a story,' Cheryl said, grinning.

'Professional curiosity. Can't turn it off just because I'm unemployed.'

'Yeah well, I don't think anyone will ever really be able to prove what happened. Graham uses our bar and restaurant a lot, told me about his problem with housing for his lads, and Cheryl and I decided to bite the bullet.'

'I get why you did it, but I'm surprised you got planning permission.'

'We had to jump through hoops,' Drew admitted. 'But Graham has a lot of sway with the local council. I don't know what strings he pulled, and I don't want to. We put the units to the side, so guests in the main house don't have to look at them.'

'What we didn't realise when we agreed to do Graham a favour—'

'—And save our own bacon...' Drew added.

Cheryl waved the reminder aside. 'We didn't know it would affect our five-star status.'

'You lost a star because of them?'

'We don't have tennis courts any more,' Cheryl explained. 'None of the guests ever used them, but it seems they matter when it comes to a hotel's place on the totem pole. Anyway, the annexe is fully occupied year round, the residents fend for themselves, and we send in cleaners once a week to make sure they haven't completely trashed the place.'

Alexi could see Cheryl and Drew were putting a brave face on things. 'I'm glad they saved the day, and I promise never to say another word about the way the huts look.'

'If things pick up, or when Graham rebuilds his own staff accommodation, we can have them taken down again,' Cheryl said.

'We're just about making ends meet right now.' Drew sighed and stood up. 'Come on love, I'll get your stuff from your car and show you up. You've got the big room, centre front.'

'But that's your best room,' Alexi protested. 'Cosmo and I don't expect star treatment.'

'We don't have anyone else in the main house right now, although we're booked up for the weekend,' Cheryl replied. 'You deserve to be pampered, at least until then.'

'All right, but I insist upon paying the going rate.'

'Are you trying to insult me?' Drew asked indignantly.

Alexi refused to back down. 'You're in business,' she reminded them.

'We'll work something out,' Drew said gruffly. 'Come on now, let's get you settled, then we'll have drinks before dinner and you can catch us up with your news.'

'I can't have drinks,' Cheryl said, patting her belly and pouting. 'But I can inhale yours vicariously *and* feel all virtuous in the morning when you two have headaches from hell.'

Alexi laughed. 'The sacrifice will be worth it.'

'You hear that,' Cheryl said to her stomach. 'You are going to be *so* worth it.'

'Don't forget,' Drew said as he lugged Alexi's bag up the stairs. 'You can stay with us for as long as you like. Take some time to think about what you want to do. Cheryl will be glad of the company.'

Alexi the hardnosed, self-sufficient journalist who didn't need anyone and never accepted favours, glanced out the window and noticed spring shower-clouds building on the crests of the downs. For no apparent reason, the sight caused her eyes to swamp with tears.

2

Cosmo stalked up the stairs with them, Toby following two paces behind.

'A right pair,' Drew said, laughing at Toby's expression of total adoration.

'If Cosmo takes a liking to someone, he tends to inspire devotion. Mostly he doesn't like people and is suspicious of them—'

'He's a feral cat, right?'

'Yeah.'

'Well then, it stands to reason that he'll have learned to be selective. It's a survival skill. But I have to say, he's the largest moggy I've ever seen, especially since he doesn't have an ounce of fat on him.'

'I'm not sure why he's so svelte. He eats me out of house and home.'

Drew opened the door to her room and placed her case on the stand. He chuckled as Cosmo, erect tail twitching, prowled imperiously around his temporary accommodation. 'What made you take on a wild cat?'

'I was doing a feature a few years back about the homeless

living under Waterloo Bridge. He was there, keeping both humans and rodents in line. He was a feral tom in every sense of the word, but for some reason, he took a liking to me. The third time I went down there, he followed me back to my car, jumped into the passenger seat and hissed at anyone who went anywhere near him.' Alexi shrugged. 'What could I do?'

Cosmo leapt onto the four-poster bed, took a position in the middle of it, and set about washing his face, sending Alexi and Drew occasional glances.

Drew laughed. 'He must have been a domestic cat at one time if he likes cars.'

'That's what I figured. And I think he's forgiven me for taking him to the vet—'

Drew winced. 'Tough luck, Cosmo.'

'Hey, safe sex shouldn't be restricted to humankind. Cosmo is probably responsible for a good number of stray moggies already. He doesn't need to add more notches to his bedpost.'

Drew reached forward to scratch Cosmo's head. Alexi tensed, then relaxed again when the feline pushed his head against his hand. Toby jumped up, too, and curled up against Cosmo's body.

'I'm really glad you're here, Alexi. Cheryl's been worried about you.'

'The nicer you guys are to me, the worse I feel about not having seen more of you.'

Drew shrugged. 'Life has a nasty habit of getting in the way of friendships.'

'That's no excuse.'

'You're here now and that's all that matters. Have you got everything you need?'

'This is luxury.' Alexi glanced around the high-ceilinged room with its full-length windows looking out over the downs. Those windows were covered with floral curtains that matched the bedspread. There was a comfortable sofa beneath the window and a desk and chair where she could set up her computer. Eventually. She peered into the spacious en suite with its rack of fluffy towels and basket of toiletries. 'How could I possibly want for anything?'

'Okay, I'll leave you to get settled. Come down as soon as you're ready and we'll have that bevvy.'

'You've got yourself a date.'

* * *

Left alone, Alexi swiftly unpacked her case and hung her clothes in the closet. Then she stripped off and took a long shower. Half an hour later, feeling refreshed, she dressed in cotton trousers and a light top, brushed her hair, dabbed on a slash of lip gloss, and waved the mascara wand at her lashes. Dog and cat accompanied her downstairs again and she followed an enticing aroma into the kitchen.

'Hey.' Cheryl looked up from stirring something in a pot. Kitchens terrified Alexi. She'd lived on take-away in London and would have trouble scrambling an egg. Cheryl, on the other hand, had always loved cooking.

'Can I do something? I can chop, peel, or dice without wrecking anything.' Alexi winced. 'Probably.'

'You're good. Grab a pew. I'll be right there.' Cheryl grinned. 'Although, on second thoughts, I'm betting you can still wield a corkscrew as well as you used to back in the day.'

'Show me where, sister!'

With a glass of wine in front of her, and orange juice for Cheryl, the friends sat at the kitchen table and clinked glasses. Cosmo, failing in his transparent efforts to extract food from Cheryl, sent her the feline equivalent of an injured look and curled up in Toby's basket. Toby hopped right in with him, wagging his tail as he occupied the small amount of space Cosmo allowed him.

'Congratulations again,' Alexi said. 'I'm really happy for you. I know you're going through a rough patch with the business, but you and Drew still appear to be joined at the hip.'

Cheryl grinned. 'Yeah, we're lucky that way. And on the subject of relationships, can we clear the air about Patrick?'

'Who?'

'Lexi!'

'What do you want me to say?' Alexi spread her hands. 'You were right about him. He's a skunk. He claimed he was sworn to secrecy and couldn't tell me about the impending changes at the paper. If he had, I'd have known I was for the chop and it would have given me more time to prepare a countermove.' Alexi sighed. 'If you love someone, you put their feelings first, don't you?'

'Yes,' Cheryl replied succinctly. 'Always. I'm sorry you've been hurt but I gotta say, you're worth way more than Patrick. You *will* find that elusive someone, probably when you least expect to.'

'Right now, I'm off men and definitely not looking.' Alexi leaned over and gave Cheryl a hug. 'The organisation was top heavy and haemorrhaging money. It was obvious something had to give. I just didn't figure that I'd be one of the casualties – I was in a relationship with the political editor, who wouldn't feed me to the wolves, at least not without giving me a heads-up.' She managed a wry smile. 'Quite a blow to the ego, that one.'

'You wrote brilliant, insightful pieces,' Cheryl said defensively.

'Which was my downfall, apparently. If it doesn't have *celebrity* status, people don't want to know any more.'

'You were too good at what you did. The *Sentinel* has made a mistake if it's trying to sensationalise. They seem to forget there are still people who actually have functioning brain cells and want reasoned opinion along with the cornflakes.'

'Not so many people buy papers at all now; that's part of the problem, to be fair.' Alexi leaned an elbow on the table and rested her chin in her cupped hand. 'It's all instant, online stuff.' Alexi expelled a resigned sigh. 'Anyway, Patrick is now covering the dumbed-down version of what I did, and seemed to think I'd be happy to run the equivalent of a political gossip column.'

Cheryl's bosom swelled with indignation. 'The fink!'

'Yeah well, that's not quite what I called him.'

'All this only happened last week, and yet you've arranged to let your flat and hot-footed it down here already.' Cheryl grinned. 'I like your style.'

'I haven't seen or spoken to Patrick either, although he keeps calling.'

'Any idea what you intend to do now?'

'Nope, not a clue.' Alexi took a healthy sip of her wine. 'It's liberating in a scary sort of way.'

'You have no job, no home, and your mum recently died. I wouldn't call that liberating. More like consecutive kicks in the teeth.'

'It's forced me out of my comfort zone, which is good in some ways. I was in a bit of a rut. And, on the bright side, I have no financial worries. Sorry,' Alexi added when Cheryl flinched. 'I sold Mum's property, inherited her investment portfolio, plus I got a golden handshake from the *Sentinel*. Not that they wanted to cough up. They reckoned they'd offered me an alternative role and that by refusing it, I'd sacked myself.'

Cheryl blew air through her lips. 'Cheapskates.'

'Fortunately I'd studied my contract and found a clause that said they couldn't *demote* me without just cause, so I threatened them with legal action if they tried it. I also intimated I'd write about the way I'd been treated, offer it to their rivals... it worked. They paid up, so I can take my time deciding what next *and* pay you for my keep.' She raised a hand to stop Cheryl from protesting. 'I've had a few offers from other London papers, but nothing that tempts me. I think it might be time for a complete change of direction.'

'What, move from London altogether?' Cheryl widened her eyes. 'I thought you were a city girl through and through. Do you even own a pair of wellies?'

Alexi laughed, feeling herself begin to relax as the wine worked its magic. 'Do they come with four-inch heels?'

The back door opened to admit Drew. Cosmo, seemingly resigned to the fact that he wasn't going to be fed any time soon, stalked through it, his faithful disciple tagging along behind him.

'Any luck?' Cheryl asked.

'Sorry love, no sign.'

'No sign of what?' Alexi asked, sensing their joint anxiety.

'It's Cheryl's friend, Natalie.' Drew poured himself a generous glass of wine and topped Alexi's up. 'She's missing. We're worried about her. I just stopped by her place but no one's been there since I checked yesterday.'

'Who is she?' Alexi asked.

'She moved to Lambourn a couple of years ago. She's into floral art. Does bouquets, table decorations for weddings, stuff like that. We've used her here, which is how we became friends.'

'How long has she been gone?'

'Three days.'

'Too short a time to worry, surely?'

'She *does* go away quite a bit, but never without telling us,'

Drew explained. 'We have her keys and keep an eye on the place for her.'

'It's just so out of character,' Cheryl said, frowning in a manner that drew attention to the dark shadows beneath her eyes. Either she was really worried about her friend or those visible signs of stress were caused by their financial problems.

'She isn't answering her mobile or emails either, and that's just not like her. She runs a business and has to keep in touch with her clients, or risk losing them.'

'What about her other friends? Husband. Men friends.'

'She's divorced,' Cheryl replied. 'With no significant other. No kids. Truth is, she's lonely, but never seems to have much luck with men. They take advantage of her... well, I suppose she's so desperate to be loved that she attracts the wrong sort.'

'She's got a lovely house, drives a nice car, and she's good-looking; takes care of herself. The moment those losers she dates see that, I'm betting they think they're on to a good thing,' Drew said, scowling. 'Her car is in the garage, but her laptop, iPad, and mobile are gone, along with her handbag.'

'That does seem odd,' Alexi replied, her journalistic antennae twitching. 'Have you told the police?'

Cheryl rolled her eyes. 'They didn't want to know. Natalie is over forty, she often goes away, so they say there's not much they can do. When Drew went to our part-time police station yesterday they all but laughed him out the door.'

'I know it's not what you want to hear,' Alexi said, 'but there probably isn't any action they can take. People make out of character decisions all the time and unless there's clear evidence that a crime's been committed, the police have got more urgent things to do. They'll list her as missing, make a few enquiries, and that's about it.'

'That's more or less what they told me when I reported it,'

Drew said, giving his wife's hand a comforting squeeze. 'They implied she'd taken herself off for a naughty weekend.'

'I know a few people,' Alexi said. 'I could get one of them to run a trace on her mobile.'

Cheryl's expression brightened. 'Could you? I was hoping perhaps—'

'That would give us some idea where she is. If she's in an urban area, they might be able to get within fifty metres of her location. But fifty metres in a densely populated area is still a lot of space to get lost in. If she's out in the sticks, there could be miles between antennae stations, impossible to pinpoint her exact location.'

'I told her it was a mistake to...'

'To what?' Alexi asked when Cheryl's words trailed off and she sucked in a shuddering breath.

'Natalie has signed up to an online dating service,' Drew explained.

'Ah.'

Cheryl sighed. 'What if she was being cyber-stalked by some creep, that's what I keep wondering?'

'If she's with one of the reputable... what the hell was that?' Alexi asked when shrieks and then raucous laughter interrupted their conversation.

'The grooms returning home,' Drew said, standing up and looking through the window, a broad smile on his face. 'I think your cat is providing a welcoming committee.'

'Oh god, I'm sorry! Cosmo hisses at everyone.'

'It makes up for all the times they've disturbed us with parties they're not supposed to hold,' Cheryl said.

'Whenever one of their horses has a win, the groom usually gets a cash gift from the owners,' Drew explained.

'Ah, I get the picture. Any more problems with your grooms, say the word, and I'll get Cosmo to up his game.'

'Hey, Mrs. H,' an attractive young man waved in the window. 'Can you call your guard cat off?'

Laughing, Alexi got up, opened the back door and shouted at Cosmo. Cheryl followed Alexi out of the door.

'Fine feline,' the young man said, looking at Alexi rather than Cosmo. 'Here you go, Mrs. H. The guv'nor asked me to give you this.'

'Thanks, Tod.' Cheryl took the envelope he held out to her.

'Are you going to introduce us?'

'Alexi, this is Tod Naismith, Graham Fuller's head lad and self-appointed leader of this motley crew.' She waved a hand negligently towards the annexe. 'Tod, this is my good friend, Alexi Ellis.'

Alexi shook Tod's outstretched hand. 'Nice to meet you,' she said.

'You too.' Tod waggled his brows. 'Do you plan to stay with us for long?'

'She's out of your league, Tod,' Cheryl said, laughing as she and Alexi returned to the house. 'Sorry,' she added as she closed the door behind them. 'I should have warned you about Tod. He's incorrigible.'

'He seems like fun.' Alexi winced at the sound of banging doors. 'Or not.'

'Graham's sent over the cheque he owes us,' Cheryl said, handing the envelope to Drew.

'At last!'

The noise gradually subsided, but Alexi could see the damage the grooms would do to the hotel business. People who paid through the nose for quality accommodation expected peace and quiet and the grooms' presence was unlikely to encourage repeat bookings.

'Anyway,' Alexi said, returning to their conversation. 'If your friend is with one of the more reputable dating agencies, I'd say she'd be pretty safe. Those sites conceal members' true email addresses and block their personal details.'

'Yes, but what if she's met someone and revealed those things?' Cheryl asked. 'I warned her about it, and she promised me she wouldn't, but if she really liked and trusted a man...'

'Do you know if she went on any dates?' Alexi asked.

'To begin with we had a good laugh about some of the men she'd met, and how different they were to the images they projected on the site.' Cheryl became pensive. 'But recently she'd become quite tight-lipped about her activities. She seemed distracted, and I hoped it was because she'd met someone nice.'

'She promised us she would only meet dates in public places,' Drew added. 'Bars, restaurants, stuff like that, and if she *did* invite anyone back to hers, she also promised to let us have his details in advance, just in case.'

'But she didn't do that?'

'No.' Cheryl shook her head. 'Natalie is a good business-woman, but when it comes to personal relationships, I wouldn't put it past her to have been sweet-talked into keeping stuff to herself. Some charismatic guy would only have to spin her a line and she'd fall for it.'

'It might not be so bad,' Alexi replied, even though she had a nasty feeling about the circumstances. 'Between a quarter and a half of all new relationships start online nowadays. Did you know that?' Cheryl and Drew both shook their heads. 'Welcome to the cyber age. Online dating has got an iffy reputation—'

'With good reason,' Drew said.

'It's like anything; opportunists will find a way to exploit it, but the majority of people don't have any problems, if they're careful.'

The wine bottle was empty. Drew opened a second while Cheryl dished up the food.

'Oh god, I'm in love!' Alexi cried, groaning as she took a mouthful of Cheryl's homemade lasagne. 'I'd forgotten what a good cook you are.'

'Now you know why I married her.'

Cosmo, presumably attracted by the smell of food, appeared in the open kitchen window. Toby's pathetic barks from outside had them all laughing as Drew got up to let him in.

'Do you think we're wrong to be worried about Natalie?' Cheryl asked.

'What dating agency did she use?'

'Heart Racing,' Cheryl replied, giggling at the name. 'Apparently online dating has gone interest-related.'

Alexi grinned. 'Whatever happened to opposites attracting?'

'People don't have time for *proper* relationships nowadays,' Cheryl replied. 'Like you just said, everything's virtual. Except that now, dating agencies are targeted at specific interests.'

'I got in touch with Heart Racing,' Drew said. 'I wanted to put Cheryl's mind at rest, but they wouldn't tell me who Natalie dated. They gave me all the spiel about confidentiality and wouldn't even confirm she was registered with them.' Drew scowled at the wall. 'They wouldn't open up even when I told the snotty woman I spoke to how worried we were about Natalie and threatened them with a visit from the police.'

'They could get sued, I suppose, if they revealed anyone's details.'

'Even if they have a pervert on their books?' Cheryl demanded hotly.

'They probably have a get-out clause when it comes to perverts,' Alexi said in a futile attempt to lighten the mood.

All sorts of questions filtered through Alexi's journalistic brain, but pregnant women with money worries didn't need stress so she let the subject drop. While Drew stacked the dishwasher and put the coffee on, Alexi mentally ran through the steps she would take if this was an assignment.

Locate Natalie's mobile phone, hack into her email and see who she'd been talking to, check her bank account to make sure it hadn't been cleaned out, check her social media sites to see how open she was about herself online. If she'd registered with Heart Racing under her true name and given an honest picture of herself, it would be child's play for a cyber-stalker to get all her personal information elsewhere without asking Natalie any intrusive questions. More troubling was the fact that if the guy's intention had been to steal her cash, he wouldn't want her around afterwards to identify him. But one woman wouldn't have enough cash to see him set for life, so he'd want to do this again. And again. Which meant he would go for wealthy, needy women.

Women like Natalie.

3

By the time she returned to her room, Alexi's curiosity had got the better of her. She fired up her computer, just to see what a little creative surfing might throw up about Natalie. Alexi had what the old hacks referred to as a 'nose' for a story, and right now that nose was twitching like it was hay fever season.

It couldn't hurt to poke about a bit.

The absolute peace and stillness of Lambourn – no traffic noise, no sirens, no hustle of a city on steroids – made it hard for Alexi to concentrate. She switched on the television news with the volume turned down low. The background noise helped her to focus upon what might have happened to Natalie. The more she thought about it, the more convinced she became that this other woman was still alive.

Working on the assumption that she'd been targeted by a fortune hunter, the guy had probably whisked Natalie off to some exotic location, spinning her a line about wanting her all to himself and persuading her to cut herself off from the outside world. He'd wine and dine her; give her his undivided attention, and ply her with the best of everything.

Those types of men were always charismatic, Alexi knew. They chose their victims carefully, then traded on their looks and charm, relying on the woman's desperate need for a man to nurture to seal the deal. Having gained Natalie's trust, it would be comparatively easy for a computer-savvy guy to access her online banking. Alexi hadn't lost sight of the fact that Natalie's electronic devices were all missing. If he didn't clear Natalie out, the chances were she'd take the hit and be too embarrassed to report it.

'Okay, Cosmo, where do we start?'

Cosmo completed his ablutions and then curled up in the middle of the bed, sending her a condescending look before closing his eyes.

'Fat lot of help you are,' she chided.

Alexi quickly checked her email. There was a long missive from Patrick, which she told herself she wouldn't read.

She read it.

He was sorry, and he could explain. Where was she? He loved her. He'd only been trying to protect her. He had a proposition for her. One that was right down her street and would be more financially rewarding than slaving away on the *Sentinel*.

'Yeah right,' she muttered, deleting the email with only a slight pang of regret for what they'd once had.

Cheryl didn't know what picture of herself Natalie had used on the Heart Racing site; nor could Alexi access that information unless she either hacked into the site or registered with them. She had no intention of doing the latter. The former was a possibility.

Natalie's business website was easy to navigate and professional. It showed a pleasant image of an attractive woman in her early forties with blonde hair cut in a neat bob and an open, friendly smile. There was a contact form for those wanting information about Natalie's services. It would be child's play for anyone who knew their way around a computer to trace the IP address. The chances of it not being registered to Natalie's business, which was located at the same place as her home, were slim.

'Oh, Natalie,' Alexi muttered, shaking her head.

She was on Facebook, Twitter, LinkedIn, and half a dozen other social media sites. Her chatty posts on Facebook said enough about her daily activities to offer a stalker a good idea of her interests. She liked horses which, given where she lived, wasn't exactly a surprise. She was thinking of investing in a part-share of a racehorse, which *was* news to Alexi, who audibly groaned. Easy enough for a potential date to pretend a similar interest, along with a passion for hiking, flowers, and photography.

By the time Alexi finished her initial foray into Natalie Parker's life, she'd become as worried about her as Cheryl was. Her eyes began to droop, which surprised Alexi since she normally did her best work after the witching hour. She figured the overdose of clean, country air had messed with her lungs, which were accustomed to unhealthy doses of carbon monoxide and second-hand smoke. Then there'd been the physical and emotional upheaval, too, as well as the big meal and too much wine.

'Face it, Cosmo,' she said with a wry twist to her lips. 'I can't take it like I used to.'

She had a quick wash, slipped into a tank top and boxers, and crawled between crisp, cotton sheets. Cosmo crept up to the pillows and wrapped himself around her head, a bit like a furry nightcap, purring like a traction engine.

'Shut up, baby,' she murmured, falling almost instantly asleep.

* * *

She was woken at some ungodly hour by a noisy army on the march: presumably the grooms heading for work. She felt remarkably rested, so pushed back the covers and had a good stretch. After a quick shower, she pulled on a pair of favourite old jeans and a sweatshirt. Cosmo deigned to stir only when she slid her feet into her shoes. Pathetic whining noises from outside her door indicated that Toby was pining for his new buddy.

'Come on then,' she said to Cosmo. 'I think I can smell bacon frying.'

Toby bounded in when Alexi opened the door, wagging and jumping all over Cosmo in a frenzy of delight. Cosmo gave Toby a gentle head butt and the two of them led the way down the stairs.

'Morning,' Drew said, turning back from the stove where he was frying the bacon that had lured her into the kitchen. 'Did you sleep well?'

'Like a log. I never sleep like that in London.'

Drew screwed up his nose. 'Too much going on in the big, bad city.'

'Actually, it's so quiet here, I thought it would stop me from sleeping.'

'Grab a seat. Breakfast won't be long.'

Alexi opened the cupboard where she'd stowed Cosmo's food and extracted a packet. He wound himself around her legs as she placed his bowl on the floor.

'Where's Cheryl?'

'Just getting up. I had to almost tie her down at first to make her rest—'

Alexi warded him off with the flats of her hands. 'Too much information.'

Drew laughed. 'She's finally being more sensible. Anyway, have you had any more thoughts about Natalie? I'd rather you told me first, especially if it's not good news.'

Alexi explained about her online search. 'That was just a short foray and I already know a ton of stuff about her life.' She frowned. 'That's why this so-called social media age is dangerous. Why did she feel the need to tell the world she's thinking of investing in a share of a racehorse? That implies money and will attract all sorts of unsavoury people.'

Drew put aside his spatula and gave Alexi his full attention. 'You think she's been groomed?'

'It's a possibility, but let's not jump to conclusions. I wouldn't mind taking a look at her home later, just to get more of a feel for her, then we'll decide where to go from there.'

'Where *can* we go? I mean, the police aren't too bothered, I don't suppose the dating agency will tell us anything, and—'

'I could take a peek at her email. See who she's been talking to.'

'You can do that?'

'Comes with the territory.' Alexi laughed at Drew's horrified expression. 'I did a story once on computer security and a master hacker taught me the rudiments of his *modus operandi* just to demonstrate how easy it actually is. Anyway, let's not get ahead of ourselves. Despite what you think, I don't make a habit out of invading people's privacy online, just because I can. It's a last resort.' *Well, usually.*

'Sorry, we can't come with you.' Drew placed Alexi's breakfast in front of her and she tucked in. 'We have a lunch party for twenty people this Sunday and we have to be here to talk to the customer. There's really no need, but I think they're a bit starstruck and insist upon meeting Marcel.'

'Marcel?'

'Our chef. I hope to Christ he behaves himself. It's impossible to know. He's a bit like your cat. If he takes a dislike to someone, he can be incredibly rude.'

'Ah, one of *those*.' Alexi rolled her eyes. 'Thanks. Breakfast was great, as you can see.' She nodded towards her cleared plate. 'I'll get out the way then. Give me the address and Natalie's keys and I'll find my own way.'

* * *

The gardens to the front and side of Sundial Cottage told their own story. Bursting with orderly colour, it was obvious that whoever lived there had green fingers and a talent for making flowers thrive. Jack recognised all the usual suspects for that time of year – daffodils, tulips, primroses – but that was as far as his knowledge went. There was a mass of colourful stuff crawling over a wall, and a whole patch of white things in the bed below it. An ancient sundial sat in the centre of a well-tended lawn. The curtains were half-closed and he knew before he knocked that no one would be at home.

Time for a good snoop.

He peered through the living room window and saw nothing to excite his interest. No signs of a scuffle or a hasty departure; everything neat and tidy, which told him absolutely nothing. He would have to get inside and take a closer look. Sighing, he rounded the left flank of the cottage, looking for a more discreet point of entry. This was a quiet lane with little passing traffic and no immediate neighbours, but even so, it paid to be cautious.

There was a newish, navy-blue Mini Cooper with a garish pink roof parked at the side of the cottage. It hadn't been visible from the lane. Preoccupied by thoughts of its ownership, he almost failed to notice a massive black ball of fury launch itself from the branches of a tree like a guided missile.

'Whoa there!'

He instinctively held up his arms to protect his face. The missile landed at his feet, hissing like it bore him a grudge. It was a cat. The largest, sleekest, most pissed off cat he'd ever seen. It had obviously been camped out in the branches and now seemed to be debating whether or not to attack Jack.

'Hey, puss.' He held out a hand and the feline sniffed his fingers. He wondered where such an odd-looking creature had sprung from.

Instead of attacking Jack, the moggy eventually rubbed its large head against his jeans.

'Glad we got that one sorted out,' Jack said, reaching down to scratch its flat ears. 'Who do you belong to, big guy?'

'Who the hell are you?'

A woman rounded the corner of the house, wielding a garden rake. From the hostile look in her eyes, he figured she was about to take over where her cat had left off.

'Ms Parker?' he asked, immensely relieved that Natalie Parker was at home, alive and well, even if she did seem a tad aggressive at having her privacy invaded.

'I asked first.'

'Jack Maddox.' He delved into his pocket and produced a business card from his wallet. She reached forward and took it from him with one hand, but kept a firm grip on the rake with the other. 'Private investigator.'

'Investigator? What are you investigating?'

'We received a report that you might be having trouble with a guy you were dating.'

'Who reported that?'

'Hey, no need to be so defensive.' He held up his hands, palms forward in a placating gesture. 'I'm on your side.'

She looked at him with open suspicion, which is when Jack realised he'd probably jumped to the wrong conclusion. The picture he'd been given of Natalie Parker showed a woman a good decade older, with a blonde bob and soft-grey eyes. This one was taller; at least five eight, without an ounce of spare flesh on her. She had slim legs that looked good in tight denim. She sported a waterfall of brunette hair that tumbled over her shoulders, high cheekbones, a pert little nose, a wide, lush mouth and huge, arresting, silver-green eyes. Eyes that remained fixed upon him with misgiving while he took her measure. She looked familiar, too. He'd seen her somewhere before but couldn't place her.

'You're not Natalie Parker, are you?'

Without replying, she pulled an iPhone from her pocket, placed the rake against the wall where she could reach it again in a hurry, and started pressing buttons. Jack figured she was checking him out. Smart lady.

'Fenton-Maddox Investigations in Newbury,' she said, as though speaking to herself.

'That's me.'

'I know. I'm looking at your website.' She glanced up at him, then back at her phone. 'This picture looks like you, except you've grown your hair longer.'

He shrugged, not knowing what to say to that. The silence worked for him and, appearing to make up her mind that he wasn't an axe murderer, she extended her hand.

'Alexi Ellis,' she said. 'Natalie's friends are worried about her. They sent me to check her place out.'

'You're the journalist,' Jack said slowly. 'That's where I know you from. I've seen your picture often enough above your by-line.'

'Right.' She looked as though she was about to say something more, then closed her mouth again.

'I take it you have a key to the cottage.'

She nodded. 'Who are you working for?'

Alexi Ellis could be the break in this case that Jack had been hoping for. She was a journalist, probably on the trail of a story, and he wasn't sure if he could trust her. But still, if he didn't tell her something, he doubted whether he'd get anything in return.

'Heart Racing Dating Agency.'

She brightened. 'Ah, so they're taking this seriously. Have there been other problems?'

Jack shook his head. 'You know better than that.'

She flashed a non-apologetic smile. 'Can't blame a girl for trying.'

'What did you find in there?'

'Sod all,' she replied, shrugging. 'But I don't suppose you'll accept my word for it so you might as well come in and see for yourself.'

Jack followed her into a neat cottage with a musty smell that implied it had been shut up for a while. There was a small lounge, an eat-in kitchen and two bedrooms upstairs. Books lined the walls, mostly about flowers, photography, and horses. Nothing looked out of place.

'All that's missing is her laptop and phone. I gather she had an iPad and I can't find that either.'

'When did your friends last see her?'

'Four days ago. Who was she dating? Come on, Jack,' she coerced when he hesitated.

'Let's look at the rest of the place first,' Jack replied, playing for time. 'What's that big building out the back?'

'I was about to investigate when Cosmo found you.'

'Cosmo?' Jack quirked a brow. 'Cute name.'

This time her smile was uncontrived. 'I've heard many adjectives used to describe Cosmo, but cute is definitely a first.'

'He likes me,' Jack replied, bending to give his ears another scratch, just to make a point. 'Do you always take him on investigations?'

She grinned. 'Face it, he's pretty damned efficient. He scared the living daylights out of you.'

'Flying felines with attitude are a new one on me and I thought I'd seen it all.'

'You're not the first person to mention that,' she said as Cosmo trotted along between them towards the outbuilding.

He chuckled. 'I believe you.'

Alexi sorted through her keys and found one that fitted the lock.

'This must be her work space,' she said as they stepped inside. There was a long surface with vases, ribbons, wires, and other stuff that Jack failed to recognise, all neatly arranged beneath a large window. There was a desk in one corner and, tellingly, a phone with the message light flashing. Alexi saw it before Jack did and pressed the play back button.

The first was from someone named Cheryl.

'Your friend?' Jack asked.

Alexi nodded. The second was from Cheryl, followed by several business enquiries before Cheryl's voice came through again, sounding more concerned. Then a frantic voice.

'Ms Parker, I was expecting you this morning with my husband's wreath. How could you let me down at such a time? I am very disappointed.'

Jack and Alexi exchanged a look.

'From what Cheryl has told me, she simply wouldn't renege

on an order,' said Alexi. 'I wasn't absolutely convinced that anything had happened to her, but now I'm not so sure.' She fixed Jack with an accusatory glower. 'Your clients must think so too. Otherwise they wouldn't have called you in.'

'Let's call the lady back and see what she has to say,' Jack replied. 'Then we'll talk about it.'

4

Alexi left a message for Mrs Dixon, Natalie's aggrieved client, and then turned to look at Jack, wondering if he had any ideas about what to do next. He was standing closer than she'd realised, watching her deliberate. What the heck? Did he imagine Mrs Dixon might know something about Natalie's whereabouts and that Alexi wouldn't share the information? She hated the alpha male posturing she saw all the time in her line of work and wanted to tell Jack she wouldn't have survived five minutes in the still predominantly male domain of journalism if she couldn't play the big boys at their own game.

She was unsure how she felt about having run into Jack and less sure still whether she trusted him. Working alone and guarding her sources was second nature to Alexi, but she reminded herself that this time she didn't have to worry about being scooped. It was more serious than that. Natalie's life could hang in the balance.

Part of her was glad that the dating agency was taking things seriously. Two heads were better than one, especially if Jack had access to the agency's database. She could sense he didn't entirely trust her. He would almost certainly hide behind client confidentiality and try to keep her in the dark if things look bad for his employer. *Good luck with that one, buddy.*

At least six-two, Jack Maddox was far too easy on the eye and Alexi figured he had to know it. She might be off men, but she wasn't blind. She could appreciate his rugged profile as well as the next woman without allowing his good looks to affect her judgement.

Probably.

He had thick, dark curls falling across intelligent, chocolate-brown eyes, a strong, chiselled jaw sporting a day's worth of stubble, a high forehead, and features that had no business being quite so symmetrical. To add insult to injury, Cosmo appeared to like him. Damned if her cat wasn't in danger of gaining a sociable disposition. She put it down to all that fresh country air messing with Cosmo's metabolism, and hers. They'd both return to normal once they got back to London.

If they went back.

Whoa, since when had that been in doubt? Alexi hadn't thought much about her future but had assumed she would end up back in journalism in London, which is where the action was. *So why did you lease out your apartment?*

'Let's get out of here,' she said curtly. 'You have some explaining to do.'

'Café Lambourn in the High Street. Do you know it?'

'I'll find it.'

'Okay, see you there in a bit.'

Alexi watched him climb into a BMW that was several years old and drive away. She and Cosmo locked up carefully and took their time getting into the Mini as Alexi pondered upon developments. Part of her wanted to go straight to the police and demand that they take action. But she needed to find out what

Jack knew first, and establish why Heart Racing had put him on the case. Besides, she had the edge on Jack. Before he'd interrupted her, she'd gone through Natalie's things and found statements for two bank accounts concealed beneath a pile of sweaters in her walk-in wardrobe. Hidden there by accident or design? One of the accounts was personal and one business-related. Both had healthy balances, or had the last time she'd received paper statements. Those statements were quite old so she'd probably moved onto banking online. Still, at least she now knew where she banked.

There had been files containing household bills, the usual stuff, in the drawers of a small desk in Natalie's sitting room, but nothing else pertaining to her finances. Odd, Alexi thought. Odder still that she hadn't found anything personal in the short time she'd had to search before Jack interrupted her. No birth certificate, divorce record, old letters, photographs... nothing, nada, zilch. The lady carried no emotional baggage.

She drove slowly back to Lambourn, thinking Jack wasn't much of a PI if he hadn't thought to look for Natalie's financial records while he was inside the cottage. Unless he was holding out on her and planned to go back alone later on.

'We'll see about that, Cosmo.' She took one hand off the wheel and stroked her cat's head. 'Don't get too attached to your new buddy. He might be pretty but may not be around for long. First we need to play nice and figure out whose side he's on.' Cosmo cocked his head to one side and fixed her with a sceptical look. 'Yeah, that's what I thought too.'

The café was easy to find. Alexi pulled her car into a spot next to Jack's. She cranked a window and told Cosmo to stay put. He blinked up at her and went back to his slumbers.

Jack was standing just inside the door to the café, waiting for her.

'What will you have?' he asked.

'A skinny latte, please and... er, are those blueberry muffins fresh?'

'Homemade this morning,' said a motherly lady from behind the counter.

'Then yes, please.'

Jack laughed, sounding superior as he ordered just a black coffee for himself. Men! Alexi refused to feel guilty about the muffin following so closely on the heels of a large cooked breakfast. She *was* on holiday. Kinda.

'Okay, Maddox, give,' she said, once they'd settled themselves at a quiet corner table. 'How long have you been on this case and what have you found out?'

'So you can put it in your paper?' He gave his head an irritated shake. 'I don't think so.'

'This is nothing about work. I'm doing this as a favour to my friends.'

'People in your line of work can't disassociate.'

She sent him an appraising look. 'You don't have a very high opinion of me.'

'Not you specifically, but what you do to earn a crust. Don't take it personally.'

Alexi took her irritation out on her latte, stirring it aggressively even though she hadn't added sugar. She'd lost her appetite and picked distractedly at the muffin with her fingers.

'No offence taken,' she said in a sweetly sarcastic tone. 'What have journalists done to make you so dead set against us?'

He was quiet for so long that she didn't think he intended to answer her. She stole glances at him, trying to get the measure of the real man beneath the film star looks. She prided herself on being a good judge of character and reckoned there was more to this guy than the admittedly attractive package he showed to the world.

'I'm guessing you'll check me out properly first chance you get,' he said, breaking the uneasy silence between them.

Alexi nodded. 'Count on it.'

'Then you'll know soon enough, so might as well hear it from me.' He paused, a faraway expression gracing his features. Whatever he was about to tell her, she sensed it wasn't something he found easy to talk about. 'I was a detective with the Met until a couple of years ago. The press conducted a witch hunt when a drug dealer we arrested cried police brutality.' He sighed. 'You'd think the same lament would have gotten old by now, but I guess it was a slow news day. Anyway, I was the sacrificial lamb.'

'I think I remember something about it. The tabloids made it a *cause célèbre* because the kid had some crusading lawyer grandstanding on his behalf.' She canted her head as she continued to observe him and softened her voice. 'If it's any consolation, those of us who report news objectively rather than going for the populist and sensational thought you got a bad deal.'

'Yeah well, I was encouraged to jump before I could be pushed. Not that it took much encouragement. I'd had enough. All those regulations, the impossible-to-achieve targets, endless paperwork, and all the other crap that got in the way of what most of us signed up to do, which was to keep the streets safe for Joe Average.' He lifted his shoulders, the casual gesture at odds with the tension in his expression. 'Beats me why anyone would want to be a copper nowadays when the odds are stacked so heavily in favour of the bad guys.'

'How did you get to be a PI?'

Alexi took a bite of sinfully delicious muffin and closed her eyes, groaning with pleasure as she absorbed the sugar hit. When she opened them again, he was watching her intently.

Alexi shook her head, determined not to be drawn in by him. She still wasn't sure about his interest in Natalie.

'Seemed like a logical direction to take. I had a buddy—'

'Mr Fenton?'

'Nothing gets past you.' He flashed a megawatt smile that she found it hard not to react to. 'Actually it's Ms Fenton. Cassie Fenton.'

'Your significant other?'

He chuckled. 'Not exactly.' He leaned his elbows on the table, bringing his face closer to hers. 'Now, your turn. What's a hot-shot journalist doing down here?'

Alexi opened her mouth to tell him it was none of his damned business. Five minutes later, he knew it all. How she'd been shafted by the corporation that had employed her since she'd left university. How she'd crawled her way up the greasy pole, working twice as hard as her male counterparts to prove herself at the sacrifice of a personal life, only to be left high and dry. He was a good listener, and didn't interrupt.

'Can't think why I told you all that,' she said sheepishly, staring at her hands.

'People tell me stuff all the time.'

She shook her head. 'I'll just bet they do.'

'Sounds like you and I both grew too big for the organisations that spawned us. What will you do now?'

It was Alexi's turn to shrug. 'Stay here for a while and lick my wounds. Feel sorry for myself.'

'And try to find Natalie Parker?'

'I can't seem to help myself.' She took a swig of her rapidly cooling coffee. 'Why did Heart Racing call you in?'

'They got a visit from the local plod, were worried about their reputation—'

'The police *are* doing something about Cheryl's report. She will be relieved.'

'I doubt it. They'll be going through the motions, covering their backs.'

'Well, I guess you would know.' Alexi scowled at him because what he'd just said really annoyed her, even though it didn't exactly surprise her. 'Presumably the agency had nothing to tell them that aroused their suspicions.'

'Nope.'

'But they called you in so they must have concerns.' Alexi paused to reason it through. 'I suppose the police aren't the only ones covering their backs. If something *has* happened to Natalie, they'll come across as being uncooperative and uncaring about their clients' welfare.' Alexi rolled her eyes. 'Typical. People with that sort of attitude do deserve to be crucified by the press.'

'Not this particular organisation,' he replied, an edge to his voice.

'Well, of course you would say that. They're paying your outrageous fees.'

'Actually they're not. I'm doing this one *pro bono*.'

'Why?' she asked scathingly. 'Don't tell me you're having trouble getting a date.'

He leaned back in his chair and fixed her with a penetrating look. 'My sister, Katie, owns the agency,' he said.

'Oh.' Her mouth fell open and her cheeks turned pink. 'I guess that puts a different complexion on things. Sorry if I spoke out of turn.'

'No apology necessary and yeah, it changes things.'

* * *

Jack didn't understand why he'd told her about Katie. He didn't entirely trust Alexi. How could he? She was a journalist, and journalists had tried him in the court of public opinion and found him guilty without a shred of evidence to back up their hysteria. No, he didn't trust her, but the man in him liked what he saw.

They were drawn together by a common goal in that they both had their reasons for wanting to find Natalie. If Alexi went to the papers when this was over, he'd make sure his sister's organisation came out of it with its reputation intact. He owed her that much, and a damned sight more.

'Does your sister suspect one of the men Natalie dated?' She sat forward and watched him intently.

'Nope.'

'Presumably you have a list of the men she's spoken with electronically, or has been out with. You must have looked into them.'

'Cut me some slack.' He spread his hands. 'This is my first day on the job. Katie rang me last night, told me about your friend Drew's rather aggressive accusations, and the visit from local uniforms. I agreed to come down today and take a look around for myself.'

'Ah, right.'

'Katie started this agency from scratch five years ago. She's put everything she owns into it, including re-mortgaging her house. Now she's between a rock and a hard place. If it comes to light that she's given away confidential information needlessly, she will be finished. If she doesn't and something's happened to Natalie at the hands of one of her punters, she can also kiss her business goodbye. She has liability insurance, but still, she will lose credibility.' Jack shifted position and sighed. 'It's a hell of a worry for her. She wants to do the right thing, but...'

'The agency is local to Berkshire?'

'That's the whole point of it. According to her, people are too busy nowadays to hook up by traditional means, so they go online and are drawn together by common interests. Katie lives locally. This is horseracing country, so...' He spread his hands, refraining from stating the obvious.

'Do you ever worry that computers are taking over our lives?' Alexi asked pensively. 'When I was a kid we played outside, climbed trees, fell off bikes, and god forbid, even walked to school. We got fresh air, exercise, *and* we interacted personally with our peers.' She flashed a rueful smile. 'I sound like an old crone, but you get my drift?'

'I agree with you, Grandma, but times change.'

'Not always for the better.'

'Do you want to put the world to rights or concentrate on finding Natalie?'

Her hurt expression made him regret sounding so impatient. They'd been talking like normal people, almost enjoying one another's company, but now her hackles were up again.

'Sorry.'

She shot him a look. 'You're right. Natalie is all that matters.'

'Right, well, as I say, busy professionals want to meet like-minded people with similar interests and don't want to travel the length and breadth of the country to hook up. So Katie figured keeping it local would be a good way to go. She's well aware of the pitfalls, too. The Online Dating Association—'

'The what!'

He chuckled, resisting voicing the jibe that sprang to mind about her not having done her research. 'They have a code of conduct, which she adheres to, doing all she can to protect her clients' interests. She's earned herself a good reputation, which is why she really doesn't need a scandal.'

'I understand, but—'

'Look at it from her clients' point of view.' Jack's voice cut through her objection. 'You're an average Joe, perhaps embarrassed about having to turn to the internet for a date. But you meet some nice, regular people, get comfortable with the idea, and then get the likes of us crawling all over you, accusing you of stuff you probably haven't done. If they sued, Katie would lose everything she's worked for.'

'The punters wouldn't know we were looking at them, unless there was something to arouse our suspicions. That's one way in which the internet works in our favour.'

'Katie knows that, which is why she called me in. She is worried because she hasn't been able to get hold of Natalie, either. She had a date arranged and the guy contacted Katie, complaining Natalie didn't show up.'

'When was the date for?'

'Yesterday lunchtime.'

'You're close to your sister, aren't you?' she asked after a short pause.

'She saved me from self-destructing when I left the force. It cost me my marriage, and my self-respect. I gave up for a while and viewed the world through the bottom of a glass. Katie came along and gave me a well-deserved kick up the backside. Anyway, I heard from Cassie, who was expanding her business and needed a partner with an injection of cash. That was a year ago.'

'I can relate because I'm going through the *what-the-heck* stage right now, too.'

'Don't let the bastards grind you down.' He grinned at her. 'Well, I say that now, having come out on the winning side of a deep depression.'

'Do you have any kids?'

'Come again?'

'You said you were married. I wondered if you were a dad.'

'The marriage didn't survive the test of time so no, no kids.' He stared off into the distance, marvelling at her ability to get him talking about himself. 'Grace and I were never really suited. She hated being a copper's wife, and I knew she wasn't happy about my career choice before we married. That ought to have told me something. Anyway, we're good friends now. She's got herself another guy and I wish her well.'

'I'm not the right person to talk to about relationships. Ask Cosmo.'

He smiled at her, guessing she was thinking about the guy at the paper whose name she had mentioned several times. Feeling her need to change the subject, which suited him just fine because this was getting way too personal, Jack obliged.

'Fill me in on what you know about Natalie,' he said.

'Most of what I know I gleaned online last night. The rest I learned from Cheryl and Drew. Basically, Natalie is a successful businesswoman with no close relations, stating online for the world to see that she's thinking of buying a share in a racehorse.' Jack flinched. 'Yeah, that was my reaction, too. I get the impression she's emotionally needy and really wants to be in a relationship.'

'Ideal fodder for the stalkery type.'

Alexi looked serious. 'We both know something's happened to her, don't we?'

He nodded. 'It's looking that way, but more digging's necessary before we can be sure.'

'Into her dates?'

'I'll let you know what I find out.'

'Oh no! We're in this together, buster. You want to find Natalie and save your sister's business. I want to find Natalie and put my friends' minds at rest.' She fixed him with a malevolent glare. 'How does that make us enemies? Oh, I get it,' she added, before he could reply. 'You think I'm gonna write this up and sell it to the *Sentinel*'s competitors because I'm the resentful type looking to get one over on my previous employers.'

'Are you?'

'I could do that anyway.' She leaned forward, arms folded on the table, determination radiating from hostile eyes. 'I'm not any happier with the idea of having a partner than you are, but I am going to try and find out enough about Natalie to get the police actively involved, with or without your help. It seems daft both of us covering the same ground. Accept my word for it that I won't write a single paragraph until we find Natalie, and perhaps not even then.' She held out a hand. 'Do we have a deal?'

Jack relented. What she said made sense. Besides, she was sharp, and would definitely be more of a help to him than a hindrance. He took her hand in a firm grasp. 'Deal,' he agreed. 'And in the spirit of open partnership, I think the first thing we should do is look at her financials.'

Alexi removed the bank statements she had found at the cottage from her bag and waved them beneath his nose in a flourishing gesture. 'I helped myself to these.'

'Damn, you're good!'

'Normally I'd agree with you, but I got lucky.' She explained where she'd found them and how odd she thought it that Natalie didn't keep a file for her banking documentation.

He shrugged. 'Odd, I agree, but not unheard of.'

'As to being good, I have my limitations and I'm not sure I know how to hack into bank accounts.'

'Who said anything about hacking?'

'Well, I thought...' Alexi spread her hands. 'How else can we...'

Jack took the papers from her. 'Her bank's here in Lambourn. Why don't we go and see the manager, ask if there's been any unusual activity on her accounts?'

'He won't tell us diddly squat.'

'No, but if we tell him Natalie's missing and the police have been informed, if there is anything odd going on, we could encourage him to take his concerns to them.'

Alexi pouted. 'You think like a policeman. You're used to having the authority to demand answers. I think like a journalist, used to having doors slammed in my face and having to find a back way in. Therein lies the difference between us.'

'Oh, I don't know.' He allowed his gaze to lazily travel the length of her body; what he could see of it with the table separating them. 'I can think of one or two others.'

'Get your mind out of the gutter, Maddox.'

He sent her a sheepish grin. 'Sorry.'

'Okay, let's call the bank first. Then we'll look at the details of the guys she's dated. No hacking required since you can get us those legitimately.' She gathered up her bag. 'Where are you staying?'

'Nowhere. I just drove over from Newbury for the day. I was planning on going back.'

'Well, don't take this the wrong way, but if we're in this together, it might make more sense if you stay in Lambourn.'

He sent her a long, speculative glance. 'What do you have in mind?'

'Not what you're thinking, obviously.'

He shrugged. 'Shame.'

'Cheryl and Drew have a hotel with empty rooms. I'll put in a good word with the owners,' she said, grinning. 'I might be able to persuade them to give you a discount.'

5

'Why don't you follow me back?' Alexi suggested.

He flashed another of his devastating smiles. 'Sounds like a plan.'

Damn it, Alexi thought as she climbed into her Mini, fired up the engine, and floored the accelerator, *why did he have to have such a killer smile?*

'He's wasting his time, Cosmo,' she told her cat. 'I'm immune to whatever game he's playing.'

She used the short drive back to Hopgood Hall to think over the agreement they'd reached, wondering if it was a good idea. She could simply go to the police with what she knew and use the power of her press credentials to force them to take Natalie's disappearance more seriously. What did she know about investigative work? If she played Nancy Drew down here in the valley of the racehorse, where she stood out like a townie on an away-day who didn't know a fetlock from a farthingale, she could put Natalie's life in danger.

Supposing she was still alive.

With such sobering considerations rattling around inside her head, Alexi felt a tad reassured when she thought about having Jack Maddox in her corner. He *did* know how to conduct an investigation. While they waited to see if the bank took any action, Alexi could pretend she was fully on board with Jack. Then she'd get to see who Natalie had been dating through legitimate means. It would also give her time to take a look at Natalie's email, which *would* require a basic hack. Hopefully they would be able to amass enough evidence to convince the police to up their game, minimising damage to Jack's sister's operation. It surprised Alexi how badly she wanted to help a woman whom she had never met.

'Go figure,' she muttered as she pulled in between the Hopgood Hall gateposts.

Jack parked, climbed from his vehicle, and shaded his eyes with his hand as he took a look at the house. As soon as she released Cosmo, he went straight across to Jack and rubbed his head against his legs. Toby came bounding down the steps and launched himself at Cosmo. Jack laughed as he watched cat and dog go through their meet-and-greet routine.

'Cosmo has an identity crisis,' he said.

Alexi rolled her eyes. 'Tell me something I don't know.'

'Nice place.' Jack's gaze lingered on the refined old Georgian building.

'It's been in Drew's family for several generations.'

'And we're hanging on in there. Somehow,' Drew's voice remarked.

Alexi turned to see him and Cheryl standing on the steps, eyeing Jack with curiosity. Alexi made the introductions and explained how their paths had crossed.

'It's nice to meet you, Jack. I'm so glad someone else is worried about Natalie,' Cheryl said. 'Do come in and tell us more.'

'Actually, Jack needs a room for a night or two,' Alexi said 'I said I thought you could probably oblige.'

'I expect we can find you a broom cupboard,' Drew said with a wry smile, indicating the visitors' car park, empty but for their two vehicles.

They followed Cosmo and Toby into the kitchen, where Cosmo set up an almighty racket, demanding food. Alexi relented and allowed him a snack. It had been a busy morning for him too.

Seated around the table, Cheryl gave Jack the third degree. Alexi didn't know whether she was more annoyed or amused with the way he fielded her questions without giving much away about himself.

'I managed to find Natalie's bank account details,' Alexi said, explaining what they planned to do with that information.

'Good thinking.' Drew nodded his approval.

'Given the police have already asked a few basic questions at Racing Hearts,' Alexi added, 'they can't ignore new information.'

'Let's make that call,' Cheryl said, fidgeting with impatience.

'In a mo,' Alexi replied. 'And while the bank's deciding what to do, Jack and I are going to take a look at the backgrounds of any men she might have dated and see what her email throws up.'

Cheryl elevated both brows. 'You can get into her email?'

'It's easier than you might think,' Jack told her. 'Simply a case of cracking her password and there are a ton of programmes you can buy online to do that job.'

'At least in this instance, it'll be in a good cause.'

'Can we use the guests' sitting room to set up our laptops?' Alexi asked.

'Consider the room as your personal working space, at least

until we fill up at the weekend,' Drew replied. 'I'll show Jack to his room, and he can join you once he's settled.'

As soon as Drew and Jack departed, Alexi braced herself for a barrage of questions.

'Only you could go out on a simple assignment and come back with *him*,' Cheryl said grinning.

'Don't get too cozied up. His first loyalty is to his sister.'

Cheryl shook her head. 'If you're saying he'd let something happen to Natalie rather than have his sister's reputation tarnished, or that he'd try to cover up her organisation's involvement if something has happened to her, then it won't wash. He has way too much integrity.'

'How can you possibly be so sure?'

'A mother instinctively knows these things,' Cheryl replied loftily.

Alexi guffawed. 'You're still a mother in training.'

'Even so.'

'You're letting his pretty face influence you.'

Cheryl fixed Alexi with a knowing look. 'And you're not?'

Alexi shrugged. 'I've never been in a life and death situation like this one before. I need help.'

The implication that Natalie was in danger caused the smile to fade from Cheryl's lips.

'Don't worry.' Alexi gave her friend a swift hug. 'We'll find her.'

* * *

Jack let out an appreciative whistle when Drew showed him into the room directly across the hall from Alexi's.

'I could get used to this,' he said. 'But really, you don't need me cluttering up your best rooms.'

'Since you're doing us a favour in a roundabout sort of way, you might as well be comfortable.'

'Well then, thanks.' He threw his overnight bag on the bed, thinking it was large enough to accommodate four with ease. Two could have an absolute ball. *Don't go there!*

'What are the chances of finding Natalie alive?' Drew asked bluntly.

Jack shrugged. 'Until we learn more about her activities it's hard to say, but something's definitely happened to her. There's no way to sugar coat that. Hopefully, by the end of the day, we'll have got the police fully involved, but we need more than we have right now to make them prioritise her disappearance.'

'Like a body,' Drew said, grimacing.

Jack slapped his shoulder. 'Don't think the worst just yet. If she's alive, we'll find her.'

'I'll let you get on with it then.' Drew paused in the open doorway. 'Let me know if you need anything.'

'Will do.'

Jack sat on the edge of the bed for a while after Drew left him, thinking about the speed with which this enquiry had escalated. His partner wouldn't be happy. The agency was busy right now, this assignment didn't pay, and paying work was the only kind Cassie took on. Jack needed to make her understand that he couldn't walk away and leave Katie in the lurch.

Hopefully he and Alexi could absolve Katie's clients of involvement before the police got their teeth into the investigation. It was looking increasingly unlikely that Heart Racing could keep itself out of the case. In spite of what he'd just told Drew, Jack wasn't optimistic about finding an innocent explanation for Natalie's disappearance. It was a question of degree. If they could find another thread to Natalie's life – personal or connected to her business – to account for her vanishing act, it would take the heat off Katie.

He pulled his phone from his pocket and called his sister up. She answered on the first ring.

'Hey, what have you found?'

'Good morning to you, too.'

'Sorry, Jack, but you know how worried I am.'

'Yeah, I do know.'

He told Katie where he was, who he was working with and why.

'A journalist?' Her groan echoed down the line. 'You hate journalists. Besides, I thought you were going to help me keep this thing under wraps, not have the spotlight shone on my problems.'

'She's on this anyway, sis. Better we work together, so I can keep control of what she makes public. Besides, I think she's more concerned about finding her friend's friend than she is about making headlines.'

'Well, that's something, I suppose,' Katie said dubiously. 'And you're right. Natalie's welfare is the primary concern. Let me know if you need anything and keep me posted.'

'Will do.'

Jack took a moment before making his next, more difficult, call. Jack knew that Cassie Fenton, a few years older than him, divorced and attractive, was angling to become Jack's partner in all senses of the word. Jack liked Cassie. He admired her quick mind and tough, no-nonsense attitude. He valued her friendship but didn't want more from her than that. She would be annoyed because he needed to stay in Lambourn for a bit longer. That was bad enough but if he mentioned Alexi, Cassie would put two and two together and come up with ninety-seven.

'Hey, Cas,' he said, when she picked up. 'How's it going?'

'Hectic. When will you be back?'

'Er, that's why I'm calling. There've been some developments. Looks like this woman has definitely gone missing and when the alarm's raised my sister's organisation will be in the direct firing line. I need to stay, dig around a bit more, and manage damage control.'

'Damn! I'm sorry about your sister, and about the missing woman, but we're up to our eyes here.'

'I'm sorry, too, Cas, but this is something I have to do. Get Larry in to help you,' he said, referring to an ex-copper they sometimes used when they were busy. 'I'll get back just as soon as I can.'

'Yeah, all right.'

'Oh and, Cas, can you run a few checks for me?'

She sighed. 'Okay, I guess. What do you need?'

'See if you can get a fix on Natalie's mobile.' He reeled off the number. 'It's a longshot. I'm guessing it's either switched off or in a poor coverage zone, but we need to give it a go.'

'Okay, I'm on it. Anything else?'

'Well, yeah. Natalie dated three guys.'

A longer sigh echoed down the line. 'I suppose you want background checks on all of them.'

'Just the basic stuff,' he replied in his most persuasive tone, giving her the details he had. 'Oh, and while you're at it, see what you can find for me on the missing woman herself, Natalie Parker.'

'Just the basics, huh?'

'Sarcasm doesn't suit you,' he said, chuckling.

'Leave it with me. I'll get back to you.'

'Thanks, Cas.'

Jack cut the connection, picked up the bag containing his laptop, and found his way to the residents' lounge.

'Nice,' he said, looking around the light, airy room that had been tastefully renovated and furnished with what appeared to be genuine antiques. Alexi was sitting at a walnut secretaire below a window that offered a pleasant view over the gardens.

'The furniture has been in Drew's family for generations,' she said, immersed in something on her computer and not looking up as he approached.

He peered over her shoulder. 'What are you doing?'

'Running a programme to crack Natalie's email password.'

Jack set his own computer up on a table next to her desk, and told her what arrangements he'd just made.

'Good.' Finally she looked up and gave him her full attention. 'I think it would be better if you rang the bank,' she said. 'If I give my name, the connection might be made to the paper, which doesn't always work to my advantage.'

'Whereas being a PI opens all sorts of doors,' he said flippantly.

'I've got the bank's number here,' she said, reeling it off. Jack punched the digits into his mobile. 'Put it on speaker.'

Jack elevated one brow and complied with her request. He jumped through a few hoops and was finally put through to the assistant manager, a guy called Cole. He quickly identified himself and told the man why he was calling.

'I can't tell you anything about a customer's account,' Cole replied crisply.

'She's gone missing,' Jack repeated. 'We don't expect you to tell us anything, but we do know she had healthy balances in both her business and private accounts.'

'I can't confirm that.'

Jack blew air through his lips and strove for a patient tone. 'We wondered if there had been any unusual activity on those accounts. Large sums of money being transferred, that sort of thing. If so, the police would be very interested.'

'They haven't been to see us about it. If they suspect Ms Parker has been targeted for her money, we ought to be the first place they look.'

'It's still early days and the police prefer to think she'll reappear.'

'Well then, I—'

'If you have concerns about activity on her accounts you can contact...' Jack extracted the card from his wallet that the PC had left with his sister. 'PC Taylor at this number.' He read it off. 'Concerned friends reported Ms Parker's disappearance to Lambourn Police but, as you probably know, the local station is only open part time. PC Taylor knows all about it and can be reached any time on the number I've just given you.'

Having secured a promise from Cole that he would make the call if he thought it appropriate, Jack cut the connection.

'You'd think I just asked him for the combination to his bank's safe,' Jack said, screwing up his features in disgust. 'If something happens to Natalie because he procrastinated, I shall make his life a living hell.'

'Do you think he will call?'

'If there's anything there, then he probably will. Eventually. His own arse would be on the line if he didn't and fraud is subsequently uncovered. I recorded that call so he can't deny it took place.'

'Very trusting of you.' Alexi grinned. 'I like your style.'

'All Cole cares about is his career.' Jack allowed his impatience to show. 'Anyway, if he does contact Taylor, he's just a local bobby. I'm betting he's given Natalie's disappearance a case number, made a few desultory enquiries, and left it at that. But if he gets more solid information that implies a crime's been committed, he'll have to pass the case on to the Thames Valley Police.' Jack stretched his arms above his head and smiled at her. 'Okay, so let's take a look at Natalie's dream dates.'

'How many of them are there?'

'Three.'

'And she dated all three of them?'

'Two of them just once. One of them three times.'

Alexi brightened. 'The three-time winner sounds hopeful.'

'Let's take a look-see.' He pulled up the Heart Racing site and accessed the restricted area. 'Ah, the power,' he said, grinning.

Alexi stood behind him, resting her hand on the back of his chair. She smelled of a light floral fragrance and herbal shampoo. He liked the way she smelled. He liked everything about her, which irked the hell out of him. Reporters were bad news. Reporters were responsible for him being hounded out of the police under a cloud of suspicion.

'Pull up a chair,' he said easily.

'You've accessed the female clients' list,' Alexi pointed out to him. 'Looking for a date?'

'I was looking to see what Natalie posted about herself.'

'Oh, right. Good thinking.'

There were several pictures of Natalie: arranging flowers, playing with a dog, out walking along a country path.

'They look like the real deal,' Alexi said. 'I don't think they've been photoshopped, but Cheryl will be able to tell us.'

'Tell you what?' Cheryl's voice asked from the hallway. She poked her head around the door. 'I just came up to tell you it's lunchtime and heard my name being taken in vain.'

'These are the pictures Natalie posted of herself on the dating site,' Alexi explained. 'Is this how she looks in real life?'

Cheryl peered over their shoulders. 'That's her,' she said.

'A pretty lady,' Jack said, printing off a couple of the better ones.

'Yes, she is.' Cheryl sighed. 'We're having lunch in the bar, if you'd like to join us.'

They both stood up.

'Sounds good to me,' Jack said. 'I could eat a... well, I probably won't be too popular around these parts if I finish that statement.'

'Stay, Cosmo,' Alexi said to the cat who, along with Toby, had come in from the garden and joined them. 'I'll be sure and bring you something.'

Cosmo sent her an assessing look, then curled up in a patch of sunshine on the window seat. Toby hopped up to join him.

Cheryl laughed as they made their way down the stairs. 'You'll just have to stay with us permanently, Alexi. Toby will be heartbroken if his new best friend leaves again.'

'Don't tempt me.'

* * *

A wide archway led from the vaulted entrance hall to a welcoming, tastefully appointed bar with racing memorabilia decorating the walls.

Jack knew a bit about expensively refurbished houses, and could tell a fortune had been sunk into this one. The original fireplace had been restored, with a huge mirror filling the space above the marble mantle and a leather fire seat surrounding the polished brass fender. There were shelves of old books, and his feet sank into expensive, thick pile carpet. The bar itself appeared to be well-stocked. It was tended by an attractive young woman who chatted with a half-dozen racing types occupying the stools surrounding it, all of whom nursed meagre half pints of beer. Less than half of the tables were occupied, all by men who appeared to be immersed in conversations, eating and drinking sparingly. Jack suspected they were using the place to impress, but were obviously slow to put their hands in their pockets. He wasn't optimistic about Drew seeing a return on his investment any time soon.

There were closed double doors at one end of the bar with a sign above them indicating that the restaurant was behind them.

'We don't open it at lunchtime,' Drew said, following the direction of Jack's gaze. 'It's not cost effective. The demand is for bar food on weekdays.'

'It looks good,' Jack replied, glancing at a bursting sandwich being served to someone at an adjoining table.

'So, what do you fancy?' Cheryl asked, handing him a menu.

Jack perused it, noticing a clever combination of traditional sandwiches and soups, alongside sushi, tapas, and exotic salads. The work of the temperamental chef he'd already heard about, presumably. He opted for a roast beef sandwich.

'I'll take a Caesar salad,' Alexi said. 'I've already eaten more than usual today. I can't believe I'm hungry again.'

'So,' Drew said, after he'd fetched drinks. 'How's the sleuthing going?'

Alexi told them about Jack's call to the bank.

'We're going to look at the people she dated after lunch,' she added.

'My partner's looking into their backgrounds,' Jack said, taking a swig of local beer and nodding his approval. 'It's often the things people don't make public that hide the clues.'

'Doesn't your sister's agency vet them?' Cheryl asked, toying with the stem of her orange juice glass.

'She tries, but only so much probing is possible without invading a client's privacy.'

'There must be a limit to how many things you can get away with lying about, I guess,' Alexi remarked.

'Exactly. If someone goes on a date and finds the person they hook up with has lied about something important, like... say, their occupation, or if they're clearly a lot older than they implied, or behave inappropriately, then Katie's people give the offender the equivalent of a yellow card. If it happens a second time, they will be removed from the agency's database. Like I was telling Alexi earlier, the Online Dating Association has a code of conduct which Katie's agency rigidly adheres to.'

Their food arrived, which kept them all quiet for a few minutes.

'Tell me more about Natalie herself,' Jack invited. 'My partner is looking into her background, but—'

'Why?' Cheryl asked defensively. 'She didn't abduct herself.'

'No, but I need to get more of a picture about her private life. It might help us to figure out what's become of her. Does she have a sick sister, aunt, cousin, niece... I don't know, someone she cares about enough to drop everything and dash to the rescue without telling anyone.'

'I didn't see any family pictures in her cottage,' Alexi said.

'I don't think she has any family,' Cheryl said in a considering tone. She glanced at Drew, who shook his head. 'It's funny, but we never really talked much about what she did before she came here. She said she'd been married for a while but it didn't work out, and that she didn't have any kids. It was like she didn't want to talk about her past. She always turned the conversation on to her business, or her hobbies—'

'Photography and walking?' Alexi asked.

'Yes.'

'Did she belong to a photography club, or a walking group?' Jack asked.

Once again Cheryl and Drew shared a glance and simultaneously shook their heads.

'She never said if she did,' Cheryl replied.

'We need to go back to her cottage,' Alexi said. 'Take a closer look at her files. After we've looked at her email, of course. That's the most likely place to learn more.'

'I feel bad not knowing more about her life,' Cheryl admitted. 'I'm a rubbish friend.'

'You trying to steal my crown?' Alexi asked.

Cheryl shook her head. 'I'm fairly sure she had no family at all. I do remember her telling me she was an only child and that both her parents were dead.'

'So,' Jack said musingly, 'where did a middle-aged woman who lives alone and runs a modest business out of her back garden get so much money?'

'Divorce settlement?' Drew suggested.

'Possibly, but it'll show up in Cassie's background check if that's the case.'

'We don't know how much money she actually has,' Alexi pointed out.

'No, but we know that two years ago, when she first moved here and had a paper statement from her bank, she had over a quarter of a million quid spread between her deposit account and various investments. And she didn't take a business loan to get started.'

Drew and Cheryl looked flabbergasted.

'Well,' Drew said, recovering first. 'We did wonder how she could afford a share in a racehorse. Now we know, I guess.'

'But not where the money came from,' Cheryl said. 'That's a lot of change.'

'Did she talk about horses a lot?' Jack asked.

'All the time,' Cheryl said, nodding. 'She was obsessed with the sport.'

'A lot of people are. That's why they buy shares. So they can go to the glamorous races, be in the owners' enclosure, stuff like that,' Drew said.

'Did she have any favourite trainers? Any horse she was seriously interested in?'

Drew and Cheryl looked at one another and shook their heads. 'If she'd found a horse, she didn't say anything to us,' Cheryl said.

'Same goes for trainers,' Drew added.

'Did she have any other particular friends in the village?' Jack asked.

'Not really,' Cheryl replied. 'She was friendly with everyone, but also very private. I think I was her only female friend. She dated occasionally, but there was no one special. That's why she started online dating. She said good men were rarer than an honest politician.'

Jack smiled. 'Interesting comparison. Okay, we'll have to wait and see what Cassie comes up with.'

Drew got up to speak to a couple of suits at another table when they beckoned him over.

'That happens a lot,' Cheryl said. 'It can be annoying, but if we want to succeed, we're never off-duty.'

'We need to get back to work, too,' Jack said, putting aside his napkin and draining the last of his beer. 'Thanks for lunch, Cheryl. Put it on my bill.'

6

'A lady of mystery,' Alexi said as they climbed the stairs, side by side. 'The more I learn about her, the less I feel like I know her.'

'Everyone has a past.'

'Sure, but I get the impression Natalie was being deliberately evasive. She seemed to avoid making female friends.' Alexi paused with her hand on the banister. 'I wonder if that was because she didn't want anyone getting close enough to ask awkward questions. Cheryl, the only girlfriend she had, knew nothing about her relationships and was too polite to probe. Even so, it still strikes me as odd that Natalie offered up nothing about herself.'

Jack shot her a look. 'Do *you* kiss and tell?'

'This isn't about me.' She resumed walking. 'Do you think Natalie kept people at arm's length because she had something to hide? The source of that money perhaps?'

'I can't see the issue arising. On the surface, she doesn't live the life of a woman with money to burn. Her home is modest and she works hard.' Jack opened the door to the guest lounge and ushered Alexi through it ahead of him. 'Anyway, there could be a genuine explanation for her bank balance. We don't know how long ago her parents died and if she came into an inheritance when they did. Her husband might have been well-off and she got a good settlement when they split.'

Alexi stroked Cosmo's head and fed him the pieces of chicken she'd saved him from her salad. She pulled her chair closer to Jack's table and waited while he fired up his laptop, ignoring the wave of awareness that streaked through her when their thighs accidently touched.

'Sorry.' She hastily moved hers out of the line of fire.

Jack grinned as he pulled up information on the first of Natalie's dates.

'Paul Keiser, forty-seven, a stockbroker based in Reading,' he said, reading off the guy's profile. 'Never been married. Lives alone. Interests include cycling and, obviously, horseracing. She dated him once two weeks ago. Her email will tell us if they've been in touch since.'

Alexi screwed up her nose as the image of a very ordinary-looking man, whose only redeeming feature appeared to be a kind smile, filled the screen. 'Wonder what she saw in him,' she said, making a note of the details.

'He's a stockbroker. That implies personal wealth.'

'Only if he indulges in insider trading. Otherwise it's just a job. Besides, Natalie has money of her own.'

'Perhaps she amassed it by targeting men like Keiser.'

'How? Unless she marries them, she wouldn't have access to their bank accounts. But then again, he's never been married, and would be flattered by attention from someone who looks like Natalie. That might get him spending on her.'

Jack shrugged. 'Let's leave him for a moment and see who else took her fancy.' Jack pulled up details of her second date.

'Divorced father of two grown kids, fifty-two, a freelance photographer—'

'Photography is one of Natalie's interests,' Alexi pointed out, again screwing up her nose when she looked at the guy's picture. 'Nothing else about him stands out.'

Jack shot her an amused look. 'Do you always judge a book by its cover?'

'If Natalie *does* want a personal relationship, of course appearances would matter to her. But I think she was equally concerned about what made the guys she dated tick.'

'Or she was looking for a lonely sugar daddy who'd be flattered by her interest in him, so appearances would be inconsequential.'

'Make up your mind, Maddox. One moment we suspect her dates of trying to fleece her, then you think it could be the other way around.'

'Doesn't do to focus on just one possibility. People never fail to surprise me with the lengths they're prepared to go to.'

'Fair point. But this guy doesn't fit the bill. Not if she planned to take him for his dosh. He has grown kids who would naturally be suspicious of any woman who got their hooks into their daddy, depriving them of the inheritance they probably think they're entitled to.'

Jack shook his head, grinning as he tutted at her cynicism. 'Okay, are you ready for this?' He sounded like a cheesy game show host trying to whip an indifferent audience into a fervour of expectancy. 'Guy number three is the one she dated three times, with Paul and Roger slotted in between. His name is Darren Walker, retired early aged fifty-five from the Civil Service and moved to Lambourn about a year ago.'

'He lives here, in the village?'

'In Hungerford, which is local enough and probably explains why she dated him so regularly.'

'Nothing else would,' Alexi said, glancing at his picture and grimacing.

Jack chuckled. 'Yeah, okay. Even I can see he's not god's gift, but perhaps he has a winning personality.'

'He's a widower with no kids,' she said, reading over his shoulder. 'That's a game-changer. He would be an ideal target, if she *was* the predator. I hate to admit it, but it's starting to look as though you might be right about that. We should pay him a visit.'

'Not yet. Give Cassie a chance to work her magic. Once she's found out about all three men's finances, we'll have a better idea if their interest in Natalie is fiscal.'

'I hate all this waiting around,' Alexi complained. 'Can't we go and have friendly chats with these guys?'

'And ask them what?'

She smiled. 'Okay, I take your point. Whatever we ask, as things stand, we won't have much idea if they're lying.'

'Right, and don't lose sight of the fact that we're trying to protect my sister's interests. Or rather, I am.' A hint of determination fuelled his expression. 'If we go knocking on Walker's door, we have no way of explaining how we know about his dates with Natalie. He will assume the agency broke its confidentiality clause and could kick up one hell of a stink.'

'We could pass ourselves off as friends of Natalie's. Say she's missing and we're worried about her. She mentioned dating Walker and we wondered when he'd last seen her.'

Jack shook his head. 'Let's look at her email before we decide, see what clues that throws up.'

Alexi moved back to her own computer. 'I have her password cracked.'

'Good, it's Cassie,' Jack said at the same time as an email popped into his inbox. 'Let's see what she's got for us.'

Jack read Cassie's message and then clicked to open a lengthy attachment.

'Paul Keiser isn't a stockbroker. He holds a middle-management position with an investment firm, salary forty thousand, and lives with his elderly mother. He pays for her round-the-clock care.'

'A nice guy who can't devote all his attention to a woman while his mother lives.'

'Right. So if Natalie's intention was to fleece him, she would know from one date that she was backing a loser. His mother owns her home, which Keiser presumably will inherit, but Cassie reckons it's only worth two hundred thousand. Not big bucks in this day and age.'

'No, and anyway, if Natalie is a victim, not the predator, leaving aside the fact that this guy doesn't have an obvious motive to wish her harm, he hasn't had enough time to figure out a way to kidnap her, or worse, so I agree with you. He's probably not our guy.'

'Good god, the woman agrees with me. Hold that thought.'

Alexi flapped a hand. 'Stop being an idiot and let's see what Cassie's found on Roger Dalton.'

Jack flipped to the second page of the attachment. 'Hmm, he has a photography business in Ascot, specialising in horses, but he's got a hefty business overdraft and a second mortgage on his house.'

'A good reason for Natalie not to have any interest in him, if he revealed any of that.'

'But plenty of reason for him to take an interest in Natalie.'

'We might need to take a visit to Ascot,' Alexi said.

'Looks that way. Still, let's see what's what with our number one contender.' The third page of the attachment was more detailed. 'He has a house on the outskirts of Hungerford, value half a million, bought for cash two years ago.'

'Where does a civil servant get that sort of dosh?' Alexi asked, frowning.

'His wife of thirty years died of cancer three years ago.'

'Life insurance pay out?'

Jack shrugged. 'Possibly. No kids or close relations.' He looked up at Alexi. 'If Natalie is motivated by money, or simply wants to find a decent guy to share her life with, either way Walker would fit the bill. I can see why she's dated him three times.'

'Then we must go and see him.'

'I agree, but after we've gone back to Natalie's cottage and taken a closer look at her papers.'

'I was about to say that.'

He sent her a sexy smile that caused her tummy to perform Olympic-standard backflips. 'Sorry.'

'You've redeemed yourself by finding all this stuff so quickly. How does Cassie do it?'

'We have our ways,' he said, smirking.

'Okay, don't tell me.'

'Hey, there's no big secret.' He waved her aside. 'You ought to know, in your line of work, how easy it is to find out just about anything on anyone these days, if you know where to look. The company Cassie worked for used to do some of the work the Met farmed out.'

'Is that how you met her?'

'Actually, no, that was coincidence. She was my ex-wife's close friend.'

'Oh, I see.'

Jack chuckled. 'I doubt it. Cassie got fed up doing grunt work for an organisation that thought a virus was something you saw your doctor about, and didn't pay her close to what she was worth. She set up on her own as a computer doctor, and kind of fell into investigation work as a sideline that finished up being more profitable than the day job.'

'Straying spouses, benefit cheats, stuff like that?'

'To start with. Now we get all kinds of obscure assignments.' He flipped a pen backwards and forwards between his forefinger and thumb. His body language was casual, but the business with the pen told Alexi he wasn't comfortable with this conversation. 'Anyway, my marriage broke up. Cassie stayed neutral and we kept in touch, had the occasional drink. Then, when she heard about my problems with the Met, she invited me to invest in her agency. She can make computers give up their secrets but needed someone with my background for doing the face-to-face stuff.' He shrugged. 'So far, we make a good team.'

I'll just bet you do! 'Glad to hear it. Now, what did your super-star partner find out about Natalie's background?'

'She's still working on that. Miracles, as she puts it, take a little longer.'

'Okay then, let's take a look at Natalie's email.'

Alexi moved back to her own desk and logged into Natalie's account. 'I haven't tried to crack her business email address yet,' she explained. 'I figured anything about her private life would be in her personal mail.'

'Good thinking.'

He scooted his chair over and leaned over her shoulder, distracting her. He had no damned business smelling so... well, so masculine. She wanted to put distance between them but that would imply she was affected by him.

'Do you notice anything?' Alexi asked, frowning as she scrolled through Natalie's inbox.

'Yeah, she's remarkably tidy. Very few files.'

'Make that no files, which is odd. I have tons on my personal email, and I keep my business files separate, just like Natalie must.' Alexi leaned back in her chair and glanced up at Jack. 'So, she either doesn't file her emails, or keeps them offline somewhere.'

'Actually, according to Cassie, a lot of people keep really important stuff off the web all together, simply because it's more secure. Nothing online is completely confidential. Hacking is the modern-day equivalent of tax evasion. Technically illegal, but anyone who's computer savvy can't resist having a go, and it's not really looked upon as being illegal.'

'Since I just cracked Natalie's password, I can't claim the moral high ground.'

Jack sent her a look. 'You're a journalist, so you can't anyway.'

The caustic comment took Alexi by surprise. She thought they had got past his resentment of her profession.

'Sorry,' he said, breaking the awkward silence that ensued.

'Apology accepted.' Alexi fell into momentary contemplation. 'I wonder if Cassie can find some sort of online storage for her. Dropbox, or something like that.'

Jack jotted a note on a piece of paper. 'It's worth a look.'

'Considering this is day four since she was last seen, there are surprisingly few emails waiting for her,' Alexi pointed out. 'The usual spam that we all get, but not a whole lot else. Certainly nothing from any of our suspects.'

'Anything marked dates? Or, more to the point, finances?'

Jack peered closer, all but resting his chin on her shoulder as his breath peppered her left ear. She shifted position, removing herself from the direct firing line, and caught a glimpse of his profile in the periphery of her vision. A smile flirted with his lips, leaving her with the impression that accidently touching her was a deliberate ploy. Nice try but Alexi didn't do casual sex. Then again, perhaps a no-strings-attached hook-up was what she needed to get Patrick out of her system. Only the fact that he so obviously thought he'd get what he wanted without too much effort made her determined to hold out.

'Nope.' She answered his spoken question, and the unspoken one, with the one word.

'I guess that would be too much to hope for.'

'What about the guy she stood up?' Alexi asked, turning her head so abruptly when the thought occurred to her that her hair whipped across Jack's face.

'Come again?'

'Your sister called you in because Natalie had missed a date. Had she seen that guy before? Could she have kept the date, but he said she hadn't to throw suspicion off?'

'I'll double check with Katie, but she assured me it was a first date. The two of them hadn't met at all.'

'As far as she knew.'

'Right. I'll ask for the guy's name, so we can check him out, just in case.' He fired off an email to his sister, typing with two fingers.

'What next?' Alexi asked.

'Let's take a moment and assess what we know so far. That's why the police keep whiteboards during investigations: so any new leads can be added, keeping everyone updated. Well, not always whiteboards nowadays, but fancy big touchscreen thingies. Still, I'm an old-fashioned guy and think *whiteboards*. Anyway, we know for a fact that Natalie Parker was last seen going about her normal business over four days ago. She has no close relatives that we are aware of, but Cassie will turn them up if they exist. It's out of character for her to go anywhere without telling her friend Cheryl, who looks after her place if she has to leave.'

'And she always answers her phone wherever she is because it could be business-related. But her phone is off and she's missed supplying a business commitment, which is totally out of character.'

Jack nodded. 'She has – or at least two years ago – had a lot of money in her personal account but lived modestly and didn't shout about it. Where did that money come from? I can't help thinking that if we can find the answer to that one, we'll find Natalie.'

'She's divorced, but we don't know how long she was married for, or anything about her husband and why they separated. We do know she now wants to have another relationship, hence joining Heart Racing, hoping to meet a guy with similar interests.'

Jack wrote Natalie's name at the top of a sheet of paper, and listed below it all the things they knew about her. On the right-hand side, he listed areas of dispute that needed further investigation if they weren't explained when Cassie reported her findings. Her husband's background and, significantly, the source of her wealth headed that list.

'Is she the genuinely nice, private person Cheryl thinks she is, looking for her happy ever after?' Alexi mused.

'Is she a female predator, using her sensuality to prey on vulnerable, wealthy men?'

'Or are the men preying on her need for companionship?'

'She's cautious about using the internet, but has a presence online because she's in business and doesn't stand much chance of surviving if customers can't find her on the net.'

'But,' Alexi added. 'There are anomalies. She's cautious about the internet but tells the world via Facebook that she's thinking of buying a share in a racehorse, which implies she has money. Why would she do that? It doesn't fit with her cautious approach to online activities.'

'Beats the hell out of me.'

'We need to hear from Cassie about Natalie's background.'

'And the fact that we haven't probably means there's hidden stuff to be rooted out.'

'There is one other thing to add to your list of unanswered questions,' Alexi said. 'Something rather important. Does she have a will, and—'

'And who inherits if she does turn up dead.' Jack nodded. 'Good thinking. I must be getting slow in my advancing years. That's always one of the first things we used to think about in my previous line of work.'

'Don't feel bad,' she replied sweetly. 'I have a naturally suspicious mind, and a generally low opinion of human nature. There's less chance of disappointment if you don't have much by way of expectations to start with.'

Jack grinned at her as he stood up. 'Let's go back to her cottage and take a closer look at her paperwork, then swing back past Darren Walker's place in Hungerford.'

'Come on, Cosmo,' Alexi said, standing up and grabbing her bag. 'This is no time to veg out. We have work to do.'

Cosmo got to his feet, dislodging Toby's head from his belly, and stretched.

'He looks so comfortable. Why not leave him where he is?'

'We're a team. Besides, he sulks if I leave him home too often.'

Jack chuckled. 'Oh well, we can't have that now, can we. Sorry, Toby,' he added, tugging the dog's ears. 'You're gonna have to make your own fun for a while.'

7

'Perhaps we should have looked at her business email before doing this,' Alexi said, as they followed Cosmo down the stairs.

'We can do that later if need be.'

'I'll just let Cheryl know where we're going.'

Jack nodded, still doubting the wisdom of joining forces with Alexi. He got more attention from women than he could handle, or looked for. Now he'd found one he'd actually like to get to know, but couldn't afford the distraction. His first and only concern was for his sister's business.

'Okay, let's go.'

Jack followed her out to her car and lifted the passenger seat forward so Cosmo could jump in the back. But Cosmo was having none of it. He simply sat down and gave Jack the evil eye.

'What?'

Alexi, already behind the wheel, chuckled. 'You don't really expect him to sit in the back, do you?'

Jack rolled his eyes. 'You have got to be joking.'

'Nope. Cosmo only travels up front.'

'Is that right?'

'Careful!' Alexi cried when Jack bent to pick the cat up. 'If anyone tries to make Cosmo do something he doesn't want to, it inevitably involves blood.'

'His or mine?' Jack placed the cat in the middle of the back seat. 'Hell, he weighs almost as much as I do.'

Cosmo let out an indignant meow.

'Don't listen to him, darling,' Alexi cooed as she fired up the engine. 'Apologise, Jack. You've hurt his feelings.'

Jack chuckled as he slid into the passenger seat, found the lever to push it back as far as it would go, and fastened his seat-belt. His smile abruptly faded when a feline ton weight landed on the back of the passenger seat and wrapped itself around his neck, a rattling purr coming from the cat's throat.

'You sure about that?' Alexi asked.

'I guess I can live with this arrangement,' Jack replied, stroking the cat's sleek body and creating an even louder purr.

'He likes you.'

'I like him right back but he senses I'm not about to put up with his theatrics.' He shot Alexi a cocky grin. 'Kids and animals need boundaries.'

A short time later, they parked at Natalie's cottage. Alexi and Jack headed for the front door. Cosmo stalked off into the garden. Jack took Natalie's keys from Alexi and unlocked the Mortis, then the Yale.

'There's no alarm system here on the cottage, but I noticed there was one on the workshop when you opened it up earlier.'

'Yes, Cheryl told me the code for it. I figured she'd have to have her business premises protected for insurance purposes.'

'Or because that's where she keeps anything that's important to her. It is where her laptop lives, I noticed.'

'Yes, but Cheryl says she kept her iPad in the cottage, along with a small printer and scanner.'

'The laptop for business, the iPad for pleasure.' Jack shrugged. 'That would work.'

'But there are no personal files in her office, or anywhere else. I found stuff in her living room relating to domestic bills and those old bank statements beneath some sweaters in her walk-in wardrobe, but they don't help much when it comes to figuring out who she was.'

Jack frowned. 'It seems awfully careless for such a careful person.'

'An oversight, perhaps?'

'The bank statements date back to the time just after she moved in. She was probably disorganised and they accidentally got buried.' They were now in the cottage's entrance hall. 'Show me where you found them.'

'Sure.' Alexi led the way up the stairs and into Natalie's bedroom. 'I suspect she had the walk-in closet specifically made to house her clothing. I reckon there was a third bedroom, a small one that she had converted into this closet and an en suite.'

Jack nodded. 'Makes sense.'

Alexi rummaged through the clothing that filled the racks and shelves. 'A lot of this is decent stuff,' she said. 'Designer labels that would make her feel good but don't scream money.'

'You'd know more about that than me.'

She turned her attention to the racks of shoes. 'Shoes tell you a lot about a woman,' she said. 'And all of these are top notch.'

Jack had moved back into the main part of the bedroom and methodically searched the drawers.

'Leave it to a man to find a girl's lingerie,' Alexi said, walking up behind him.

His responding grin caused her to shake her head and delve into another set of drawers. 'Oh my!'

'What you got?'

'Come and see for yourself.'

A large drawer was full of sexy – very sexy – underwear. And a number of toys. Jack let out a low whistle. 'This lady takes her pleasures seriously.'

'So it seems, but alone or did she invite men back?'

'Not much point in doing herself up in this stuff unless she had an audience to appreciate it.' Alexi nodded. 'We ought to talk to the neighbours, see if they've noticed any comings and goings.'

'She doesn't have any immediate neighbours. This place is pretty isolated.'

'Which makes it easier to have assignations that she wanted to keep under wraps,' Jack said speculatively. 'Perhaps that's why she chose it.'

'She doesn't need to keep her activities quiet. She has no ties.'

'But perhaps her caller does. And there had to be one.' He picked up a riding crop from her play drawer and slapped it against his palm. 'I doubt whether she used this on herself.'

Alexi giggled. 'She really does like all things equestrian, doesn't she?'

Jack didn't reply. This find showed Natalie in an entirely different light and had him wondering.

'Women are way more liberated these days,' Alexi said, 'and don't feel any need to apologise for their needs. But to hear Cheryl talk, Natalie Parker is Lambourn's answer to Mother Teresa.'

'Come on,' he said, 'there's nothing else to help us in here. Let's go and check out her work room.'

'Nothing other than meticulous accounts of her business transactions for the taxman, client invoices, and invoices from her suppliers,' Alexi said a short time later, pushing a strand of hair away from her forehead. 'Nothing about her personal life at all. Nothing to imply she even existed before she came here. No address book, no old birthday cards kept for nostalgic reasons, no letters... absolutely nothing.' She shook her head. 'I thought I travelled light, but this is just not natural.'

'It's lucky you found those old bank statements.'

'I would have smelt money when I looked more closely at her clothes but, yeah, that's our only break so far.'

'I wonder if she was checking her statements and was interrupted,' Jack said. 'That would account for their location. Perhaps she got a call from her guy to say he was almost there. She would have been looking through her post but then found herself in a hurry to get ready, deciding what to wear – or not. Standing in her walk-in closet, she found she still had the statements in her hand and simply dropped them on that shelf. They got buried beneath her sweaters and she forgot about them.'

'Possibly. Anyway, what now?' she asked. 'We don't seem to be—'

Alexi broke off when Jack's mobile rang. He checked the caller ID and took the call. 'Hey, Cas, what you got?'

'Are you on your own?'

Jack frowned, wondering why she'd asked, feeling the compulsion to lie. Cassie would get possessive if she knew he was with Alexi and he didn't need the hassle. 'Yeah, I'm alone.'

'Check your email. I've found a few interesting things about your saintly Ms Parker.'

'I know that tone of voice.' He winked at Alexi. 'Give me the highlights.'

'She's known to the police. Is that highlight enough for you?'

'She's been arrested?' He gaped at Alexi, whose jaw dropped open. 'What for?'

'Soliciting.'

Jack inhaled sharply.

* * *

Jack didn't look that surprised by what his partner had unearthed, but Alexi was stunned. Why, she couldn't have said. It wasn't as if she knew Natalie personally. Besides, she'd seen and heard it all during her years as a reporter and knew that women turned to the oldest profession for all sorts of reasons – usually financial necessity. The sexy underwear and extensive collection of sex toys ought to have told her something. Jack had obviously already made the connection, but she'd been slow on the uptake because she'd bought Cheryl's take on her friend. A basic error. Not that Cheryl had any reason to lie, but she did have a tendency to think the best of everyone.

'Tell me,' she said when Jack ended his call.

'Cassie says it's all in her email.' He logged into his account. 'Here we go.'

Alexi again found herself reading over Jack's shoulder.

'Natalie Parker isn't her real name,' she said.

'Nope. She's Natalie Seaton but changed her name by deed poll some years ago. She was given up for adoption at birth. No information available on her birth parents.'

'Since she never knew them, she can be excused for saying her parents died.'

'Perhaps she meant her adoptive parents are dead,' Jack suggested. 'She would have thought of them as her parents, presumably.'

'Most likely.'

'Her adoptive mother was a gardener, into floral art, whatever the hell that is.'

'Flower arranging,' Alexi told him. 'Natalie's adoptive mother's example must have persuaded Natalie to go down that path. How old was she when she got arrested?'

'Fourteen.'

'Fourteen?' Alexi was rendered temporarily speechless.

'Her juvenile records will be sealed so Cassie hasn't been able to look at them.'

'Will it be impossible for her to get them?'

Jack shot her an ironic look. 'You trying to insult my partner's abilities?'

Alexi answered his question with one of her own. 'Why did you tell Cassie you were alone?' She frowned when Jack hesitated to answer. 'You haven't told her about me, have you, Maddox?' A slow grin spread across her face. 'You're scared of her.'

'Yeah, right!'

Alexi wasn't buying his denial and the opportunity to have a little dig was too good to let it go. 'I thought you said your relationship wasn't personal,' she remarked sweetly.

'I *have* told her, but perhaps I underplayed the amount of co-investigating we're doing. She's already annoyed with me for spending more time down here when the paying jobs are stacking up. No point in making matters worse. She can be a tad overprotective.'

She tilted her head, pretending to be affronted. 'And thinks you're being traumatised by exposure to my conniving company?'

'Something like that,' he agreed with a self-deprecating smile.

Alexi shook her head, thinking she'd just learned something useful. Cassie Fenton had her sights set on Jack. Jack obviously knew it since he was prepared to go that extra mile not to antagonise her. Not personally involved, indeed!

'I wonder if Natalie's adoptive father got over-friendly,' she said in a speculative tone. 'It happens. A lot. I did a feature about abuse in the social welfare system once. The stories I got out of foster kids were heartbreaking. Those that tried to tell weren't believed and were labelled as troublemakers.'

'Don't jump to conclusions.'

'I don't work on conclusions. Just so you know, I always triple check my facts, otherwise the paper's lawyers would be all over me. I was thinking aloud, that's all.'

'Hmm.' Jack was reading Cassie's email and clearly only giving Alexi part of his attention.

'If she was a high-class escort then it would explain all that dosh.'

Jack let out a long, appreciative whistle. 'Wow!' he said.

Alexi looked at the screen and had to agree with him. The pictures that came up were from a website on which Natalie had advertised her former trade. She went by the name of Natalie Dwight and looked classy, sexy, and sophisticated all at the same time.

'This website is long gone, but Cassie found it. That's what took her a while.'

'Presumably she retired when she moved here two years ago,' Alexi said, watching as Jack flipped through the pages; each of them devoted to a different female, every hair, skin and eye colour featured, every customer's taste catered for. 'She was part of a classy escort agency. Does it say where it was based, Jack?'

'Mayfair Escorts. I'd put money on that being in London.'

Alexi rolled her eyes. 'Nothing gets past you.'

He grinned and winked at her. 'Cassie will be able to find out exactly where, and if it's still in business.'

'How will that help us? And why would the website be gone if they're still operating?'

'I'm not sure yet, but I'm guessing this agency, or whoever ran it at the time, was a big influence in Natalie's life. Top end joints like that one are very selective.'

Alexi regarded him quizzically. 'And you'd know this because...'

'I just do. The madams take a motherly interest in their girls. This one might actually have been the saving of Natalie, if she was going off the rails. And perhaps the agency has the type of exclusive reputation that no longer requires a website, or any advertising at all.'

Alexi nodded thoughtfully. 'She must have changed her name to Parker just before she moved here but perhaps she still sees a few of her old clients, which would be why she retained the tools of her trade.'

'That's possible, but if she was serious about settling down, why would she continue turning tricks in her own backyard?'

'I haven't figured that part out yet.' She frowned. 'Maybe she doesn't. Cheryl says she often goes away for a night or two on business.... she obviously neglected to say what kind of business.'

Jack chuckled. 'Good old Cas. She got into her bank accounts.' They peered together at the figures scrolling down the small screen. 'She retired with over half a million in the bank.'

'We already knew that.' Alexi sighed. 'I'm in the wrong business. None of the careers advisors at my school pointed out the financial advantages in Natalie's particular line of work.'

'Girls in the high end of the business get taken to swanky business parties and need to be able to look and talk the part,' Jack told her. 'If they're canny, like Natalie obviously is, they can make a small fortune.'

'Yeah, I get that part.'

'It looks like she bought this place for cash, then she applied for planning consent for the annexe. She got it approved, got business use, and paid for all of that in cash, too.'

'That must have made a dent in her nest egg,' Alexi said.

'It did.' Jack continued to read the figures. 'Those statements we saw dated back before she shelled out all the cash. She was down to less than a hundred thousand by the time her business premises were finished.'

'And now?'

'Double that amount.'

They looked at one another. 'Her business can't have made that much money so quickly, can it?' Alexi asked.

'She's been getting regular payments of a thousand quid a time ever since she moved here. But they've gone into her personal account, and we know that she only keeps fastidious records for her business activities.'

'Payment for services rendered? Would she be able to ask that much?'

Jack shrugged. 'Depends on how good she is at her job.'

Alexi took a closer look at the figures as Jack scrolled through the pages. 'What about these amounts? Seven thousand, nine thousand. There are quite a few deposits in four figures.'

'Made quite recently.' Jack looked pensive. 'What the hell did you get yourself mixed up in, Natalie?'

'Those amounts would fly beneath the banking radar, so she wouldn't need to explain where they'd come from,' Alexi said slowly. 'Where *did* they come from, Jack?'

'Beats the hell out of me.' He leaned back and stretched his arms above his head. His T-shirt rode up, giving Alexi a close-up view of washboard abs and the trail of curling chest hair that disappeared beneath his waistband. 'Putting the squeeze on ex-clients, perhaps?'

'Blackmail? The sort of thing that would get her killed?'

'Yeah, if she was daft enough to go down that route. And Natalie doesn't strike me as being stupid. She knows how the game's played and which lines are never crossed.'

'But if she crossed them?'

'Then we will definitely have to delve deeper into her murky past and see what's what.'

'You don't have to do that. Once we're sure this has nothing to do with your sister's agency, you can leave the sleuthing to me.'

He subjected her to a slow, lazy appraisal. 'Fed up with me already?'

'Your partner wants you back.'

'She's my partner, not my mother. And this business with Natalie has got me intrigued, so I'll hang around for another day or two, then see where we are.'

'Okay, but for what it's worth, I still think Natalie was serious about finding Mr Right and putting her previous life behind her. If she wasn't, she wouldn't have joined your sister's organisation.'

'I'm inclined to agree with you. Although she could have joined because she was lonely. From what she told Cheryl, she wanted normal.'

'Cassie didn't find any evidence of a husband?'

'No, she must have lied about that, too.'

'We haven't found a will, or even any mention of a solicitor.'

'We can find out easily enough who represented her in the purchase of this place and for building the annexe.'

'Except they won't tell us diddly-squat.'

Jack conceded the point with a nod.

'Well, I don't think we'll find anything else here,' Alexi said. 'Time to go and call on Walker, although I'm thinking it less and less likely that anyone connected to the dating agency has anything to do with her disappearance.'

'Katie will be glad to hear it.'

They froze when Natalie's landline rang. Alexi glanced at Jack, suspecting he felt as much like an intruder at that point as she did. The answerphone cut in and they heard Natalie's voice: a soft, well-modulated voice, asking the caller to leave a message. It was the first time they had actually heard her speaking voice. To Alexi, it made her seem more human somehow and reinforced her concerns for her welfare. She hated herself for the conclusions she'd jumped to. The fact that she'd started to think less of her since discovering how she'd amassed her nest egg. That was wrong, and Alexi gave herself a mental dressing down. Natalie had had a tough start in life and, without knowing more about her, Alexi was in no position to stand in judgement on the choices Natalie had made.

'Natalie,' said a male voice into the phone. 'This is Charles. I'll be down your way on Saturday and wondered if you could make some time for me. Please let me know.'

'Damn,' Alexi said when the message ended. 'He didn't leave a number.'

'And he withheld his,' Jack added, having dialled 1471. 'Never mind: he can't hide from Cassie.'

* * *

Alexi resisted the urge to make a noise and give her presence away while Jack chatted with his possessive partner. He asked her to check Natalie's phone records and discover Charles's identity.

'Right,' he said, pocketing his phone. 'Let's get ourselves over to Hungerford.'

They left Natalie's workshop, having set the alarm and locked the door behind them. Cosmo materialised from the undergrowth and preceded them to the car.

'How does he do that?' Jack asked.

'He's very perceptive, to say nothing of protective. He stopped you in your tracks this morning when you crept up on me.'

'He scared the heck out of me.'

Alexi chuckled. 'That's my clever boy!'

'Anyway, just for the record, I was not creeping; I was investigating. I do not creep.'

'If you say so,' Alexi replied with a knowing smile. 'You might want to change your technique in that case. It looked a lot like creeping to me.'

8

It was gone five in the afternoon by the time they left Natalie's cottage. What sunshine there had been had given up trying to compete with the heavy clouds, and a light drizzle fell on the Mini's windscreen.

While Alexi concentrated on the road, Jack used the opportunity to steal glances at her, noticing things that hadn't previously been apparent. The line of faint freckles across her nose. A tiny scar just below the hollow at the base of her neck. The cute way she mangled her lower lip between her teeth when she concentrated. A tough career lady who probably didn't realise she oozed femininity. She had worked her backside off to establish herself, only to have the rug pulled out from under her. She was feeling a little vulnerable because of it, and Jack could tell that annoyed her.

'I wish to god it would rain or not rain,' she muttered. 'I hate half-measures.'

'Want me to drive?'

'No one, but no one other than me, *ever* drives Fabio.'

Jack quirked a brow. 'Fabio?'

She patted the steering wheel. 'Fabio, meet Jack. Jack, Fabio.'

'Pleased to meet you, Fabio.' He grinned. 'What happens now? Is there a protocol? Should I shake his gearstick?'

'Absolutely not! You hardly know one another. Keep your hands to yourself, Maddox.'

Alexi continued to look at the road ahead as she fought a grin. He wanted to tell her to let it out. She had a lovely laugh, throaty and uncontrived. When she did let her guard down her smile was sincere, pushing up into her eyes and emphasising the silver flecks dancing in their depths. Jack had been told once by a doctor he'd briefly dated that the muscles needed to smile with one's eyes are involuntary, only becoming engaged in an authentic smile as opposed to the courtesy variety. Watching Alexi, he could well believe it.

'Should we have called ahead?' she asked. 'What if Walker isn't home?'

'Better to catch him off guard. If he's retired, it's a good bet he'll be home at this time of day.'

'I guess.'

Walker lived in a substantial house on a large plot. It was fronted by a pristine lawn, trimmed to within an inch of its life, not a flower or shrub in sight. The barren garden screamed of a man living alone. Jack wondered if garden-loving Natalie had seen it and, if so, what she'd made of it. Would it leave her feeling challenged or depressed?

'Stay, Cosmo,' Alexi said to the cat when Jack disentangled his feline neck-warmer and placed him on Alexi's vacated driving seat. 'We won't be long.'

'It's a tough life, mate,' Jack told the cat as he too exited the car.

They were encouraged to see a top of the range Audi parked in front of Walker's garage. Jack pressed the bell and waited. A short time later the door was opened by a short man wearing casual trousers with razor-sharp creases and a navy polo shirt. He didn't look as good in the flesh as he did in the picture they'd seen online, but there was a warmth and openness about the man that Jack thought women would find attractive. Far from seeming annoyed at being interrupted by strangers, he offered them a pleasant smile.

'Darren Walker?' Jack asked.

'Yes, what can I do for you?'

'We were hoping to have a word with you about Natalie Parker. I believe you know her.'

Walker's brows disappeared beneath his sparse hairline. 'Natalie – has something happened to her?'

'What makes you think that?' Alexi asked. So much for letting him do the talking, Jack thought. Still, it was probably unrealistic to expect a reporter to keep her mouth shut.

'Why else would you be asking about her?' His smile faded. 'Actually, do you mind telling me who you are?'

'I'm Jack Maddox, Private Investigator,' Jack said, holding out a hand which Walker instinctively grasped. 'And Ms Ellis is assisting me.'

Jack ignored Alexi's glare, aware that he'd hear about arbitrarily demoting her later. Walker released Jack's hand and offered his own to Alexi, eyeing her with evident appreciation. Not that many men with eyesight and a pulse could fail to be impressed by Alexi, he conceded, but Walker's approval was apparent in the not-so-subtle once-over he subjected her to. *In your dreams, mate.*

'A PI.' Walker took the card Jack handed him and studied it. 'I've never met one before. Never imagined that I would have reason to.'

'You haven't done anything,' Alexi said.

'That's reassuring. But if you're here about Natalie, I have to assume something *has* happened to her.'

'We just have a few questions.'

'Then you'd better come in.'

Walker opened the door wider and ushered them into a sterile hall. The walls were blindingly white, the carpet beige, the only piece of furniture – a teak hall stand with an ornate mirror above it – expensive but... well, unexciting. A set of golf clubs leaned against one wall but there were no coats occupying hooks, no discarded shoes or junk mail.

'This way.'

Walker opened the door to an equally unexciting living room that stretched the full width of the back of the house, also painted brilliant white. The beige carpet continued in here and was echoed in the colour of the leather furniture. The man was either addicted to beige or had employed an interior designer who lacked vision.

There were a couple of half-decent paintings on the walls to relieve all that white, a large TV in one corner, a few tables and lamps scattered about, and not much else. No plants, ornaments, books, framed family photos, or knick-knacks. The items that had made it through the door were in perfect alignment, not a speck of dust in sight. It was a bit like he'd just moved into a place that was already furnished and hadn't bothered to stamp his personality onto it.

'Please, sit down.' Walker addressed the comment to Alexi. Jack assumed he was included in the invitation and sank into a beige leather chair which was, he had to admit, sinfully comfortable. 'Can I get either of you anything to drink?'

'No, thanks,' Jack replied. 'We won't keep you for long.'

He took a seat across from them. 'Then how can I help you?'

'We've been asked by friends of Natalie's to see if we can find her,' Jack said, seeing no point in beating around the bush. 'She's been missing for four days and—'

'Four days. Oh dear.' Walker scratched his head. 'Still, that's not so very long.'

'It is when you have a business, obligations to fulfil, and you haven't made arrangements to cover them in your absence, or warned anyone that you would be away.'

'And you don't answer your mobile,' Alexi added.

'Oh yes, I see what you mean. How distressing. But I'm afraid I can't help you.' He paused. 'I assume you know I met Natalie through a dating agency.' Jack and Alexi both nodded. 'I'm a widower, recently retired and, to be frank, I'm finding retirement a bit lonely. Perhaps I should have remained in London. Not that I had any friends up there really, just colleagues and acquaintances, but still, it might have been easier than starting completely afresh.'

'Making new friends attracts fortune hunters,' Alexi suggested, casting her eyes around the room. Sterile it might be, but any female clapping eyes on the outside, on the neighbourhood generally, would know it had cost big bucks.

'Exactly.' Walker seemed relieved that she understood. 'One hears such terrible things nowadays, Jack. I know I'm not much to look at, or especially interesting, so when attractive women throw themselves at me, I'm not stupid enough to think it's my irresistible charm that draws them in.'

Jack felt sorry for the guy, but was glad he understood the score. Appearances mattered at any age. Unjust, but that was the way the world worked.

'So you joined a dating agency where the clientele have interests in common?' Alexi suggested.

'Quite. I was attracted to Natalie the moment I saw her

picture. She's elegant, educated, interesting, and very easy to talk to.'

'I understand,' Jack said aloud. 'How often did you date?'

'Three times.' His expression was self-effacing. 'We got along really well but, to be honest, I was surprised when she agreed to see me a second time, much less a third.'

'Why do you say that?' Alexi asked.

'Have you met her?'

Jack and Alexi both shook their heads.

'Ladies who look like Natalie don't choose men like me. I might have a few bob, but she doesn't know that. We chatted by email for a while before we dated, talked about our likes, our interests, but all she knows is that I retired early from the Civil Service. She doesn't know where I live, so she can't know about the house, or that I have no mortgage on it.'

Jack knew that wasn't true. If Natalie was aware of Walker's full name, finding his address would be child's play. Perhaps she really had meant to work a number on him. It was obvious that he was already smitten, so the hard graft had been put in. 'Anyway, we met twice more. I planned to ask her over here next week. It's time I was completely honest with her about my circumstances. I mean,' he added, sounding as though he was trying to convince himself, 'if she liked me before, all this can't hurt.' He waved his arms vaguely around. 'Although what she'll make of the garden, goodness only knows. I've been meaning to get someone in, land-scapers or something, but I haven't got around to it. Natalie loves gardens and says she can make absolutely anything grow.'

'That's true,' Alexi replied. 'I've seen her garden. It's beautiful, but I'm like you, Mr Walker. I don't know a dandelion from a daffodil.'

'Please call me Darren.'

'Did she mention any friends or relations?' Jack asked. 'Anyone she was close to?'

He shook his head slowly, as though dredging his memory. 'No, she told me that she's divorced and has no contact with her ex. Her parents are dead and she has no siblings. I thought she was alone, like me.'

'So you can't think of anything that would have made her take off?'

Walker answered Jack's question with one of his own. 'Can't you put a trace on her car, or something?'

'Unless the car has a tracking device, it would be next to impossible. Besides,' Jack added softly, 'her car is still in her garage.'

Walker paled. 'Oh my god! This doesn't sound good.'

'It's certainly odd, but—'

'Can I ask how you knew Natalie and I dated?'

'We found your name on a piece of paper beside her phone,' Jack replied.

'Oh, right.' That appeared to satisfy him. 'What's being done to try and find her, apart from the two of you, I mean?'

'Her disappearance was reported by friends to the police,' Alexi said.

'I expect they'll come to see me as well.'

'Unfortunately, they aren't doing much to try and find her, because—'

'—because she's an adult, there's no obvious signs of an abduction, presumably, and no body.' He set his lips in a tight line. 'I do watch TV.'

'Which is where we come in,' Jack explained. 'The dating agency wants to keep their client base confidential, but they don't want to hamper efforts to find Natalie.'

'That's perfectly understandable. I imagine you'll be talking to all the men she met through the agency.'

'Yes, although you're the only one she saw more than once.'

'Am I really? 'Walker seemed both surprised and pleased. 'Well then, you must let me know if there's anything I can do to help find her. It would be such a shame if anything's happened to her.'

'Quite.' Jack paused, legs stretched out in front of him, and crossed at the ankles. 'Did she happen to mention anything about the work she did before she moved to Lambourn?'

'She said that she worked in public relations and travelled a lot.'

Well, Jack thought, that would cover it. 'Not to worry,' he said aloud.

Jack nodded to Alexi and they both stood. It took a moment before Walker also found his feet and Jack could see he was genuinely distressed about Natalie's situation. They thanked him for his time and promised to let him know if they found her.

* * *

'Your assistant?' Alexi asked as she drove them off, conscious of Walker watching from his front window.

'People in your line of work get a bad press,' Jack replied, deadpan.

She shot him a sideways glance. 'Seriously?'

'Would I lie to you?'

Alexi harrumphed. 'What did you make of him?' she asked.

'I think he couldn't believe his luck when he linked up with Natalie and that he's genuinely upset about her disappearance.'

'Yeah, that's what I thought, too. He's lonely and regrets

leaving London.' She paused. 'Let that be a lesson to you, Alexi,' she added *sotto voce*.

Jack seemed surprised. 'I didn't know you had plans to leave the capital.'

'There's no reason why you should. Besides, I haven't made up my mind yet. Anyway, back to Darren Walker. Natalie might have been planning to work a number on him, but I'm convinced it wasn't the other way around.'

'I agree with you.'

'Okay, that leaves the other two guys.'

'I'll get Larry to check them out.'

'Larry?'

'He's an ex-cop who works for the agency from time to time.'

'Cassie won't like that.'

'I won't tell her if you don't.' He shot her a killer grin. 'And Larry sure as hell won't.'

'Old cops sticking together?'

'Hey, not so much of the old.'

She treated him to a seraphic smile. 'I speak as I find.'

Jack chuckled and shifted position. Cosmo shifted right along with him, while Jack absently scratched his ears. Alexi shook her head, astonished at her cat's total adoration of Jack.

'You two need to get a room,' she quipped.

'Is it my fault if your cat's a good judge of character?'

Alexi rolled her eyes as she stopped in a queue of traffic at a red light. 'You don't think it's worth paying the other two personal calls?' she asked.

'Nope. Time is of the essence, so we need to manage it well. I'm getting increasingly convinced that Natalie's disappearance has something to do with her previous occupation. We need to find out who Charles is, and if there's anyone else she's been seeing regularly. A jealous ex,' he said, fixing Alexi with a probing glance, 'or someone at the agency where she worked who feels they're being short-changed if she's branched out alone and taken their clients with her.'

'Is that likely?'

'Damned if I know, which is why we need to find out. In the meantime, Larry can look at the other two. I trust his judgement. If he thinks there's anything there, he'll sniff it out, then we'll go check on them.'

'Fair enough.'

Alexi pulled her car into the Hopgood Hall car park.

'I guess we'd better let Cheryl and Drew know what we've found out,' Alexi said as she climbed from the car. 'I wonder if they had any idea. About Natalie's secret life, I mean.'

'We'll soon know.' Jack placed his hand on the small of her back and guided her towards the door. It was an intuitively polite, albeit old-fashioned gesture that she couldn't object to without making a big deal of it. 'You go ahead. I'll give Larry a quick call, check in with Cassie, then join you.'

'Fine.'

* * *

Cosmo led the way to the kitchen, where Toby hurled himself at the cat in a frenzy of delight. Alexi smiled at the sight, threw her bag onto the table and looked up at...

'Patrick?' She stared at her ex, who'd made himself comfortable at the kitchen table, where he and Cheryl were sharing a pot of tea. Cheryl jumped up and threw Alexi an apologetic glance.

'He just turned up,' she whispered. 'Said you were expecting him.'

Alexi patted her friend's shoulder. 'It's okay.'

'Hey.'

Patrick stood up and tried to pull Alexi into an embrace, which she evaded. His lips landed fairly harmlessly in the vicinity of her left ear. Cosmo had just noticed Patrick. His back arched, his fur stood on end, and he emitted a series of angry hisses. Cheryl, who'd probably sensed the tension even before Cosmo's reaction, looked totally bemused.

'What are you doing here? How did you find me?' Alexi asked.

'I'm a reporter. It's what I do.'

'You'd damned well better not have tracked my phone,' she said, moving away from him with her arms folded.

'I'll leave you two to talk,' Cheryl said, beating a hasty retreat.

The door closed behind Cheryl, leaving Alexi trapped with her determined ex, an angry cat, and whimpering dog. The only sound in the room was Cosmo's hissing and Toby's confused yelps. Alexi, struggling to contain her anger, had absolutely no intention of relieving the tension with small talk.

'You haven't answered my calls,' he said.

'Any reason why I should?' Alexi looked away from him.

'Come on, Alexi, cut me some slack. I couldn't tell you what was going on ahead of time. It would have been more than my job was worth.'

'But not mine, apparently.'

He grasped her shoulders and turned her until she was compelled to look at him. Cosmo's hissing got louder. 'If there was something, anything, I could have done to secure your position on the paper, don't you think I would have done it?'

She shrugged. 'Does it matter?'

His sigh was deep and heartfelt. 'I love you, and want to spend the rest of my life with you. I thought you felt the same way about me.'

'I thought so, too.' She paused, looking up into his handsome face as she waited for regret to grip her and felt... nothing. It was liberating to have it confirmed that she really was over him. But it did make her wonder about her own constancy. She had really thought she was in love with him. She spent two whole days crying up a storm after she lost her job and then dumped him because she could no longer trust him. Perhaps he hadn't been the love of her life after all. 'Once,' she added.

'You know how the newspaper game's played, Alexi. It's all about the bottom line and cutting cloth accordingly. You were too good at what you did. You'd priced yourself out of the market.'

She arched a cynical brow. 'Nothing to do with the paper reducing its standards?'

'I had it all worked out. If you'd taken the position that was offered to you, I had plans to get you doing what you do best through the back door. Once management realised how badly the readers missed you, they would have had to let me.'

'Run the equivalent of a political gossip column and lose face in the eyes of the industry, to say nothing of readers?' She glowered at him. 'Is that the big master plan you've been at pains to talk to me about?'

He shook his head. 'You've changed.'

'Getting fired does that to a girl.'

'If you'd agreed to see me, or even taken my calls, I could have explained that you *would* get your job back. But you were so damned hot-headed, wouldn't listen to what anyone told you, and insisted on being paid off. You're angry, and you have every right to be,' he said, his voice softening. 'Now it will be harder for me to get you reinstated, but I can make it happen.'

'How do you plan to do that?'

Alexi expected more prevarication, empty promises. 'The Rachman feature.'

Her head shot up. That wasn't what she'd expected at all. Following the Morecombe Bay cockling disaster there had been an outcry about the exploitation of illegal immigrants forced to live in primitive conditions while worked, sometimes literally, to death. The apathetic public had been shocked into taking an interest in the problem. No one knew quite what to do about it, but everyone agreed someone had to be held to account.

Before she got fired, Alexi had been delving into a similar scandal in London, where illegal immigrants were housed like sardines in garden sheds, lacking even the most basic facilities, and charged a small fortune for the privilege by rich landlords. She'd given her project the code name 'Rachman' after the notorious Notting Hill landlord who had taken exploitation of tenants to new levels in the fifties and sixties. Alexi's story was potential dynamite, but everyone involved was too scared to talk on the record.

Alexi told herself Patrick was employing a few underhand tactics of his own to tempt her back into the fold and refused to show too much interest.

'What about it?' she asked, hating herself for asking. Once a reporter...

'Someone's come forward who's willing to talk.'

'Who? One of the people I'd been trying to cultivate? Why did they come to you?'

'Write that story and it will go a long way to getting your position reinstated.' He briefly removed his hands from her shoulders and spread them wide. 'Hell, you could probably take my job, to say nothing of all the awards you'd win.'

'Perhaps I've had enough of all the cut and thrust.'

Patrick laughed. 'You thrive on it.'

'I did once.'

'I called by your flat. Are you really letting it?'

'Yep.'

'Where will you live?'

She shrugged. 'The world's a big place. I can live or work just about anywhere I like. Here, for instance.'

Patrick's mouth fell open. 'You hate the country.'

'Well, you said it yourself just now. I've changed.'

'Cheryl said something about you looking for her missing friend.'

Alexi made a mental note to murder Cheryl later. She should know better than to mention something like that to a reporter, untrustworthy bunch that they were once they sniffed the possibility of a story!

'Promise me you'll think about it. The whistle-blower won't wait forever and I can't let the story slip through my fingers. If you don't want it, I'll have to give it to someone else.'

He was right and, damn it, she was salivating at the prospect of finally getting the story written. 'Yeah, okay, I'll give it some thought.'

His hands returned to her shoulders, his fingers digging almost painfully into them. Cosmo hissed louder. Patrick shot the cat a wary glance before dropping his hands to her waist and pulling her against him. 'Don't give up what we had together just because you're angry.' He whispered the words into the top of her head, while the fingers of one hand worked their way up her back and beneath her hair. 'We were good together and I miss you so damned much it hurts. Come back to London and we'll work this all out.'

'I've said I'll think about it. Don't push me, Patrick.'

'It's this guy you're working down here with, isn't it?' he said, his voice turning hard.

'What guy?'

'Aw, come on, Cheryl told me.'

'Cheryl talks too much.'

'She cares about you.'

'This has got nothing to do with anyone, other than me.'

'Your feelings are hurt. I get that part. And you deserve to be pissed off, but don't shoot the messenger. I have to deal with the owners *and* try to get the best deal for everyone on my staff, including you. I owe it to them all. The best way to fight fire isn't always with more fire.'

She nodded half-heartedly. Give him his due: Patrick always had played the game of office politics with the hand of a master. She, on the other hand, tended to speak her mind without first engaging her brain, especially when she was angry. Not a good idea but, hell, it had felt good to tell the owners of the *Sentinel* where to stick their job.

Alexi screwed up her features, angry, upset, and confused, wondering if Patrick knew how self-centred he sounded. 'You want me to feel sorry for you?' she asked. 'Okay, you have my sympathy. Now get out of here.'

'I thought I'd stay for a few days.'

'I don't want you here. Besides, you have a paper to run and Cheryl is full this weekend.'

'You think you don't want me, but I seem to remember when you couldn't get enough of this.'

Without warning, his lips covered hers, hard and demanding. Cosmo's hissing turned into indignant yowls and Alexi half feared for Patrick's calves. The other half of her befuddled brain was encouraging Cosmo to attack when the door behind her opened.

'Oh, sorry,' Jack's voice said. 'I didn't realise you had company.'

9

Larry was happy to fit the other two guys Natalie had dated into his schedule first thing the next day. Cassie was a harder nut to crack, proving resilient to Jack's most persuasive arguments, and blaming Alexi for his failure to return to the day job.

If Natalie was dead, Jack patiently explained to his recalcitrant partner, her body could turn up at any time. If that happened, damage control would be out of Jack's hands. He needed to find Natalie before anyone else did, preferably alive, and put his sister's mind at rest. Cassie didn't sound impressed but finally agreed to take a look at Natalie's phone records and get an identity for Charles.

Jack's disgruntled frame of mind didn't improve when he walked into the kitchen and found Alexi cosying up with some guy he'd never seen before. He apologised and turned to leave the room.

'Don't go, Jack.'

Her voice halted him at the door. Cosmo stopped making a god-almighty racket, blinked up at Jack, then stalked across to rub his big head against his calves. The man with Alexi – Patrick – looked on with open astonishment.

'Patrick Vaughan, Jack Maddox,' Alexi said curtly, walking away and half-turning her back on them both. She didn't embellish the introduction, but then she didn't need to. Vaughan was obviously her ex-boss, and ex-lover. It looked as though he wanted a reconciliation and Alexi didn't seem too averse to the idea. Vaughan extended his hand with obvious reluctance. Jack accepted it with an equal lack of enthusiasm.

'Patrick's just leaving,' Alexi said, breaking the brittle silence that prevailed as Jack and Vaughan continued to size one another up.

'Drive safely,' Jack said, heading for the door.

Drew and Cheryl were both already in the bar when Jack walked into it.

'What're you having?' Drew asked, beckoning Jack over.

'A beer would hit the spot.'

'I should have warned you Patrick was here,' Cheryl said, chewing her bottom lip, while Drew went to get Jack's drink. 'I should have warned Alexi, too, for that matter. He's definitely not her favourite person right now.'

'Could have fooled me,' Jack replied absently.

'He just turned up.' Cheryl looked conflicted. 'What was I supposed to do? Deny that Alexi was here?'

Jack allowed his surprise to show. 'He didn't know?'

'She hasn't been taking his calls.' Cheryl screwed up her features. 'I've never liked Patrick much, but it's not me he's trying to impress.'

'Yeah, well.'

Jack shrugged, unsure what else to say, or why he was so disgruntled. Drew placed a foaming pint in front of him before he'd reached any decisions. He took a long draught and felt himself beginning to unwind. He'd disliked Vaughan on sight, and had learned during his years on the force to trust his instincts, but it really wasn't his problem.

'How did you get on this afternoon?' Cheryl asked. 'Did you find out anything else about Natalie?'

'More than you could possibly imagine.'

Jack turned at the sound of Alexi's voice. She was alone. She pulled out the chair next to Jack and sat down.

'White wine, Alexi?' Drew asked.

'How large do your bar staff pour them?'

'That bad, huh?'

Drew laughed as he went off to get her drink.

'Sorry, Alexi,' Cheryl said. 'Did I screw up by letting on you were here?'

'It's okay.' She let out a long breath. 'He would have found me regardless. He's gone now.'

'He said he thought you'd be going back to the paper with him.'

'He was wrong,' Alexi replied succinctly.

The largest glass of chilled white wine Jack had ever seen materialised in front of Alexi. She took a healthy swig and sighed with pleasure.

'Is that a glass or a vase?' he asked, amused.

'Jack says you found out some stuff about Natalie,' Cheryl said, her expression grave.

Jack and Alexi exchanged a glance and prepared the Hopgoods for a shock before telling them just about everything they'd discovered.

'She was an escort?' Cheryl's mouth fell open.

'A high-class escort,' Jack amended.

'There's a difference?' Cheryl shook her head.

'A huge difference, not least in terms of earning power,' Drew replied.

Cheryl fixed her husband with a speculative look. 'And you'd know that because...'

Drew laughed. 'Not from personal experience.' He paused, his expression playfully regretful. 'I don't have that sort of money.'

Cheryl punched his arm. 'She's attractive enough to make a living that way. She has a way about her.' Cheryl frowned. 'I'm not sure how to describe it. A presence, an awareness? It's in the way she carries herself. The way she listens to what you have to say and appears fascinated. That's rare. People seldom want to talk about anything other than themselves but she never did.'

'Sensual is how Jack described her, and he's never seen her in person,' Alexi remarked, flashing an amused smile.

'What can I say?' Jack spread his hands. 'I'm a trained observer.'

'A tough job, but someone's got to do it,' Drew added with a boyish grin.

Their banter momentarily lightened the mood.

'So, let's see if I've got this right,' Cheryl said, her expression sobering. 'Natalie was born Natalie Seaton but used the name Natalie Dwight to ply her trade, then changed it to Parker when she moved here. She was adopted at birth, Seaton being the name of her adoptive parents, and her adoptive mother was keen on gardens and flower arranging.' Cheryl counted off the points on her fingers. 'Something happened. She ran away from home and was picked up for soliciting when she was... how old?'

'Fourteen,' Jack replied.

Drew winced. 'Bloody hell!'

'That's all we know, and we're lucky Jack's partner was able to find out that much,' Alexi said.

'Did she go back to her family?' Drew asked.

'We're still trying to find that out,' Jack replied, thinking it would take Cassie a long time to do the finding. She had a point to make. Like Jack didn't already get the message – loud and clear.

'My guess is probably not,' Cheryl said. 'I mean, she chose to enter the oldest profession there is. I'm betting she did that through necessity. If I was her adoptive mother, I wouldn't stand by and let her sell herself.'

A tall man wearing a flat cap, silver hair showing beneath it, entered the bar and nodded to Cheryl and Drew.

'Who's that?' Alexi asked.

'That's Graham Fuller, a local trainer.' Cheryl twitched her nose. 'It's his lads who occupy our annexe.'

'I recognise the name,' Jack said, watching as Fuller ordered a half with a whisky chaser and took a seat on a barstool. He kept glancing at his watch, as though waiting for someone.

'Yeah, he's a big shot around these parts,' Drew replied. 'Which is saying something because the place is riddled with training yards and locals aren't easily impressed by reputations. But his old man was a force to be reckoned with. Charming and charismatic, yet rumours abound still about his tough stance with his own family.'

'And yet Graham followed in the old man's footsteps,' Jack remarked.

Drew lifted a beefy shoulder. 'Word is, he never stopped trying to live up to his expectations. Graham's married to a rich American woman now and has a couple of grown kids.'

'He looks angry, or furtive. Not sure which,' Alexi remarked, watching him as he struck up a conversation with another barfly.

'He has a high opinion of himself,' Cheryl said.

'You don't like him?' Alexi asked.

She shrugged. 'I don't like his attitude. He thinks he walks on water.'

'He *is* royalty in this neck of the woods,' Drew pointed out.

'That doesn't mean he has to flaunt it, or use it as an excuse to be rude to people,' Cheryl replied. 'Just because he's had a few big winners. Not recently, mind.'

'Going back to Natalie and her chosen profession,' Jack said. 'Her adoptive mother may not have known what she got herself involved with since we have no idea what made her go that way so young.'

'She dated one guy three times,' Alexi said. 'We've just been to visit him and we're convinced he knows nothing about her disappearance.'

'What about her other dates?' Drew asked.

'One of my guys is looking into them,' Jack replied. 'But they don't look likely.'

'So, it all comes back to her mysterious past,' Drew said, leaning back in his chair. 'Do you think she moved to Lambourn at random? I mean, I know she's interested in horses—'

'Or claims to be,' Cheryl added. 'All the things we thought we knew about her are no longer set in stone.'

'Good point. But I still want to know, why Lambourn? Is there a reason for that choice? Some ulterior motive?'

'Hard to say until we know more about her,' Jack replied, drinking more of his beer.

'The problem,' Alexi added, 'is that the more we find out, the more complicated her background becomes.'

'Shame she isn't addicted to the internet, like everyone else nowadays,' Cheryl remarked.

'Being secretive goes with the territory if you're trying to hide your past,' Jack said. 'Quite a few people nowadays are shunning social media if they want absolute confidentiality.'

'Because the net is so easy to hack?' Drew asked.

Jack nodded. 'Any geeky teenager with a bedroom, computer literacy, and a grudge against the world in general—'

'Most of them, in other words,' Alexi said.

'Right, kids like that have a command over the net you can only dream about. They can't resist showing off and causing mayhem. So, it's safer to put nothing online unless you're prepared for the entire world to know about it.'

* * *

Jack noticed another man walk into the bar. He met Fuller's eye but didn't acknowledge him as he purchased a pint and took it to a corner table. Jack was unsure what it was about the newcomer that held his attention. He didn't look out of place and was unexceptional in every way. Even so, Jack noticed him get up after a few minutes and head for the gents. Fuller followed him almost immediately.

His curiosity piqued, Jack excused himself as well, convinced that the man had come with the specific intention of meeting Fuller. Jack wanted to know what was so private about their business that they felt the need to conduct it in the bathroom.

Fuller and the newcomer were huddled together beside the hand basins, talking in whispers. They both looked up when Jack walked in, frowned at him, and stopped their conversation. Jack nodded at them and headed for a cubicle. It had the desired effect. With a flimsy wooden door separating them from Jack, the two men continued their muted conversation.

Jack, with his ear pressed against the door, heard horses' names mentioned along with race meetings and, he was pretty sure, specific races. Shortly after that the two men left the facilities but Jack remained inside the cubicle, leaned against the door, and mulled things over. The newcomer had to be a bookie's scout and Fuller, the renowned trainer with his ear to the ground and a wealth of information inside his head, was giving him tips.

Either that or he was colluding in race-fixing.

Both activities were highly illegal, dangerous, and stupid things to do. Why would he take that chance? And why do so in the men's room in a Lambourn hotel? Jack had no idea how to answer his first question, but he figured the second was less of a conundrum. Jack knew next to nothing about the types who hung around the racing scene, but was pretty sure from what he'd overheard that he'd pegged Fuller's associate for what he was. Locals, who lived, worked and breathed horseracing, would have even less trouble identifying him if they were seen together in a public place, causing speculation about Fuller's association with the man. But who could possibly read anything into a chance meeting in a men's room?

'What are you up to, Fuller?' Jack muttered aloud as he washed his hands and returned to the bar. Fuller had struck up a conversation with a group of locals upon his return to the bar. The scout's empty glass sat on the table he had occupied and the man himself was nowhere in sight.

'Are you okay?' Alexi asked him. 'You look preoccupied.'

'Sure.' Jack wasn't ready to share what he thought he'd just witnessed. It didn't have any bearing on Natalie's disappearance and Jack didn't have time for distractions, even though the policeman in him still yearned to knock Fuller's game on the head. 'Where were we?'

'We were talking about Natalie's online presence,' Drew reminded him. 'We have to ask why she would be so cautious about her email and stuff like that, yet have a Facebook page and openly talk about buying a share in a racehorse?' He shook his head. 'It makes no sense.'

'That is a very good question,' Jack replied.

'What do you plan to do now?' Cheryl asked. 'Since you've satisfied yourself that your sister's clients aren't involved, will you keep on digging?'

'I don't think they're involved but I want to find an alternative reason for Natalie's disappearance that will point the police in a different direction, if it comes to that. Preferably one that will end with us finding her alive and well.'

'How?' Drew asked.

'The escort agency where she worked,' Jack replied. 'I'm hoping they will be able to enlighten us since I'm convinced her past life is the key to her disappearance.' He turned towards Alexi and grinned. 'Fancy a trip up to town tomorrow?'

* * *

Cosmo was confined to the kitchen while Alexi and Jack, at Cheryl's insistence, dined in their restaurant. They were shown to a round table in an intimate corner. There was an orchid in its centre, and a waiter lit a candle as he handed them menus. Alexi thanked him, then hid behind hers, pretending to study it as she tried to figure out why Jack was suddenly so distant.

She put her menu aside while Jack had a long discussion with the waiter about wines and selected a bottle. They ordered their food but before either of them had time to instigate a conversation, the waiter returned with their wine. Jack went through the ritual of tasting it and giving it the seal of approval. The waiter filled Alexi's glass and she took a sip. Water was poured, a basket of bread with olive oil dip placed between them and finally... finally, they were alone.

'What?' she asked crossly when she had absorbed the heavy

weight of Jack's gaze for several tension-filled minutes prior to the delivery of the bread.

'I can't help thinking it isn't me you really want to be having romantic dinners with.'

'What do you mean?'

'I obviously interrupted you and your boss at a vital point in your negotiations.' Sarcasm dripped from his voice and Jack knew he was behaving like a jerk. He just couldn't seem to help himself and dipped bread into the oil-balsamic mix as he tried to get himself together. 'Are you going back to London and your old job?' he asked.

'I haven't had a chance to think about it.'

'He offered you your position back?'

'Not exactly.'

'Then what?' Jack leaned back as the waiter placed their starters in front of them.

'There's a big exposé I put a lot of work in on,' she replied, piercing a seared prawn with her fork, lifting it to her mouth, and taking a bite.

'Tell me about it.'

Tight-lipped when it came to stories she was working on, Alexi surprised herself by opening up to Jack, telling him about the legwork she'd already put in and how much she wanted to see it through.

'Not just for personal glory, believe it or not,' she said. 'I really care about those poor people. One or two of them told me, off the record, that they would be better off returning to their home countries but can't afford the fare, or the shame they'd face once they got there. Their families scrimped and saved to send them to England, where they were promised a better life, unimaginable earnings... the usual hype those unscrupulous traffickers come up with to sell the dream.'

'They don't want to admit they were duped,' Jack said. 'I can understand how they feel, and why you're so obsessed with this story but, here's the thing – if you were the only one in direct contact with these people, how come the whistle-blower contacted Vaughan?'

'That's a very good question.' She paused while the waiter cleared their empty plates. 'He had my mobile number but... well, I hate to admit it, but I went into a bit of a downer when I left the paper and didn't answer my phone. Patrick had taken to calling me from numbers I didn't recognise and I didn't want to talk to him. Perhaps when he couldn't reach me, my contact rang the paper direct, trying to find me, and the call was diverted to Patrick.'

Jack fixed her with a probing gaze. 'Do you think he would have done that?'

'Why would Patrick lie?'

'Taking a wild guess, I'd say he's crazy about you, desperate to get you back to town, no matter what it takes.'

'But I would have found out he'd got me there under false pretences when my contact failed to deliver.'

Jack shrugged. 'But you'd be back where you feel most at home, and would have had time to calm down about the paper downsizing.'

'I don't think he seriously believed I'd leave London. He just thought I was avoiding his calls.' Alexi leaned her elbow on the table and her chin on her clenched fist, her gaze averted from Jack's to avoid watching him watching her with such unnerving stillness. 'He called at my apartment, saw I'd put it up for rent, and that spooked him.'

'The guy's in love with you,' Jack replied softly.

She finally met his gaze, the tension between them replaced

by something more fundamental. Something she preferred not to put a name to.

'Thank you.' She flashed a wan smile. 'I think.'

'What will you do?'

She sighed. 'I'm seeing a different side of Patrick now. A controlling, manipulative side, and I don't much like the view.' She shook her head. 'I want that story, I want my old job back, but I don't want Patrick.'

'You're not in love with him?'

'I don't think I ever was. Not really.'

His slow, somnolent smile tugged at Alexi on a level over which she had absolutely no control. The waiter appeared with their main courses, and Alexi was grateful for the interruption.

'Is Cassie working on Natalie's background?' she asked in a deliberate change of subject.

'Not exactly.' His knife slid through his locally-produced steak as though cutting through butter.

'What do you mean, *not exactly*?'

'Cassie has other priorities right now.'

'She's still annoyed with you.' Alexi shook her head. 'That's not helpful. We need to know about Natalie's arrest, who her adoptive parents were, and whether she went back to them after her arrest. If possible, we need to talk to them. We also need to know Charles's identity. If her activities are motivated by her past, then that information is essential.'

'That's why I'm hoping we'll learn more from the agency tomorrow.'

'I'm kinda looking forward to that. I'll be interested to see what it's like.'

They ate in thoughtful silence for a moment or two.

'Why would the agency tell us anything about Natalie's history?' Alexi asked. 'I should have thought their business relied upon absolute discretion.'

'I'm sure it does, at least in so far as the identity of their clients goes, but—'

'But if they think one of their own is in danger, perhaps at the hands of a client, they might be more forthcoming.'

'We can but hope.'

'I assume we're not going to ask for an appointment.'

Jack grinned. 'Absolutely not.'

'Do you have an address for it?'

'Yep. Cassie found it.'

'Of course, she did.' Alexi rolled her eyes. 'So, how do you want to play it when we get there?'

'I figured on the truth, but you'll have to let me think on my feet. It really depends upon who we see and how responsive they are. If they clam up, you might have to go from being my... *assistant*,' he said with a cocky grin, 'to your true self.'

'On the trail of a hot story?' She returned his grin. 'You'd be surprised what people tell me in confidence if I give them my word that I won't publish.'

The waiter cleared their empty plates and they both declined the dessert menu.

'I've been thinking,' Alexi said as they waited for their coffee. 'If Cassie's backed up, I might be able to get a line on Natalie's arrest, and her adoptive parents.'

Jack sat a little straighter. 'How?'

'I did an exposé once on the foster system.' He nodded. 'A lady high up in Social Services gave me a very frank interview highlighting the obstacles in the system that prevented them from doing their jobs as well as they would like. Most of it was off the record and she actually contacted me when the article was printed because she said that for once the argument was balanced. She reckoned I'd highlighted how her department was hampered and Social Services were shown as victims of... well, of government red tape and cut backs, which is true, by the way.'

'So, I take it you have the lady's contact details and think she owes you one.'

Alexi grinned. 'No harm in trying, especially since I have a valid reason to ask and she knows I won't reveal her involvement.'

'Worth a try, I guess.'

He drained his coffee cup and pushed his chair back. 'Come on, let's hit the computers for a while, see if anything new has come in.'

10

Jack and Alexi left Lambourn at ten the following morning. This time Jack insisted upon driving and Cosmo was bribed with a tin of organic tuna and a catnip mouse to stay at home.

On their way out, Jack hit the brakes and allowed a string of thoroughbreds returning from the gallops to cross the road in front of them.

'Aren't they magnificent?' Alexi eyed the spirited horses with appreciation.

'Makes you want to get your jodhpurs out again, does it?'

'Hardly,' she said. 'Hey, that's Tod, I think,' she added when the last jockey in line waved his thanks to Jack. 'It's hard to recognise him beneath that skullcap.'

'Who's Tod?'

'Tod Naismith. He's one of Graham Fuller's trainee jockeys. Lives in Cheryl's annexe.'

'Oh, right.' Jack moved the car forward once the horses were clear, thinking there was no getting away from Fuller. 'I haven't had a chance to ask. Did you manage to get through to your contact at Social Services this morning?'

'Yes. She was off to a meeting and couldn't talk for long, but I explained what we wanted to know about Natalie and she promised to get back to me later today.'

'Ah, the powers of the press.'

'Don't mock. I seem to be getting more co-operation out of my unpaid sources than you are from your business partner. Sorry,' Alexi added when Jack inhaled sharply. 'Sore subject?'

'Cassie has her... issues.'

'So I gathered.' Alexi sent him a look. 'Wanna talk about it?'

'Nothing to talk about. I don't like being at odds with her is all. I thought she'd understand my need to help my sister. Still, she'll get over it and come through with what we need.'

'Is it me that's caused her to get her knickers in a knot?'

'Hard to say.' He shrugged. 'Perhaps it's just that we're not getting paid. Cassie always has an eye for the bottom line. Cassie thinks that because we've excluded the men Natalie dated, my involvement is at an end. I don't agree. We argued about it.'

'I see.' Alexi changed the subject. 'So, where is this Mayfair Escort Agency? I'm betting it's not in the West End.'

Jack grinned. 'Clapham.'

'Clapham? That's not far from my old stomping ground. The property's expensive but it's not an exclusive address.'

'You seem to think we're going to a house of ill-repute.'

'Well, aren't we?'

'I doubt it. Interested parties in need of a *bona fide* escort sign up online and make their selection from pictures like the ones we saw on the site.'

'Not a website that anyone can access?'

'I'm guessing it's more exclusive than that nowadays. Anyway, they pay the agency for the escort's time and anything else that happens between them is, presumably, negotiated between the punter and the escort.'

'Is it an unwritten rule that the girls *must* give out?' Alexi snorted. 'That doesn't seem very fair.'

Jack pulled onto the slip road and filtered into the traffic on the motorway heading for London. 'You think they don't know what they're getting themselves into?'

'Damn sight better than standing around on street corners, I suppose.'

'These girls travel the world, first class, at their clients' expense. When it comes right down to it, what they do is not much different to being trophy wives. They have to look good, be inventive in the bedroom, and pander to the rich man's ego. Think about it that way, if it helps.'

She screwed up her nose. 'I'd rather not.' She sighed. 'Part of me can't help thinking the girls are being exploited, even though I can see that Natalie was canny and came out of it with enough money to set herself up for life.'

'Well, there you are then.'

The radio in Jack's car was tuned to a classical station. Presumably it was the motion of wheels on Tarmac and the soothing strains of Beethoven that caused Alexi to stifle a yawn. Her eyes fluttered to a close.

* * *

Alexi only stirred when Jack pulled off the motorway and slowed, snarled up in traffic as he hit the outskirts of London. She sat up, blinked, and then stretched her arms above her head.

'Sorry,' she said sheepishly. 'I'm not much company, am I? Where are we?'

'Getting close,' he said, checking his GPS as he waited at a red light.

Five minutes later, Jack was feeding a parking meter situated in a side street lined with elegantly restored Edwardian houses.

'This is as close as we're likely to get,' he said, placing a hand on Alexi's elbow and guiding her along the crowded pavement. 'The agency is in this side street.'

A discreet plaque situated in the centre of a black door confirmed they had found the right place. Alexi looked up at the rather grand, well-maintained exterior of the building and grinned.

'Can't judge a house by its façade,' she said flippantly.

Jack pressed the bell and the door swung open. They found themselves in an airy entrance hall with a tiled floor. There were open archways on either side of it, leading to sitting rooms. There wasn't a person in sight. Presumably the front door was covered by a camera, which accounted for its opening on its own.

'Not quite what you expected?' Jack asked.

Before she could respond, a young woman of no more than twenty appeared from the back of the house. She wore jeans and a sleeveless top, her hair pulled back into a ponytail, no make-up on her pretty face.

'Definitely not,' Alexi belatedly replied.

'Can I help you?' the girl asked pleasantly.

'We're here to see Athena De Bois.' Jack told her.

'Do you have an appointment?'

'No, but I'm hoping she can spare us a few moments. My name is Jack Maddox. I'm a private investigator.'

'Oh.' The girl lost a modicum of poise. 'I hope there isn't going to be any trouble.'

'I'm sure there won't be.' Jack handed her his card and treated her to a full wattage smile that made her blush. 'We just need to ask her a few questions about Natalie Dwight.'

'I see.' It was obvious the name meant nothing to the girl. 'If you'd like to take a seat in there,' she said, indicating one of the sitting rooms, 'I'll see if Athena's free.'

'Thanks.'

'Who's Athena De Bois?' Alexi asked as they sat.

'The woman who now runs this place.' Jack grinned at her. 'I did my homework.'

'Evidently.'

A short time later, the same girl returned.

'Athena will see you, if you'd like to come this way.'

* * *

The girl led them up a wide staircase and tapped at an open door at one end of the corridor. She ushered Jack and Alexi into the room and closed the door behind them. An elegant woman sat behind a marble desk in the tastefully appointed office. The walls were painted a soft shade of yellow. A large abstract painting dominated one of them and an equally large mirror reflected light projected through the full-length window directly behind the woman's chair.

A fig tree flourished in a ceramic pot in one corner of the room and a small, cream-coloured dog was fast asleep in a soft basket. The view looked over a decked garden with strategically placed tubs of flowering plants and expensive-looking outdoor furniture. The only indication of the nature of business carried out in the establishment was a statue of Aphrodite.

Athena De Bois was, Jack figured, probably pushing fifty but ageing gracefully, her poise and elegance immediately apparent as she stood to greet them. She wore tailored trousers, a fuchsia, silk blouse that clung to her slender body and her hair was swept back into a perfect chignon.

'Mr Maddox,' she said, extending a slim, manicured hand,

her nails varnished the exact same shade of pink as her blouse. Jack imagined such attention to detail was *de rigueur* in her line of work. 'I'm Athena De Bois.'

'Jack Maddox. Thank you for seeing us without an appointment.'

The hint of a smile flirted with her lips. 'A private investigator,' she said, picking up his card from her desk and twisting it between her fingers. 'My curiosity got the better of me.'

'This is my assistant, Alexi Ellis.'

The ladies shook hands.

'I know that name,' Athena said, a note of suspicion entering her voice as she subjected Alexi to an appraising glance. 'But not, I think, in the role of investigator. Help me out here, Alexi. Why do you look so familiar?'

'Jack's the investigator,' Alexi replied. 'You probably know me from the *Sentinel*.'

'Of course.' If Athena was discomposed to have a journalist in her office, she gave no sign and remained perfectly calm. 'I admire your work.'

'Thank you.'

'Please,' she said. 'Take a seat and tell me why an investigator and journalist are interested in my friend, Natalie Dwight.'

'She's gone missing,' Jack replied bluntly. 'And we're rather concerned about her.'

'Missing?' Athena raised a perfectly plucked eyebrow and appeared slightly less composed. 'How long for?'

'We're now into the fifth day.'

'Oh.'

'Do you know her?' Alexi asked. 'Well, presumably you do since you referred to her as your friend.'

'Excuse me, but before I answer you, I need to understand why you're here, Alexi, and in what capacity.'

'That's easily explained. I'm staying with a close friend in Lambourn at the moment. She and Natalie have become friendly. It's Cheryl who alerted me to Natalie going on the missing list. I agreed to take a look into it, and met Jack along the way. You have my assurance that I won't be writing about this, and if I ever do, I shall seek your permission before I say a word about your organisation.'

'Please don't take this the wrong way, but why should I believe you?'

Alexi flashed a wry smile. 'We're not all bad. I'm doing this as a favour to a friend, and because I feel as though I've come to know Natalie a little over the past day or so. I want to find her.' Alexi leaned forward. 'I can sense she's in danger and needs help rather badly.'

Athena leaned back in her chair, apparently satisfied. 'Very well, what do you need to know?'

'You said you and Natalie are friends,' Jack said.

'Oh yes. We worked here together for some years. I was coming to the end of my career as an escort. She was in training.'

Alexi frowned. 'Training?'

'There is a great deal more to this profession than you might think.' Athena appeared resigned to Alexi's misconception. 'How long do you think a person would last at your newspaper if they just assumed they knew how to be a reporter?'

Alexi conceded the point with a nod and a smile. 'I hear you.'

'Presumably you're aware that Natalie moved to Lambourn and set up a business in floral art,' Jack said.

'Yes, I did know that.'

'You keep in contact with her?'

'We're still friends.' Jack could tell from the slight tightening in her expression that he had offended her. 'It might surprise you to learn that escorts are capable of forming friendships, just like anyone else.'

'It doesn't surprise me in the slightest,' Jack replied composedly.

'Sorry.' Athena briefly lowered her head. 'Sore subject.'

'I can imagine.'

'Apart from my friend Cheryl Hopgood, who's a hotelier in Lambourn,' Alexi said, 'you're the only other friend of Natalie's we've come across, and we didn't actually know the two of you were friends when we came here today.'

'Natalie is a very private person.' Athena fiddled abstractedly with Jack's card. 'We *do* form friendships, but are cautious about whom we trust.'

'Which, presumably is why she changed her name when she stopped working and no one who knows her in Lambourn is aware of what she used to do for a living.'

'What conclusions do you think they would draw if they did?'

'Good point,' Jack acknowledged.

'If she wasn't driven out of town by jealous females, you can be sure those females would lock up their husbands.' Athena's smile became strained. 'Take it from me, it would be a waste of breath to tell them they had nothing to fear from her. Entertaining gentlemen professionally is one thing. When it comes to our private lives, we can enjoy the luxury of being considerably more selective.'

'I can understand that,' Alexi said.

'So, tell me how you think I can help,' Athena said.

'When did you last speak to Natalie?'

'About a month ago. She came up to town for a couple of days and we arranged to meet for lunch.'

'Did she tell you she planned to join a dating agency?'

'Yes, she wants to settle down, like a normal person,' she said quietly. 'She asked me if I thought she should do it and I told her to go for it.'

'It's a problem for her because if she finds someone she likes and tells him the truth about her background, he's unlikely to continue with the relationship,' Alexi said pensively. 'If she doesn't tell him, she'll be living a lie.'

Athena nodded. 'It's all right for men to have a chequered past but the same rules don't always apply to women.'

'We've investigated the three men she dated,' Jack said, 'and are satisfied that none of them know what's happened to her. So we decided to dig a little deeper and that's how we came across her past life.' Jack leaned back in his chair and hooked one foot over his opposite thigh. 'Our problem is that we can find out very little, other than that she worked here.'

'We know she was adopted,' Alexi said.

'And we also know she was arrested as a minor for soliciting.'

'She was.'

'But unfortunately we have no way of knowing if she returned to her adoptive parents, or how she became an escort,' Jack explained.

'I can't see how any of that information will help you. It's ancient history.'

'Perhaps, but I'll bet my pension on her disappearance not being random,' Jack said. 'She was targeted.'

'How can you be so sure?'

'There was no sign of a struggle in her home, her car is still in the garage, and she isn't answering her phone or email,' Alexi said. 'She's also missed one business commitment that we know of, which is totally out of character.'

'Yes, it is.' Athena frowned, looking genuinely concerned now. 'All right, I'll tell you what I know. She was arrested at the

Park Lane Hotel for trying to shake down a rich guest.' Athena's
eyes were softened by a smile. 'It was obvious that she was under
age and didn't have a clue what she was doing. Ordinarily girls
like her wouldn't get through the front door of such establish-
ments, but she must have slipped past the concierge when his
back was turned.'

'You sound as though you witnessed the event,' Jack said.

'Oh, I did,' Athena replied calmly. 'I saw it all.'

* * *

Alexi blinked. 'You saw Natalie as a teenager trying to pick up a
rich man in a five-star hotel?'

'I was there in the lobby, waiting for a client to finish a tele-
phone call. Natalie was totally out of her depth, but even then
she had a certain something about her that made her stand out,'
Athena said with a sardonic smile. 'Natalie, I later learned, was
adamant that she didn't intend to return to her adoptive parents
but, of course, Social Services knew best and forced her to. I
knew she would run away again, and they probably did too, but
since she refused to tell them what had gone wrong, they had no
choice.' Athena sighed. 'Suffice it to say, I told Bella—'

'Bella?' Alexi asked.

'The lady who ran this establishment when I was still an
escort. I told her about Natalie and that I thought she had potential. When she ran away a second time and was picked up by
vice, my contact tipped me the wink, we bent the rules by
excluding Social Services, and I took responsibility for her.'

'Just like that?' Alexi asked, unable to keep a faint note of
censure out of her voice. 'Without knowing why she was so
determined to run from the only home she'd ever known?'

'I didn't need to know. I could see it in her eyes that she had her reasons. Compelling reasons that probably forced her to try and sell herself in the first place. I also knew that if she was sent back to the Seatons, she would run away again. Someone had to look out for her.'

'Weren't you asking her to sell herself by bringing her here?'

Athena sat a little straighter. 'Do you know how many beautiful young girls aspire to enter this profession?'

'Enlighten me.'

'As many as those who wish to become models or actresses and, believe me, as ambitions go, becoming a top escort is almost as unattainable. Take the girl that let you in just now, for example. What did you make of her?'

'She looked like the girl next door,' Alexi replied slowly. 'Fresh and young, and yet...' She glanced at Jack. 'She got your attention, even dressed casually as though not trying to make an impression.'

'Then we're doing something right.' Some of the tension left Athena's body. 'That's what we teach here. It's not all about sexy clothing and thick make-up. Just the opposite, in fact. The gentlemen on our books require understated sophistication. Look upon this place as an academy from which only one in ten ever graduates.'

'Blimey!' Alexi muttered.

'Natalie was fifteen by the time we took her in. She was angry with the world, with just cause, and didn't want to listen to anything we tried to tell her about the pitfalls of the occupation. She knew better, of course.' Athena's shrug was impossibly elegant. 'Well, what teenager doesn't? Most kids with that attitude refuse to toe the line and get shown the door, but Bella agreed with me about Natalie's potential and allowed her some leeway.'

'Please don't take this the wrong way,' Alexi said. 'But how do you learn to become an escort?'

'How much time have you got?' Athena smiled. 'Natalie was bright, so it was easy to get her to develop an interest in all the right things she'd need to keep herself informed about in order to make polite dinner conversation... politics, current affairs, stuff like that. She had to read the papers every day and answer questions intelligently upon a whole range of subjects. She learned to speak properly, to walk, to dress, to use make-up and style her hair. Trainees also get investment advice.' A ghost of a smile flirted with Athena's lips. 'We have an accountant on staff, believe it or not.' Alexi nodded. She believed it. 'Natalie's apprenticeship lasted two years.'

Alexi flexed both brows. 'That long?'

'We charge our clients a lot of money. In return, they expect the very best, which is what we pride ourselves upon giving them.'

'It sounds as though Natalie was your protégée,' Jack remarked.

'She was in many respects. I brought her in so felt responsible for her. We became friends, and I value that friendship. I hope you find her safe and well.'

'Can you think where she might have gone?' Alexi asked.

'No, I'm sorry, I can't. If I had any ideas, I'd tell you.'

'Please don't take this the wrong way,' Jack said. 'But it did cross our minds that she might have befriended a wealthy date with a view to exploiting that wealth.'

Shades of irritation clouded Athena's expression. 'Natalie was wealthy in her own right. Even if she was not, she wouldn't do that.'

'She purchased her house and paid for an extension from which to run her business. That made a big dent in her nest egg, but since then regular large amounts have gone into her account. You can see how it looks to an outsider.' Jack paused. 'Especially to the police, if they start digging.'

Athena shuddered. 'Let's hope it doesn't come to that.'

'We have managed to see her financial records through, shall we say, roundabout means. We've also alerted her bank manager to her disappearance. If he reports any financial discrepancies to the police, it will escalate their enquiry,' Jack explained. 'Which means her past will inevitably come to light.'

'We found out about it,' Alexi added. 'So they will too.'

'Yes, I see.' Athena turned her head to one side, as though she didn't want them to see her frown. 'I want her found, but I don't want any adverse publicity for this agency. We have a lot of high-profile clients who won't appreciate it.'

'Natalie used my sister's dating agency,' Jack said. 'Which is how I got involved, and my main concern is in protecting my sister's interests, just as yours is in protecting your own.'

'Do you know why Natalie ran away from home?' Alexi asked.

Athena pursed her glossed lips. 'Her father is a sports agent. Represents a number of top footballers, tennis players, people like that. He is well-known, very charming and highly respected.'

'Gerald Seaton?' Alexi said, frowning. 'Of course. I know that name. Who doesn't?'

Athena nodded. 'He took Natalie to some flashy awards ceremony when she was fourteen. Her mother, for some reason, wasn't there, so Natalie had a posh hotel room all to herself.'

Alexi shivered. 'Let me guess: the Park Lane Hotel.'

'Precisely. She told me how excited she'd been. How grown up she'd felt. She idolised her father, you see, and would do anything to please him. Well, anything except what it transpired he actually wanted from her.' Athena sighed. 'He told her afterwards when she went into meltdown that nobody would believe her if she talked about it. She owed him for taking her in and giving her such a luxurious lifestyle.' Athena frowned. 'All the usual garbage. But most worrying of all, he made it clear he didn't plan to stop. From that moment on, she was his whenever he wanted her.'

Alexi shuddered.

'He underestimated Natalie's strength of will, though. His actions shattered her hero worship and opened her eyes to the real world. She told me she grew up that day and accepted what she'd spent years trying to deny. There was obviously something fundamentally wrong with her. There must be or her birth mother wouldn't have given her up. And now, the man she looked upon as her father seemed to think he could use her as he pleased. Well, it didn't please Natalie, and she was determined it wouldn't happen again. She also decided that if she was attractive to older men she might as well make a living for herself on her own terms.'

'Hence her return visit to the scene of her worst nightmare,' Jack said softly.

'Quite.'

'Are her parents still alive?' Alexi asked.

'As far as I know. I would imagine her father has retired now. They live in Woldingham, Surrey.' Alexi knew of the village. Stockbroker central, with property prices to match. 'I'd love to see Seaton get his comeuppance, but I very much doubt there was anything Natalie could have done to get back at him after all this time. It would still be her word against his.'

'Was she bent on revenge?' Alexi asked. 'In her position, I suspect I would be.'

'She never really got past it. She told me more than once that it was like an obstacle, stopping her from being her own person.

I've often thought that's why so many people come out of the woodwork years later, accusing celebrities of nefarious wrong-doings, because finally the world is prepared to believe them.'

'Just a couple more questions,' Jack said when Athena took a glance at her watch. 'Natalie was exceedingly cautious about what she posted online.'

'In this line of work, caution becomes second nature.'

'I would imagine that carrying little physical baggage does as well.' Athena nodded. 'Which explains why there were so few papers, personal or otherwise, in Natalie's cottage. But she must have *some* things she needs to keep. Can you think where they might be?'

'Sorry, she didn't confide in me.'

'Did she make a will?'

'Most likely. We all use the same solicitor.' She rummaged in a drawer and produced a card. 'You can ask these people if they represent her interests.'

'Thanks,' Jack replied, smoothly pocketing the card. 'One last thing. Do you know if she had a client called Charles?'

Athena frowned and looked as though she wouldn't answer. But Jack could see that the name was familiar to her.

'He left a message on her answerphone, wanting to see her,' Alexi explained. 'He isn't a man she dated through Jack's sister's agency so we wondered—'

'Yes, I know who you're talking about. Occasionally clients form an attachment to a particular escort and continue to see her privately even after she leaves the business.'

'Don't you mind?' Alexi asked. 'I mean, you're cut out of the financial arrangements that way.'

Athena smiled. 'Not in the least. We have a business arrange-ment with our escorts while they are employed by us. They have a contractual obligation to work here for a specific time period that ensures we recoup the cost of their training and make a profit. When they leave, they are free to behave as they please.'

'But Charles is registered here?' Jack asked.

'Yes, he is.'

'Regular payments of a thousand pounds a time have gone into her bank account. Would Charles pay her that much?' Alexi asked.

Athena's lips twitched. 'She's selling herself short.'

Alexi's mouth fell open. 'She charged more than that when she worked here?'

'Considerably more.' Athena looked complacent. 'We're very good at what we do, and Charles does have very specific requirements.'

'Obviously.'

'I'm prepared to help you by contacting Charles, explaining the situation and asking if he's willing to speak with you. I know for a fact that he won't have seen Natalie over the past two weeks because he's been abroad on business.' Alexi and Jack exchanged a glance. 'One of our girls went to Paris to attend a party with him last week, which rather puts him in the clear in terms of being involved in Natalie's disappearance, doesn't it?'

Jack nodded. 'I guess it does.'

'Besides, they are very fond of one another and he has no reason to harm her.' Athena held up her hands. 'And before you ask, she would never even *think* of exploiting him, so don't go there.' She stood, indicating the interview was at an end. 'I assume it's all right to give Charles your number?'

'Of course.' Jack stood also and offered her his hand. 'And thank you for your time.'

'You're welcome. Please keep me informed, and let me know if there's anything else I can do to help you.'

'You'll be the first to know,' Alexi said.

'Oh, one more thing I've just thought of.' Alexi and Jack, on the point of walking through the door, turned to look at Athena. 'In her final year here, she started seeing a psychiatrist and talking her problems through. He encouraged Natalie to write it all down, get her feelings out on paper.'

Alexi and Jack exchanged a glance. 'We didn't find anything like that.'

'Well, she wouldn't leave it hanging around. It was way too sensitive.'

Especially if she planned to take her revenge, Alexi thought.

'Why did she decide to see a shrink?' Jack asked. 'What we have found out about her points to a private, self-contained person.'

'Absolutely, but when she told me she was thinking of giving up this work... well, let's just say that all our escorts are actively encouraged to talk the decision through with professionals. You'd be surprised how many of us got into the business for reasons similar to Natalie's, and how difficult it is for us to adjust to normality without help.'

'Yes,' Alexi said. 'I can imagine.'

'The doctor encouraged her to explore her feelings about being given up for adoption.'

'About her birth mother?' Alexi shared a glance with Jack. 'Did she try to find her?'

'Not to my knowledge. But there is something I've just remembered... I'm not sure if it's significant. She received some unexpected news that expedited her departure from this establishment.'

'Do you know who from?' Alexi asked.

'She said very little about it, but seemed profoundly affected by whatever it was. I tried to persuade her to postpone her decision to retire. I was running this place by then. Natalie was still only forty, but looked ten years younger and was in great demand. She could still have made a lot more money, but I could tell the mysterious communication had made up her mind so there seemed little point in trying to get her to change it.'

'Do you have the name of her shrink?' Jack asked. 'I know he won't tell me anything about their sessions but he might know something that will help.'

Athena smiled as she handed Jack another card. 'We have a resident psychiatrist on speed dial too,' she said.

11

'What did you make of that?' Jack asked as they left the house.

'That I'm in the wrong business. A thousand quid for...' She wrinkled her nose. 'On second thoughts, perhaps not.'

'Come on,' he said, grinning. 'I'll buy you some lunch while you reflect upon lost career opportunities. Then we can plot our next move.'

They made their way to the nearest pub. It was crowded with the lunchtime mob but Jack managed to nab a small corner table. Over sandwiches and soft drinks they reviewed all they'd learned.

'It sounds as though Natalie fell on her feet, at least initially, to be adopted by such a well-off family like the Seatons,' Jack said.

'She would have had the best of everything, I imagine, especially if she was an only child.'

'A good education and mixing with better off people would have been useful grounding for becoming an escort.'

Alexi nodded. 'It certainly made her self-assured. Perhaps

that's what Athena saw in her. I mean, how many fourteen-year-olds would have the confidence to walk into a five-star hotel and try to do what she did?'

'Fourteen-year-olds are very streetwise nowadays.' Jack took a bite of his ham sandwich.

'Natalie's safe, comfortable world had crumbled around her and she lost all self-worth.' Alexi ground her jaw. 'Bastard!'

'The one man she trusted above everyone exploited her. Of course she felt worthless. He would have told her it was her fault, and she probably half believed it. Her birth mother had given her up. Now the man she thought of as a father had abdicated that role because he didn't deem her a worthy daughter.' Jack shook his head. 'Poor kid!'

'Do you think it's true, though?' Alexi said reflectively. 'I was at a function once and Seaton was there. He has such presence, such charm. I never would have thought him capable of doing something so horrific.'

'The charmers, people in positions of authority, make vulnerable kids feel special when they're noticed by them. Look at all the high-profile cases that have come to light recently. Television celebrities abusing their positions for years and getting away with it – until now.' Jack abandoned his half-eaten sandwich. 'Still, we need to keep an open mind. Perhaps Natalie was a little princess, spoiled and indulged, and decided to rebel for no reason other than that she wanted some fun, which got out of hand.' Jack smiled across at her. 'There could be any number of other explanations.'

She folded her arms on the table and leaned towards him, her expression intent. 'Tell me you weren't thinking about your own trial by media when you recommended giving Seaton the benefit of the doubt.'

He flashed a sheepish grin. 'You've got me there, but still, it *does* pay to examine all the angles before passing judgement.'

'I keep thinking about her bank account. And those payments. I wonder if they're connected to the mysterious information she received. Do you think she blackmailed her father into paying up in exchange for her silence about what he put her through?'

'*If* he put her through it.'

'Well, even if he didn't, she could make up a convincing story that would see his reputation ruined.'

Jack nodded. 'The same thought had occurred to me.'

'Was Lambourn a random choice, or did that also have something to do with whatever news Natalie had received? As far as we know, she'd never been to Lambourn before she decided to settle there and you have to admit it's pretty quiet unless you're into horses. And, like me, she'd always lived in town before her move.' Alexi pursed her lips, frustrated. 'I know she wanted to make a fresh start, but still...'

'If we ever find the account of her life she's supposed to have written, we'll probably be able to nail the whole case. But, blackmailing her father?' Jack shrugged. 'I'd say it's a distinct possibility.' He paused. 'And a very good way to get herself killed.'

Alexi gasped. 'You're not saying—'

'It's just an observation.'

Alexi frowned into the distance and absently twisted the ends of her hair around her forefinger. 'I wonder if she tried to tell her adoptive mother what happened.'

'Why don't we go and ask her?'

'That was going to be my next suggestion.'

'The solicitors and the shrink definitely won't see us without appointments, and probably won't tell us anything we don't already know even if we do get past their gatekeepers. We need to prioritise and follow up the most promising clues first. If Natalie turns up alive and well, with some plausible explanation for her disappearance, we'll pack up shop and go back to our lives. If she doesn't...'

'If her body's found, you mean?'

'Yeah, if that happens the police will be all over this and we'll lose control, so let's leave the shrink and lawyer until later.'

Alexi was already Googling away on her iPhone. 'Gerry Seaton is a co-founder of Sporting Initiatives. He's now in his late sixties and retired as an active director five years ago, but retains a position on the board.'

'See if you can find an address for them.'

She shot Jack a grin. 'They still live in Woldingham. I'm wondering how much of an effort was put into finding Natalie when she took off for the second time. I dare say there's stuff online about it but that search will have to wait until later.'

'If Seaton *did* abuse her, he'd have been keen on covering his tracks, so I'm betting not much was done.'

Alexi grimaced. 'You're probably right.'

'Okay, let's go.'

They drained their glasses and left the pub.

'I've been to Woldingham a few times,' Alexi told Jack as he pointed his car in the direction of Croydon. 'It's on the North Downs. Very upper class. Has a thriving golf club, of which, I'll bet good money Seaton's a member.'

'Undoubtedly, especially if he's retired.' Jack slowed to thirty as they entered the village. He indicated left, past a row of shops that included a saddler's, a sporting goods store with a display of fishing rods, green wellies, and shooting sticks in its window, and the ubiquitous convenience store. Even posh people ran out of sugar, it seemed. 'This is the road,' he said, taking another left.

'And I'll bet that's the house.' Alexi pointed to a large pad in a good acre of ground, its front garden bursting with vibrant blooms.

Jack shrugged. 'All I see is lots of colour, so I'll take your word for it.'

'You haven't told me what you plan to say to them,' Alexi pointed out. 'You can hardly swan up to the door and ask Seaton if he would kindly 'fess up to abusing his daughter thirty years ago.'

Jack winked at her. 'I'll think of something.'

'Well, thanks for sharing,' she replied, sounding miffed.

'I'm not holding out on you. It's simply a situation that calls for improvisation. Until I gauge our reception, I've no idea which way to play it.'

'I suppose you think you can take one look at Seaton and decide if he's predator or victim?'

'All those years on the force did give me an edge, but I'm not always right.'

'Did I just hear you admit to having faults?' She offered him an incredulous look. 'You're fallible?'

Jack grinned. 'I didn't say I was often wrong.'

* * *

The house with all the flowers did indeed prove to be the Seaton residence. Jack drove his BMW through tall wrought iron gates that were wide open and followed a smooth, block-paved drive, halting the car in a turning circle at the front door.

'Nice,' he said to Alexi as they got out the vehicle and looked up at the modern, extensive, and immaculately maintained building.

Alexi merely grunted. Jack pressed the front door bell and it was opened by a short, plump woman with a pleasant, rather timid smile.

'Mrs Seaton?' Jack asked.

'Yes, can I help you?'

'My name's Maddox. I'm a private investigator.' He handed the bemused woman his card and turned on the charm. 'I'm sorry to call unannounced but I wondered if we could have a few moments of your time?'

'What's this about? Is it Na... have you news?'

'This is Alexi, my assistant. May we come in?'

'Yes, of course.'

She took them into a large lounge with full-length glazed doors leading onto a wide patio. A huge conservatory spanned one end of that patio and Jack could see the turquoise water of an indoor pool sparkling through the glass. The extensive back garden was also a riot of colour and didn't have a leaf out of place.

'You have a lovely home,' Jack told her.

'Thank you. Please sit down. May I offer you something to drink?'

'Tea, if it's not too much trouble,' Jack replied, flashing his most engaging smile.

'No trouble at all.' Mrs Seaton bustled towards what was obviously the kitchen. 'Make yourselves at home. I'll only be a moment.'

'Does that smile ever let you down?' Alexi demanded to know.

Jack turned the smile in question upon his partner-in-investigation. 'Not often,' he said. 'Don't judge. I'm betting you're not above using your own physical attributes to get interviewees to open up.'

She bit her lip. 'Why did you ask for tea?'

Without replying, Jack walked towards a sideboard crammed with family photographs. Almost all of them featured a girl – obviously Natalie – in various stages of adolescence, always smiling broadly. The photographs ended when she'd become a stunning teenager.

'Our daughter.'

Mrs Seaton had re-entered the room so quietly that the sound of her voice startled Jack. He almost dropped the picture of Natalie that he'd picked up to examine more closely. The child couldn't have been more than four years old. It made Jack feel indescribably sad to think how things had turned out for that little girl, innocent or otherwise.

'She's very pretty.'

'Thank you. Yes, she was.'

'*Was*?' Alexi asked as she helped clear a space on the coffee table for the tea tray.

'She disappeared, a long time ago now, but I still miss her every single day. I half-hoped, when you said you were an investigator, that you might have news of her. We did hire someone years ago but my husband dispensed with his services when he failed to find anything out. Even so...' Jack slowly shook his head, and saw the anticipation fade from Mrs Seaton's eyes. 'I've never given up wondering what happened to her. She's still alive somewhere; I'm absolutely sure of it. But what drove her away from home, I've never been able to fathom. She had everything she could possibly wish for, and two parents who loved her absolutely.'

Can she really have no idea, or is there nothing for her to know?

'It must be hard,' Alexi replied sympathetically, seating herself across from their hostess and nodding her thanks for the cup of tea, handed to her in a bone china cup and saucer.

'It is. I blame myself. I obviously did something wrong.'

'I doubt that,' Alexi replied.

'Would you like a biscuit?' Mrs Seaton proffered a plate. 'I baked them myself.'

'Well, in that case.'

Alexi selected a biscuit, took a bite, closed her eyes, and sighed.

'Delicious!' she said.

The older lady preened at the compliment. Based on what they knew of her husband's persona, Jack figured they had to be polar opposites, which didn't surprise him. He'd seen it more times than enough, and was already starting to understand why Natalie hadn't felt able to tell her mother what had been done to her, assuming something *had* been done and that she didn't actually try to talk about it. Mrs Seaton would have trouble believing the man she married capable of such depraved behaviour. She was devastated by the loss of her daughter, as evidenced by the photographic shrine in her living room, but if she'd had to choose between them, Jack wondered which way she would have jumped.

One of life's victims, was Fay Seaton. That's why they appealed to strong men like the one she'd married, who would find her easy to manipulate and control. Perhaps she even came from a moneyed background, giving Seaton the financial wherewithal to get his business off the ground. But Jack hadn't met Seaton yet and he might be jumping to erroneous conclusions.

But there again, he might not.

'We were just admiring your garden,' Alexi said.

'Why thank you.'

'It must be a lot of work.'

'It is, but I get help with the heavy stuff, which leaves me free to lose myself in the things I most enjoy doing. It's my passion, you know.'

'It shows.'

'I don't mean to be rude, but I don't have a lot of time. There's a gardening club meeting I need to attend very shortly.'

'Well then, I'd best come clean.' Jack flashed another of his winning smiles. 'I wasn't entirely honest with you earlier, Mrs Seaton, for which I apologise.'

'Oh,' she said, blinking in confusion. 'Then what—'

'I am an investigator, but Alexi isn't my assistant. She's a reporter with the *Sentinel*.'

Mrs Seaton cast Alexi a considering look. 'But, I don't understand—'

'Alexi is working on an article about children who go missing.' Mrs Seaton gasped. 'We don't mean to upset you, but your name came up during the course of her investigation and we wondered if you would be willing to talk about it.'

'Well, I...' Mrs Seaton fell into momentary contemplation but, fortunately, didn't ask how a PI came to be working with a reporter. 'I'm not sure what I can tell you after all this time. Besides, my husband says we shouldn't talk about Natalie. It upsets us both too much.'

Jack glanced at the gallery of pictures, suspecting that keeping them on display was one of the few areas in which Mrs Seaton had found the courage to defy her husband.

'From what our research threw up, it seems Natalie had the best of everything,' Alexi said softly. 'Did something change to make her want to leave home? Teenagers aren't always easy, are they?'

'Natalie never gave us a moment's bother.' Mrs Seaton frowned, suddenly looking decades older. 'That's why I've never been able to understand why she left.'

'Was she a good student?' Alexi asked.

'Oh yes, she was very diligent when it came to her studies.

She wanted to be a vet, specialising in horses, and she would have made it, too. Natalie could do whatever she set her mind to.'

'But she got herself arrested,' Alexi said, her voice soft and sympathetic, inviting Mrs Seaton's confidence.

'Oh, that was a misunderstanding. She was cross with us about something and tried to punish us by running off. She'd been to that hotel with her father a week or two before. It was familiar to her, which is why she must have gone back there, but the police jumped to the wrong conclusion.'

'Yes,' Alexi said gently. 'I expect they did.'

'I thought she'd got in with the wrong crowd at school and that they'd had a bad influence on her. It happens at that age, no matter how hard you try to steer them on the right path.' Yes, Jack thought, she would believe that. 'They have bad apples, even in good schools like the one we sent Natalie to. Anyway, we thought we'd set her straight. She promised us, but she hadn't been home for two days before she took off again, and this time she didn't come back.' She wiped a tear from her wrinkled cheek. 'I'm still hoping that one day she will.'

'What did she like to do?' Jack asked.

'Oh, she loved horses, just like most girls do.' Jack shot Alexi an *I-told-you-so* sideways glance. The admission also put Natalie's choice of Lambourn into perspective. If the love of horses had never left her, perhaps she genuinely wanted a share in a race-horse, explaining her need to shout about it on Facebook. 'She had her own pony, you know?' Mrs Seaton sighed. 'We eventually sold Dandy Kim, when it became apparent she would never return to ride him.'

'That must have been very hard for you.'

'For both of us. Natalie adored her father. They were so close I sometimes felt excluded.' She shook her head. 'That's ridiculous, I know, but we can't help the way we feel, can we?'

'No, we can't.'

Alexi leaned forward to touch Mrs Seaton's hand, her empathy for the woman's plight effortlessly seeming to communicate itself. Jack was starting to understand how she managed to get people to overcome their suspicion of reporters and open up to her. In this case it was the way she turned huge eyes, moist with sympathy, upon Fay Seaton and focused her complete attention on her.

'And then, of course, there was Perry.' Mrs Seaton reached across to the sideboard and picked up the picture of four-year-old Natalie with the puppy that Jack had examined earlier. 'It broke his heart almost as much as it did ours when Natalie disappeared. He sat at the gate every day waiting for her to come home from school but, of course, she never did.' Mrs Seaton sighed. 'I felt like giving up myself. I still don't know how I got through that terrible time.'

'You had your husband to lean on.'

'He was grieving too. It's funny, we ought to have been able to talk about it to each other, comfort one another, but we just seemed to skirt around the issue. Gerry buried himself in his work and I had... I wasn't very well. But I had my garden, which was a passion Natalie shared with me. It was unusual, I always thought, for a young girl but she had naturally green fingers and didn't mind getting them dirty.'

'She got that from you,' Jack said.

'Actually, no. Natalie was adopted. I wasn't able to have any of my own.'

'Oh, I see.'

'How thorough was the police investigation when Natalie went missing?' Jack asked.

Mrs Seaton shook her head. 'They were in and out of here for days, weeks... I don't really know. Like I said, I wasn't well. I had a bit of a breakdown, couldn't handle it, and my doctor kept me medicated. My husband handled it all and tried to protect me from it.'

The sound of a key in the front door had Mrs Seaton almost leaping from her chair. Her reaction confirmed Jack's suspicion that she was afraid of her husband, dominated by him, which is why the marriage had endured. 'And that will be my husband now. He's back from golf early.'

The man who strode into the room was tall, ramrod straight with not an ounce of spare flesh on his frame and a headful of silver hair. He wore expensive, casual clothes and the air of a man used to getting his own way. His gaze passed briefly over Jack and lingered a little too long on Alexi: a mixture of politeness, irritation, and very obvious appreciation of the female form. Definitely the sort arrogant enough to take what he wanted if it wasn't volunteered. He hadn't opened his mouth yet and Jack already disliked him. Mrs Seaton seemed too flustered to say anything so Jack took over, standing to introduce himself.

'Investigators,' he said jovially, turning on the charm. 'What have we done?'

'They were asking about Natalie, dear,' Mrs Seaton explained in a timid voice.

Seaton's smile faded. 'Do you have news of her?'

'Not exactly,' Jack replied, 'but there are a few—'

'Then why bring it up and upset my wife?'

'I'm not upset, dear. I like talking about Natalie. But I do need to leave now or I'll be late for my meeting. Perhaps you could answer any more questions our guests might have?'

'Of course.' He patted his wife's shoulder. 'You get along now.'

'Thank you for your time, Mrs Seaton,' Jack said, standing

and taking her hand in both of his. 'It was very nice to meet you and I hope you find out what happened to your daughter.'

'I doubt that we will ever know, not after all this time.' She shook her head in resignation. 'Still, it was nice talking about her again. I don't often get the chance.'

12

Left alone with Seaton, Alexi half-expected the charm to fade and his true character to show itself. If he was the reason for Natalie's disappearance and had kept it secret all these years, he had good reason to be worried, which would make him defensive. She was disappointed when instead of turning into a raging bull, he focused the full force of his smile upon her.

'Well now,' he said. 'Perhaps I can interest you in something stronger than tea.'

'Not for me, thanks,' Jack replied, even though the question had been directed to Alexi.

'Nor me,' she said.

'I hope you don't mind if I do.'

Without waiting for a response, he went to a well-stocked drinks cabinet and poured himself a substantial measure of single malt. With his back turned towards them, he took a long swig and then faced them.

'You didn't explain why you were asking about Natalie,' he said.

'You've seen what an effect your daughter's disappearance

has had on your wife,' Jack replied. 'Why haven't you done the decent thing and told her she's still alive and well?'

'I'm sorry.' Seaton blinked at Jack, his face a study of innocent bewilderment. 'I don't understand what you're getting at.'

He seemed so confused that Alexi was almost certain he must be innocent.

'We both know that isn't true,' Jack said, his voice tight with controlled anger.

'Look, we've tried to put this mess behind us. It was a terrible time when the child we both loved absconded but we've finally come to the conclusion that she must be dead. At least that gives us some sort of closure.'

'Dead?' Alexi asked. 'Why do you think she's dead?'

'It's the only explanation that makes any sense. She was a good kid, and we hadn't had any sort of falling out.' He shrugged. 'She had absolutely no reason to turn her back on all of this,' he added, gesturing around the opulent room. 'Besides, if she was still alive, she would have contacted us long before now. She knew how much we both adored her. Fay especially.'

'But there is another explanation, isn't there?' Jack said.

'What explanation?' he asked, deep grooves appearing in his forehead. 'Have you ever lost a child? No, I don't suppose you have, otherwise you wouldn't be asking such ridiculous questions.' He knocked back the remains of his drink and turned to refill his glass. 'Now, unless you have any specific knowledge of Natalie's last movements, I don't think there's anything else I can tell you, especially since you've avoided telling me why you're asking.'

'When did she first contact you again?' Jack asked, surprising Alexi probably as much as he shocked Seaton with the bluntness of the question.

'What the devil are you talking about?'

His bluster was almost convincing. Almost. A tic working beneath his left eye and the slightest of tremors in his hands gave him away. As did the fact that he glanced away to his left when he made his feeble attempt to deflect Jack's question.

'You raped her at the Park Lane hotel when she was fourteen.'

'What the devil do you think you're—'

'Pretty as a picture, wasn't she? All the laughter you shared, the come-ons she gave you, the way she idolised you. She was asking for it. Fourteen is the new twenty-five.'

Seaton's expression was set in granite. 'I don't have to listen to this slander.'

'You thought she'd be grateful,' Jack said, his voice silk on steel. 'Instead she ran, and tried for years to get over what you'd done to her. When she couldn't, she came back for her revenge and hit you where it hurt you the most. In your wallet.'

'You're deluded. Get out of my house!'

'Fine, but if we go, we'll be back, with the police.'

'And I'll sue for harassment.'

'Good,' Alexi said contemptuously. 'A courtroom is precisely where we want to get you. Even if you win, the publicity will ruin your reputation, to say nothing of your marriage. I'm betting your reputation, and appearances,' she added, taking her turn to spread her arms to embrace the elegant room, 'are all that really matter to you. You'll go to any lengths to protect them.'

'Even if Natalie did come back, making up some absurd story, why would I pay her to go away again?'

Alexi was wondering the exact same thing.

'Natalie was encouraged by a shrink to put down in writing what had happened to her.' Alexi watched Seaton carefully as Jack spoke. 'We've seen what she wrote and know what she had on you.'

Alexi crossed her fingers behind her back, praying he wouldn't ask what it was.

'She told you she wanted a one-off payment, but like all blackmailers, she came back again. And again. She was bleeding you dry, but part of you was willing to pay, if only for the pleasure of seeing her again. In spite of everything, you still wanted her. But it got too much. She became increasingly greedy. Threatened to tell your wife the truth, perhaps, even though you'd paid up.' Jack paused. 'Is that why you killed her?'

Seaton's head shot up. 'Now just a minute! One moment I'm a rapist, then a murderer. Make up your minds.'

'I think you're very likely both.'

Seaton remained silent, standing rooted to the spot like a deer blinded by headlights, his empty glass clutched in the slack fingers of one hand.

'You're deluded,' he eventually said with a negligent wave. 'If you really thought this was true and could prove it, the police *would* be here.'

'Oh, they will be, once Natalie's body is found. It's only a matter of time.'

'And even if it isn't,' Alexi added. 'We have her written account of what happened to her, as well as the diaries she wrote at the time of the rape.'

Jack shot Alexi a warning glance. They had no way of knowing if Natalie actually kept a diary, but Alexi thought it highly probable. Most girls of that age wrote down every single thought, feeling, and aspiration. Alexi certainly had.

'Natalie and her damned diaries.' Seaton fell into a chair, shared a glance between them, then shook his head and dropped it into his hands. Alexi sensed he was about to tell them the truth, or his version of it. 'Natalie, in spite of all we tried to do for her, had a genetic fault that meant she would never stay on the straight and narrow. It wasn't really her fault.'

Alexi's jaw dropped open.

'I warned Fay. I warned her.' He thumped his thigh with his clenched fist. 'You just don't know what you're getting when you adopt a child. But Fay stood her ground. She wanted a baby and wouldn't stop going on about it until I relented. Much good it did her. Bad genes will out, no matter how hard you try to instil your own standards and values into the child. Whatever happened to Natalie is down to genetics. How she can now cry rape is beyond me, especially given her chosen profession.'

'You have got to be kidding me,' Jack muttered.

Alexi was equally disgusted by his pathetic attempts to justify the unjustifiable. Even so, she wanted to punch the air in jubilation. By admitting he knew what his daughter had become, he had also admitted to having had contact with her since she became an escort.

'She'd been looking at me in a certain way for months,' Seaton sighed. 'Flaunting herself in a bikini as she climbed out the pool, knowing damned well what she was doing to me. I only gave her what she wanted.'

'Which will see you do jail time,' Jack snarled. 'She was underage.'

'She was looking at you, her daddy, for approval, not sex,' Alexi snapped. 'She trusted you.' She shook her head, feeling sick.

'I don't know how it all got so out of hand.' He looked up at them, as though expecting their understanding, sympathy even. 'It's not as though I planned it. Something inside of me just snapped. I guess I never was cut out to be a father. My own wasn't much of an example so I had to make it up as I went along. Kids don't come with instruction manuals.' He glared at them, a touch of his defiance in his eyes. 'But you have to believe I didn't mean to do what I did, and it never would have happened again.'

'Even though you told her she was yours whenever you wanted her?' Alexi asked.

Seaton's head shot up. 'Those words never passed my lips. I swear it.'

'And we should believe you because...' But oddly, Alexi did believe him, even as she voiced the question. It was impossible to fake such genuine surprise.

'When she came back, I tried to tell her how sorry I was, that I would make it up to her. I'd stolen her innocence and things could never be the way they once were. But at least I could make her see she had nothing more to fear from me. Or so I thought.' The brief defiance evaporated and he looked like a broken man. 'I knew when she went the second time that she wouldn't come back.'

'Why did you go to Lambourn?' Jack asked in an abrupt change of subject.

'Lambourn?' He appeared confused. 'Why would I go there?'

'To see your daughter. To persuade her to let up on the blackmail.'

'Is that where she lived? I've never been there. I've seen Natalie a few times, to hand over the money she demanded, but always in London, in public locations of her choosing.'

'How many times and how much did you pay her?'

'Three times. Ten grand each time.'

Jack let out a low whistle. 'How did she make contact with you?'

'The first time she was waiting for me when I left my office in London. I didn't recognise her at first. We went to a bar and I could feel all the pent up anger radiating off her.'

'I just bet you could,' Alexi muttered.

Jack touched her hand to stop her from interrupting.

'I tried to tell her again how sorry I was. She didn't want to know and laughed herself silly when I suggested she come back home. That her mother would have adored seeing her.' He sighed. 'Instead, she said she wanted a hundred grand. I said I couldn't get my hands on that sort of money. We settled on an initial payment of ten, but I knew she'd be back for more.'

'And you couldn't let her bleed you dry.'

'Actually, I felt kind of relieved in some respects.'

'To be blackmailed?' Alexi asked, frowning.

'To make amends in some small way. Not that I ever could. I don't expect you to believe this, but I'm not proud of what I did.' He dropped his head and rubbed his forehead with his thumbs, leaving white indentations in the tanned skin. 'If I could turn back the clock...'

'But you couldn't,' Jack pointed out. 'Natalie started taunting you, didn't she, even though you'd paid up? Extracting money from you was only part of her revenge. She wanted to spoil your peace of mind too. Keep you on the back foot by leaving you wondering what she intended to do next. She threatened to phone here and tell Fay what's you'd done. You couldn't take the risk. Natalie was the only aspect of your comfortable married life over which you couldn't control your wife's reaction. It all got too much, so off to Lambourn you went to put an end to it all.'

'I think you'd better go now,' he said. 'I've said all I have to say. I did pay Natalie to keep her mouth shut, but if she's dead, it's nothing to do with me. And don't try coming back with the police and shouting rape because I shall deny this conversation ever took place.'

13

'Jack, I don't believe he fell for that!' Alexi cried, bouncing up and down in her seat as they drove off. 'You were brilliant, making him admit to what he did.'

'I figured there had to be some sort of incontrovertible proof, otherwise, why pay up?'

'We didn't know for sure that he had.'

Jack grinned mirthlessly. 'We do now. I risked pushing it because he didn't throw us out the moment I mentioned rape. An innocent man would have been straight on the phone to his solicitor.'

'Very clever, but what if he'd just denied it, or asked us what the proof was?'

He paused at a T-junction. 'I assumed it has to be something super-personal, and embarrassing. Some habit he indulges in while having sex that no one other than his wife would know about—'

'Something he wouldn't admit to in front of strangers? He assumed Natalie had written about it and we've seen what she wrote.'

'Right.' Jack nodded, his expression grim. 'We caught him off guard and the bluff worked when I brought murder into the equation. But people like him don't go down without putting up one hell of a fight. He'll have explanations for the withdrawals from his account if the police get around to questioning him about them.'

Alexi was momentarily quiet. 'Do you think he did kill her?'

'He certainly had motive. But, if he told the truth about how often he saw Natalie and how much he paid her, then he probably wasn't the only person paying her to keep quiet.'

'Yes,' Alexi replied. 'The same thought had occurred to me. There are more large payments in her account, more recent too, than the ones Seaton made. But we do know he took her virginity and robbed her of her dreams. If Natalie had all that bottled up anger, I'm betting it was directed towards the man who set her on the road to ruin. I know mine would be. But if he did kill her and dumped her body anywhere near Lambourn, he won't go near the place again.'

'No.' Jack's smile was tight. 'But if he thinks there's anything in writing about what he did to her he might try to recover it, just to cover his back. If the police find her papers first, they'll be all over him. He knows that, especially since he'll assume we'll tell them about the conversation we just had. But, if we do go to the police with what we know, it means Mrs Seaton will learn how her daughter's been making her living all these years.'

'Ah.'

'Precisely. If she is still alive, I don't want to do that to Natalie, or her mum.'

'I agree, but it means that sick pervert continues to get away with it,' Alexi protested indignantly.

'I know, but even if he didn't kill her, he knows we know

about the blackmail and he *thinks* something exists in writing to incriminate him. That'll be enough to spoil his beauty sleep.'

Alexi screwed up her features. 'I really want to be there when they slap the cuffs on him. The way he looked at me made my skin crawl.'

'I wanted to push his teeth down his throat. I couldn't, so I hit him with words instead.' He winked at her.

'So, what do we do now?'

'We go back to Lambourn, I'll buy you dinner and we have another think about where Natalie might have hidden her papers. We now know that something definitely exists and it must be somewhere in that cottage of hers. We just didn't search thoroughly enough.'

* * *

Jack's phone rang just as he pulled off the motorway. Cassie. Again. They hadn't ended their conversation the previous evening on the best of terms and now wasn't really a good time to pick up. Not when he had Alexi sitting right next to him and Jack would have to use the hands-free facility because he was driving. There was no telling what Cassie might say and Alexi would hear every word. Still, she might have something for him relating to Natalie so he took the call.

'Hey, Cas. What's up?'

'Where are you? I've got some information on Natalie's phone records but, more to the point, there's some important stuff in the office on your *paying* investigations you need to see.' She placed heavy emphasis on the word *paying*.

'I'm ten minutes away. I'll stop by.'

'See you shortly.'

Jack disconnected. 'You don't mind, do you?' he asked Alexi.

'I don't mind, but I don't think your partner will be too happy to see me.'

'She'll get over it.'

'I'll wait in the car.'

'Not a chance.' Jack firmed his jaw. 'We're in this thing together. Besides,' he added flippantly, 'I'm not ashamed to be seen with you.'

'Good to know.'

He drove to his office, situated in a converted flat above a tobacconist's establishment on the outskirts of Newbury.

'Be it ever so humble,' he said, sliding his arm along the back of Alexi's seat as he reversed his car into the only available space. 'Come on, let's face the inquisition.'

'You are such a wuss, Maddox.'

He chuckled. 'I prefer to think of myself as a pacifist.'

Jack opened the outside door with a key and led Alexi up a narrow staircase. Cassie was on the phone when he ushered her into their two-roomed office suite. She smiled when she saw Jack. Then her eyes fell upon Alexi and that smile faded. She finished her call and stood up. Jack made the introduction and sensed the two women sizing one another up as they shook hands.

'I didn't realise you weren't alone, Jack,' Cassie said, making it sound like an accusation.

He told Cassie where they'd been and what they'd discovered.

'You think the father killed her to stop the blackmail?'

'We think someone did,' Alexi replied. 'We don't think her father was the only one she was blackmailing but don't know who the other person was yet.'

'Not anyone connected to your sister's agency,' Cassie said pointedly to Jack.

'What do you have on Natalie's phone records?' Jack asked.

Cassie handed over a sheaf of papers. 'I haven't had a chance to check them all out, but two numbers that she called regularly stand out. One is to a floral supplier. Another is a local trainer, Graham Fuller.'

Fuller again, Jack thought, recalling the incident in the cloak-room the previous night.

'Fuller.' Alexi's head jerked up. 'A lot of the people working for him live in Cheryl's annexe.'

'It might be worth having a word with them when we get back to Lambourn,' Jack said. 'If she was interested in buying a share in one of his racehorses they'll know about it, and it will explain the calls.'

'You're going back?' Cassie asked. 'Is that really necessary? All the stuff you were waiting for on the credit fraud case has come in.' She indicated a pile of paper on Jack's desk. 'The client's been on the phone several times. He wants to meet with you tomorrow.'

Jack knew she had a point. Still, Lambourn and Newbury weren't far apart. 'I'll be back tomorrow to take care of it,' he said, scooping up the papers. 'I'll look at them tonight and call him.'

Cassie pursed her lips. 'Fine,' she said shortly, returning to her desk and immersing herself in whatever was on her computer screen.

'Nice meeting you,' Alexi said as she walked through the door Jack held open for her.

Cassie mumbled something unintelligible in response.

'That went well,' Alexi said with a wry smile as she slid into Jack's car.

'Sorry she was so rude. There was no call for that.'

'She's under pressure. I recognise the signs.'

'Sometimes Cassie makes her own pressure. We're busy, but not *that* busy.'

'She likes to control things,' Alexi replied. 'Especially you.'

'She's certainly welcome to try.'

* * *

They remained silent for the short drive back to Lambourn. When they got close, Jack pulled his car into a space outside The George.

'This place was built in the eighteenth century, apparently,' he said, cutting the engine. 'It's the oldest licensed pub in Lambourn.'

Alexi smiled. 'You sound like a tour guide.'

'I am *such* good value.'

She laughed. 'Keep thinking that way, Maddox.'

'You ever been here?' He clutched both hands over his heart. 'They do real ale from Arkell's Brewery.'

'O... kay, just so long as you don't expect me to drink any.'

'Leave that to the experts,' he replied, chuckling as he opened the door to the bar.

A short time later Jack had a pint of the desired ale, Alexi a large glass of wine.

'So,' she said, once they'd ordered their food. 'I think we need to go back to that cottage, tear it apart, and find Natalie's private papers. The longer she remains missing, the more convinced I become that she's dead. The police could pile in at any time and if we don't find her documents, they sure as hell will.'

'The police won't take too much interest unless there's a body.'

'So you keep reminding me,' Alexi said, shuddering.

'Got to hand it to the girl, she was clever. We know Seaton paid her three lots of ten grand but she didn't bank all of it.'

'Different amounts each time to avoid raising suspicion, *and* keeping it below the level that would have the bank's regulators asking questions about its origins.'

Jack took a swig of beer and wiped the foam from his mouth with the back of his hand. 'I can see why the police wouldn't take our concerns seriously without anything to back them up. Now, if we find her papers, it would be a whole new ball game. We'll have to hand them over, of course.'

Alexi grinned. 'Only after we've read them.'

'Talking of which...' Jack pulled Natalie's phone records from his inside jacket pocket and checked them against the list of numbers his sister had given him for her three dates. 'She didn't call any of them,' he said, feeling relieved. 'They must have communicated only by email.'

'That looks good for your sister. Natalie was being cautious and hadn't got close enough to give any of them her phone number.'

'Unless she had a pay-as-you-go we know nothing about. One she used for her blackmail business.'

'You have a suspicious mind, Mr Maddox.'

He fixed her with an unrepentant grin. 'Goes with the territory, Ms Ellis.'

Their food was placed in front of them, bringing a temporary halt to their conversation.

'Okay, so how do find out what Natalie discovered?' Alexi asked musingly. 'Whatever it was that made her decide to retire. I have a feeling that's the key to everything.'

'Her papers,' Jack said. 'Everything comes back to her papers.'

'I know she didn't want to trace her birth mother, but

supposing she changed her mind and actually did. She probably wouldn't want anyone to know, just in case she was rejected again.'

'But why would she, after so many years?'

'Good question, but *if* she did, it would be easily done. At age eighteen, she would be entitled to apply for a copy of her original birth certificate, and details of her adoption, wouldn't she?'

'The law changed to allow that, but only for people born after '72. She would have just missed the boat, which means she would have had to see a shrink appointed by the state and explain her reasons for wanting to see the records after all this time.'

'Ah.'

'Besides, she'd disappeared, remember, changed her name. She didn't want her adoptive father to find her and, presumably, didn't want to upset her adoptive mother. There would be a risk of them discovering she'd been asking questions and then Fay Seaton might find out what she did for a living.'

'I thought all these things were confidential.'

'They are, and the risk of the Seatons finding out would be slim, but don't forget how obsessive Natalie is about her privacy.'

'Do you think she was ashamed of what she'd become?'

Jack shrugged. 'As the years went by, I'm guessing she became increasingly determined to have her revenge. You have no idea the extreme sorts of crimes committed in the name of revenge.'

'You don't need to tell me. I'm a journalist, remember?'

'Yeah, you are.' He sighed. 'Anyway, we'll ask Natalie all those questions if we find her.'

'Athena said it was her shrink who wanted her to trace her birth mother but the only way to do that was to talk to another shrink, one not of her choosing. How's that for irony?'

'Maybe her own shrink will tell us why he thought she should go down that route.'

Alexi laughed. 'Maybe the moon's made out of cheese.'

He affected surprise. 'You don't have a high opinion of shrinks?'

'They have their place, but I sometimes think they do more harm than good. People bury bad memories for a reason and being forced to confront them often backfires.' She pushed her empty plate aside and leaned towards him. 'You agree with my assessment of the psychiatric profession, don't you? Come on, Maddox, 'fess up. What turned you against such a fine body of professionals?'

'Working as a policeman requires a cynical mind-set, but that's a discussion for another day. Back to business. Did you know there're over fifteen hundred racehorses in training in this valley?'

'No, but it doesn't surprise me. There seem to be way more horses than people.'

'Right, and it costs a small fortune to keep them in training, which is why a lot of people sell shares. Doesn't it strike you as odd that Natalie only negotiated with one trainer that we know of?'

Alexi wrinkled her brow as she pondered the question. 'Perhaps a particular horse had taken her fancy.'

'Possibly, but it doesn't fit with what we know of her character. Any sentimentality she might have had in her dissipated the night her father raped her.'

'You can't know that for sure.'

'I can make an educated guess, based on what I've seen of her cottage and what we've learned from people who know her.' Jack leaned back and fixed Alexi with an intense look. 'When she ran away from home the second time, according to Fay

Seaton, she took nothing with her except a few clothes and the contents of her father's wallet. She loved her dog and her horse but didn't take any snapshots of them, nothing. It was as though she pulled a curtain across that part of her life and started afresh which, in my opinion, shows the makings of one very single-minded, strong-willed teenager.'

Alexi tilted her head to acknowledge his conjecture. 'That's a good point.'

'Right, so why only enquire about the share in one horse? She was in a strong negotiating position because she had the cash to make it happen. Why didn't she capitalise on that?'

'I wish I knew.'

The waitress cleared their plates, they both declined coffee, and Jack asked for the bill.

'Cosmo will think you've been unfaithful,' Jack quipped.

'He knows better than that. I'm a one-cat woman.'

Jack chucked. 'Right.'

'Tell me about you and Cassie,' she said. 'Why is she so possessive?'

'We've never discussed it.'

'Come on, Maddox!'

'Okay, I suppose you could say she picked up the slack when I got divorced.'

'You dated?'

'I wouldn't call them dates exactly.' Jack waggled one hand from side to side in a considering gesture. 'More soul-searching conversations during which I did most of the talking and she just listened. There was nothing more to it from my perspective, but I sometimes wonder if I gave out the wrong signals.'

'Which is why you tread on eggshells around her?'

'Is that what I do?' Jack was genuinely surprised by the

suggestion. 'I was distracted by the divorce, blamed myself for putting too much time into the job and neglecting my wife.'

'You didn't want to divorce?'

'I think I knew it was inevitable, and I was upset rather than heartbroken. I just didn't want to feel it was all my fault. Cassie was a good sounding board because she knew us both and could be objective.'

Alexi turned sideways on her chair and looked at him more closely. 'You ended up in bed with her?'

'No, but it got close. I was drinking too much, drowning my sorrows, she was there, available and... well, you know.'

'Going into business together has reinforced her belief that you're interested in her.'

'I don't see how.'

Alexi sent him a droll look, accompanied by an impatient huff. 'Of course you don't. You're a man and haven't taken the time to think it through. You told Cassie you felt your work had driven a wedge between you and your wife, then agreed to work with Cassie. What message do you think that sent?'

'You're saying Cassie imagines I've partnered with her with a view to having a relationship that work can't interfere with.'

'Give the man a prize.' Alexi's smile faded. 'If you don't want her that way, you need to straighten it out with her. It's not fair to leave her hanging.'

He sighed. 'You're right. I hadn't thought it through in that way.'

The bill arrived and Jack picked it up. 'Let me get this.'

'An old-fashioned gentleman. How refreshing.' She leaned across the table and planted a kiss on his cheek. 'Thank you.'

'My pleasure.' He placed his credit card on the plate and waited for the waitress to come back with the necessary machine. 'Consider it payment for the soul-searching.' Jack treated her to a languid smile. 'So, your turn. What do you plan to do about Patrick?'

'Unlike you, Maddox, I know my own mind. Patrick and I are history.'

Jack knew she meant it, but wondered if she realised just how deeply Vaughan was hooked on her. The man wouldn't go quietly.

'What about his offer of work?'

She shook her head. 'I can't work with him. I haven't had much time to think about it, but I'm already starting to like the idea of going freelance.' Her eyes sparkled. 'Just think of the story I could write about Natalie's life. Don't worry, I won't,' she assured him, presumably in response to his horrified expression. 'I can't as things stand, but it's made me realise how much freedom there is in having the luxury of pleasing myself rather than an editor.'

'If you don't mind not eating.'

'I'm okay financially, for a while anyway.'

'Good.' He inserted his pin number into the machine, thanked the waitress when she handed him his copy, and then stood to pull the table out so Alexi could get up. 'Come on then, let's go and put your cat out of his misery.'

* * *

They drove the short distance back to Hopgood Hall in companionable silence. Alexi had enjoyed the intimate dinner with Jack. If she was honest with herself, she'd also enjoyed having the complete attention of a man who made female heads turn. But she had no intention of becoming another Cassie. He'd be gone in another day or two, once they got the business of Natalie sorted, and she could get on with her life, free from distractions.

'Here we are,' he said, breaking the silence as he pulled his car up next to her Mini.

They walked through the hall, directly into Cheryl's kitchen. It was empty, but for Cosmo and Toby, curled up together in Toby's basket.

'Hey, Cosmo, we're home,' Alexi said, dumping her bag on the table.

Cosmo lifted his head and blinked at them like an outraged parent demanding to know why they'd stayed out so late. Then he stood up, pointedly turned his back on them and curled back up again with his face to the wall. Jack laughed aloud.

'He's sulking.'

'Women don't have a monopoly on that particular trait.'

Cheryl pushed through the door, her hands full of menus, looking distracted. 'Oh, you're back. Have you eaten?'

'Yes thanks,' Jack replied. 'We grabbed a bite on the way.'

'Are you okay?' Alexi asked, concerned. 'You seem a little stressed.'

'Bloody Marcel,' she replied, tossing her head. 'We just got the weekend's menus printed up, then he throws a wobbly over the signature dish *he* insisted upon including. Something about consistency of the sauce that made the entire dish inedible.' She shrugged. 'I tasted it and thought it was divine. Honestly—'

'You should stand up to him,' Jack said, relieving her of the menus and placing them on the kitchen table. 'Let him know who's boss.'

'In *his* kitchen he reigns supreme, and don't we all know it.'

Alexi nodded sympathetically. She'd heard more than one verbal eruption coming from the vicinity of the kitchen since her arrival. 'Why are chefs such prima donnas?' she asked.

'Because we let them be, I suppose,' Cheryl replied. 'But we can't risk upsetting Marcel. He's part of what keeps this place afloat. He's too good for us, and we all know it. I think he only stays because he likes the gee-gees and gets a few tips from the guys who come in here. But still, it's only a matter of time before he packs up his knives and legs it.'

'Just so long as he doesn't do any back-stabbing with them before he departs,' Jack remarked.

'This is *not* funny, Jack,' Alexi said crossly.

'But probably accurate.' Cheryl threw herself into a chair. 'Tell me what you found out. Anything to take my mind off domestic royalty.'

Before Alexi could reply they were joined by Drew. Also muttering a few choice words about stroppy chefs, he made a beeline for the corkscrew. Seated around the table, Alexi and the guys shared a bottle of wine.

* * *

'Let's get this straight,' Cheryl said, looking a little taken aback when Jack and Alexi had filled them in. 'You found Natalie's adoptive parents, went to see them, accused her father of rape and he admitted it. Phew!' She fanned her face with her hand. 'You guys don't take any prisoners.'

'The man's a total creep,' Alexi replied, wrinkling her nose. 'But so charismatic that, at first, I was inclined to believe he was innocent.' She shrugged. 'It just goes to show how much stock we put on appearances. If he'd been a grumpy old bastard with bad breath and yellowing teeth, I probably would have automatically assumed his guilt. No wonder Natalie didn't speak out. No one would have believed her, not back then.'

'You weren't taken in by him?' Drew asked, addressing the question to Jack.

'There were a few things about his reaction that didn't add up, despite the fact that Fay Seaton told us Natalie was a happy, well-adjusted child and had no reason to run away.'

'Seaton loves the limelight, is always ready to be the mouth-piece for the athletes he represents, and doesn't shy away from the camera,' Drew said, screwing up his features in disgust. 'He thinks on his feet and knows how to play his audience.'

'Right,' Jack agreed.

'But would he really harm Natalie?' Cheryl asked.

'He seemed genuinely surprised when we suggested that he might have done away with her to put a stop to the blackmail,' Alexi replied. 'But, like I say, his performance almost fooled me. He certainly had a motive, but none of that gets us any closer to finding Natalie. Unless she turns up and wants to press charges there's sod all we can do to make him pay. And probably not even then, given that she's blackmailed him over it.'

'So, what next?' Cheryl asked.

'Jack has some stuff to do for his day job before the morning,' Alexi replied. 'I thought I'd go through Natalie's phone records, see if I can identify any of the numbers she called less frequently.'

'I'll look at them with you,' Cheryl volunteered. 'If they're local numbers, I might recognise them.'

'Thanks.'

'In that case, ladies, I'll leave you to it.' Jack patted the wedge of papers Cassie had given him and pulled a face. 'I have home-work and my teacher is likely to test me on it. Catch you in the morning, Alexi.'

'Okay, good night.'

'And I'm needed back in the bar,' Drew said, bending to kiss his wife's head. 'There's no rest for the wicked.'

Laughter sounded from the annexe. 'That'll be the grooms

returning from the pub,' Cheryl said. 'One day, they'll remember to do it quietly.'

Alexi grabbed the printed picture of Natalie she'd been carrying about in her bag and went to the back door. 'I need to ask Tod if he remembers seeing Natalie at Fuller's yard and, if so, what she was doing there.'

Cosmo stirred and deigned to follow her from the room with Toby tagging along. Alexi met the returning revellers before they reached their accommodation.

'Hey,' Tod said, his eyes lighting up at the sight of her. 'Sorry. Were we too noisy?'

'Actually, I wanted a quick word with you.'

He offered her a sweeping bow. 'I am entirely at your service.'

Alexi laughed as she unfolded Natalie's picture. 'Do you recognise this lady?' she asked.

Tod took the picture from Alexi and held it beneath one of the outdoor lights. 'Sure, that's Natalie. She's a local florist. Why do you ask?'

'Has she ever been up to your yard?'

'Yeah, frequently as it happens. She's interested in taking a share in Super Nova. He's a promising two-year-old Graham's just taken into training.'

'You say frequently. How often has she been to see the horse?'

'Dunno. But I've seen her hanging around at least three times. Maybe more.'

'Is that normal?'

Tod smiled. 'It's a big investment she's considering, so I guess she needs to be sure.'

'Why big? Surely a lot of people take shares in horses?'

'Yeah, you've no idea how many pieces a horse can be chopped into, figuratively speaking. Up to twenty isn't unusual.

But Natalie is considering a quarter share so Graham's job is to convince her the horse has real promise, which he does. It's a big deal.' Tod shrugged. 'There again, perhaps she just likes hanging about the yard and soaking up the atmosphere. Some people are like that.'

'Who dealt with her enquiries about Super Nova?'

'The guv'nor.'

'What, every visit? Is that normal?'

Tod grinned. 'She's very attractive.'

Alexi laughed, but when it became apparent Tod couldn't tell her anything more, she thanked him and said good night.

'Hey.' His voice caused her to turn back. 'Why are you asking me these things? Why not ask Natalie herself?'

'I would if I could find her.'

'She's probably gone off with some bloke somewhere,' Tod replied. 'I bet she gets plenty of offers. Do you want me to ask the boss if he knows anything?'

'No, it's okay, thanks Tod.'

Alexi planned to visit Graham Fuller and do the asking herself.

She returned to the kitchen, poured the remainder of the wine into her glass, and told Cheryl what she'd learned from Tod.

'I suspect Jack will need to go to his office tomorrow, at least temporarily, so I'll go and see Fuller on my own.'

'I hope we're not going to lose the pleasure of Jack's company.' Cheryl grinned. 'He certainly makes the place look pretty.'

Alexi conceded the point with a wry twist of her lips. Cosmo, having forgiven her for abandoning him all day, leapt gracefully from the floor and landed on her lap. She smoothed his big head and the cat responded with a thundering purr.

'He likes you, Alexi.'

'Cosmo? Of course he does. I feed him, don't I?'

Cheryl tutted. 'You know very well I'm talking about Jack.'

'Even if that's true, I'm not in the market for romance. Besides, he already has a very overprotective partner lusting after him.'

'I get the impression your Mr Maddox doesn't allow anyone else to tell him who he should or should not date.' Cheryl grinned. 'Besides, Cosmo likes him. That has to count in his favour.'

'I wish I knew what made Cosmo decide if a person is worthy of his notice. His instincts are almost human... no, better than human when it comes to judging character. I thought he just liked people who were no threat to me, but he disliked Patrick from the word go.'

'There you are. He *is* a good judge of character.'

Alexi smiled. 'He's a very unusual feline.'

Cosmo purred louder, obviously aware that he was being admired. 'Come on then, help me plough through these phone numbers.'

'Slave driver.'

14

Alexi and Jack were both up early the following morning and encountered one another in the upstairs residents' lounge. Jack had his car keys in his hand, about to leave.

'Hi,' he said. 'I missed you last night.'

'You were on a long phone call when I came up. I didn't want to disturb you. Thought you might be whispering sweet nothings to a girlfriend.'

'If only. What did you get from Tod? I saw you talking to him through the window.'

Alexi told him. 'Sounds genuine enough, but I'm planning to go up there now and see if I can talk with Fuller myself.'

'Be careful.'

Alexi blinked at him. 'Why?'

'I'm not sure.' Jack scratched his neck. 'There's something about him that doesn't add up.'

Alexi was surprised when Jack told her what he'd overheard in the men's room.

'Blimey, you think he's hard up? I find that difficult to believe. He's a famous trainer. Even I've heard of him. I'd have thought owners would be clamouring to have him take their horses. Why would he risk it all?'

'He might have expensive habits. Don't forget his staff accommodation burned down in mysterious circumstances, which probably resulted in an insurance claim. And Drew says he's always having to chase him for outstanding rent.'

'True, but I don't see how he can have anything to do with Natalie's disappearance. If she was thinking of taking a share in that horse, it would be in his best interests to have her alive and well. Anyway, we haven't unearthed any connection between them.'

'Just take care, that's all I'm saying.'

'I'll do that. Then I'll go on to Natalie's cottage and see if I can find her hiding place.'

'Don't pull up all the floorboards,' he said with a grin. 'Oh, and there's no point in going to see Fuller yet. He'll be up on the gallops, watching his horses being put through their paces at the crack of dawn.' He consulted his watch. 'Leave it another couple of hours.'

'I knew that.'

His grin widened. 'Course you did.'

Alexi actually didn't have the first idea how the racing world worked and evidently it showed.

'You going into Newbury?' she asked.

'Yeah, I have a meeting scheduled with a client, but I should get that cleared up this morning. I need to put some time in at the office after that but I'll be back this evening. If you find anything significant, or need me in the meantime, call my mobile.'

'I *can* manage without you.'

'I'm just saying. We don't know what we're dealing with, so tread carefully and trust no one.'

'Have you heard back from the guy you had checking out Natalie's other two dates?'

'Actually, yes. Both guys seemed surprised and genuinely concerned about Natalie's disappearance. They confirmed individually that they'd only dated once, communicating by email. They admitted they couldn't believe their luck when they saw Natalie and weren't surprised when she didn't want to hook up for a second time. Anyway, Larry's pretty sure they're not hiding anything, which is good enough for me.'

'Okay, we'll put them to the bottom of the suspect list.'

'We don't really have any suspects, other than Seaton.'

'How many more do we need? He has motive, means and opportunity. Isn't that the yardstick you cops measure these things by?'

'It's hard to apply those criteria when we don't have a crime to apply them to.'

Alexi folded her arms defensively. 'We ought to bear Walker's name in mind. I don't think he had anything to do with her disappearance, but she *did* date him three times and we haven't found anyone else she allowed to get that close. He planned to move their relationship on by inviting her to his house. Maybe she refused.' She shrugged. 'People have killed for less.'

'That's a reach. But I agree, we should keep him in mind.'

'Okay, so we have a suspect list of two. That makes me feel as though we've achieved something. Now, what about her solicitor and shrink? Are you going to try and get appointments with them?'

'I'll put calls into them when I get to the office, but unless they're willing to reveal anything significant, which I doubt, there's not much point in going up to town again.'

'Oh, I don't know. I can be quite persuasive, given the right motivation.'

Cosmo stalked up to them and wrapped himself around Jack's legs, purring.

'Take this guy with you today,' Jack said, bending to scratch his ears. 'It'll make me feel better.'

'I will, but only because I can't deal with another of his strops if I leave him behind.'

The corners of his lips lifted. 'Good enough. Right, I'm out of here. Take care.'

He grabbed his iPad and phone and waved over his shoulder as he flew down the stairs, taking them two at a time. Alexi shook her head at his retreating figure. He was incorrigible. Dressed in a long-sleeved shirt that hung loose outside his jeans, his hair still damp from the shower and flopping over his eyes, she had to agree with Cheryl's assessment of him. But she'd cut her tongue out before she admitted it.

'Okay, Cosmo,' Alexi said. 'You ready for another day's hard sleuthing?' She stroked her cat's sleek back. 'I'm determined to show Newbury's answer to Dick Tracy that he's not the only one who knows how to get results. Natalie's hidden her personal stuff somewhere. I'm a woman. I ought to be able to think like she does and figure out where.'

* * *

Alexi had been unsure what to expect from Fuller's venture when she arrived there much earlier than Jack had suggested. She was a reporter, on the trail of a story, and always concerned about being scooped, she didn't do waiting under such circumstances. She looked about the trainer's pristine establishment with a combination of surprise and interest. Spick and span, everything was neatly in place, not so much as a blade of hay littering the cobbled yard and barns beyond. There were several rows of loose boxes set around a quadrangle. Some, but not all, were occupied by leggy horses munching away at hay nets. One or two of them glanced at her as she walked past, displaying refined heads with widely spaced, intelligent eyes, and long, arched necks.

She had left Cosmo in the car, thinking there would probably be dogs around and not wanting him to take them on. Having Fuller's dogs coming out on the losing end of a fight with her cat, or having him traumatise one of the horses, wouldn't be the best way to encourage his cooperation. Alexi chuckled as she considered the possibility of threatening Fuller with letting her cat loose in his yard if that cooperation wasn't forthcoming.

She wondered what Cosmo would make of these noble creatures. For her part she was starting to appreciate why it was known as the sport of kings. Just standing there, she felt a sense of history and tradition permeate her soul. She allowed the smell of warm horseflesh and sweet molasses, the sound of contented munching, and the tranquillity of her surroundings to soothe her.

'I feel a feature coming on,' she muttered to herself. 'Why would such strong, noble creatures allow themselves to be dominated by considerably weaker men?' She thought of *Animal Farm* and conceded that Orwell had probably been onto something.

'Can I help you?'

Alexi turned at the sound of a voice. The voice in question belonged to a girl of no more than twenty wearing muddy boots, jodhpurs, and a body warmer over a polo shirt, her long hair pulled, appropriately enough, into a ponytail. Alexi wondered if she was one of the residents of the annexe. She was very slight of build. Perhaps a trainee jockey – or were they apprentices? Whatever, women rode right alongside their male counterparts nowadays, didn't they? It was one of the few sports where they supposedly competed on equal terms.

'I'm looking for Graham Fuller.'

'Do you have an appointment?'

'Do I need one? It'll only take a minute.'

'He doesn't usually see people without appointments. Can I tell him what it's about?'

'Super Nova.'

'Oh, are you a prospective owner?'

'Something like that.'

The girl's attitude became less guarded as she led Alexi to one of the boxes. Its inhabitant was a rich bay colour, indistinguishable to Alexi's untrained eye from all the other horses she'd seen, most of whom were also brown. But there was no question that he was handsome. He looked up and whinnied when he saw the two of them looking at him over his half-door. The girl produced something from her pocket and offered it to the horse on the flat of her hand. He snuffled and crunched on whatever she'd given him.

'What was that?'

The girl looked at her askance. 'A mint. Horses love them. If you're thinking of becoming an owner, I should have thought you'd know at least that much.'

'I have a lot to learn.'

'Evidently. Hang on a minute. I'll go and see if the guv'nor's about. They came back from the gallops a while ago and are at breakfast. Won't keep you a moment.'

Super Nova discovered Alexi had no supply of mints of her own, lost interest in her, and returned to his hay. She seemed to be kept waiting for ages and was on the point of giving up when a slim, muscular man strode across the yard in her direction, two spaniels at his heels. The same man who had been in the bar the other night, only Alexi had barely spared him a glance on that occasion.

Fuller looked to be in his late sixties, with a weathered face and a smile that didn't trouble his eyes. He'd probably once been a handsome man, but time and the ravages of the outdoor life had left their mark. As he got closer, she noticed a network of fine broken blood vessels decorating his face and nose. A drinker, she thought. Wisps of grey hair poked out from beneath the brim of a flat cap that appeared to be surgically attached to his head. She was repulsed by the traces of grease creeping up the outside where it clung to his scalp.

'I'm Graham Fuller,' he said without preamble. 'I gather you are interested in Super Nova.'

'Alexi Ellis.' She shook his proffered hand, waiting for him to recognise her name. When it became apparent that he didn't know who she was, Alexi was relieved. If he had any useful information to impart, he was less likely to tell a reporter for fear of adverse publicity. 'Thanks for seeing me without an appointment.'

'Not a problem. What do you need to know about Nova?'

Breakfast was obviously over and the yard gradually filled with knots of people, chatting and laughing. They noticed Fuller and the huddles dispersed with lightning speed. Alexi thought it interesting that all his workers appeared frightened of him.

She watched the grooms go about their business. Horses with coats that already shone brightly enough for a person to see their own face in them were being vigorously brushed. She noticed a groom doing something clever with a piece of plastic that left the horse he was working on with diamond shapes on its quarters. A couple more wore rugs and things to protect their legs and were being loaded into a lorry. One of them didn't want to go up the ramp and it took two grooms, with a rope around its backside, to persuade it. Was there a race meeting today? She didn't even know if Fuller trained chasers or flat racers. Face it: she barely knew the difference between the two except, obviously, one lot had to jump over obstacles and the others just ran like hell.

'Is there somewhere we can talk?' Alexi asked.

'You don't want to look at the horse?' The friendliness in Fuller's smile, such as it was, evaporated. 'I'm a busy man.'

'Okay then, I'll try not to waste your time. What can you tell me about Natalie Parker?'

She watched him carefully and was convinced there was a momentary shift in his expression when she mentioned Natalie's name. It was gone before she could be sure, leaving her with no opportunity to decide if it was guilt, fear, or merely recognition.

'She's thinking of taking the remaining share in Super Nova. I guess the two of you must be friends, which is what brought you here.' He leaned closer and Alexi caught a whiff of alcohol on his breath. It was only ten in the morning. She knew these people got up at some ungodly hour, so probably worked on a different time clock to everyone else, but still... 'What I don't understand is why. Oh, and in case you're wondering about the horse, I haven't heard from her for a while, so I don't know what she's decided.'

'She's gone missing. I'm trying to find out what's happened to her and your name appeared a lot on her phone records.'

'So you're not interested in Super Nova?'

Thanks for your concern about Natalie. 'I didn't say I was interested in a share. Your girl just assumed. Anyway, I should have thought you'd be keen to help me find Natalie, seeing as you appear to have so much invested in... well, her potential investment.'

It was true. Fuller seemed awfully keen to shift the

remaining share, reinforcing Jack's impression that he was strapped for cash. Then again, there could be a perfectly innocent explanation. Perhaps the principal owner was a personal friend, or someone who couldn't afford to keep the horse in training with Fuller unless another investor took up some of the slack. Part-owners were responsible for a share of the training fees, she thought. If the horse had the potential Tod implied, Fuller would be keen to hang onto it.

Perhaps he actually owned the horse himself, as opposed to simply training it. If he did, and needed others to take up shares, he must definitely be harder up than this top-notch set-up implied. Appearances, Alexi knew full well, could be misleading. Were trainers allowed to be owners? What Alexi knew about the rules and regulations pertaining to horseracing was woefully negligible. She was usually far more diligent about her research and blamed Jack for distracting her. Even so, her journalist's nose seldom let her down when something wasn't quite right, and at that precise moment it was twitching like she was in danger of developing serious allergies.

She knew next to nothing about racehorse syndicates. She knew next to nothing about a lot of the stories she'd worked on in the past, but that hadn't stopped her from sticking her oar in. The only difference this time was that she hadn't made sure of her basic facts before piling in. Hitting the ground running on a live investigation changed all the rules.

'Aren't racehorse syndicates managed through an agency of some sort?' Alexi vaguely recalled reading an article in the *Telegraph* a while back.

'Usually, but Nova's owner doesn't want a ton of people muscling in on the act.'

'Who owns him?'

Fuller shrugged, evasive. 'What's that got to do with anything?'

'I can find out easily enough.'

'Then that's what I suggest you do.' He scowled off into the distance, but continued to stroke Nova's sleek neck. 'Look, syndicates can work, but just as often they don't. People disagree. They know sod all about training but if their horse wins a couple of races, they get flushed with success and think they're experts all of a sudden, entitled to interfere. If an owner wants to keep a majority share in a horse, but doesn't want the hassle of a load of armchair experts looking over his shoulder, he might seek a private investor. Someone who has some spare cash, enjoys the sport, but who's content to take a back seat.'

Someone like Natalie, who wouldn't want to put herself into partnership with a load of strangers asking questions about her background. 'I see,' Alexi replied pensively. 'How much does it cost to train a decent horse?'

'After the initial cost of purchase?' She nodded. 'Well, buying a horse as good as Nova could cost anything up to a hundred thou. Then training fees add up to a good thirty K a year, and that's without entry fees, veterinary costs, insurance...'

'Blimey,' Alexi said faintly. 'You really do have to want to do it, don't you?'

He actually smiled. 'You really do.'

'What if a horse breaks a leg?'

Fuller said nothing. He appeared to be deep in thought and she wasn't sure if he'd even heard her speak. She would give a lot to know what was going through his mind.

'I'm sorry,' Fuller said after a prolonged silence that was in danger of becoming embarrassing. 'Of course I'm concerned about Natalie. It certainly explains why she hasn't returned any of my calls. I was annoyed with her, if you want the truth. She'd all but committed to the horse, then gave me the silent treatment. If she'd had a change of heart, it wouldn't have killed her to let me know.'

Unfortunate choice of words. 'When did you last see her?'

'Not sure.' He paused to think about it, but something told Alexi he didn't really need to. 'I suppose a couple of weeks ago. She was very keen on Nova and said she'd be in touch again in a few days, once she'd organised the necessary funds. I'm still waiting to hear from her.'

'Did she ever bring anyone with her when she came here?'

'Not that I recall.'

'How often did she come?'

He shrugged. 'A few times.'

'Did you always deal with her?'

'No, I think I only saw her the last time, or maybe twice.'

Which didn't jibe with what Tod had told her. He'd implied the two of them always seemed to have a lot to say to one another. Alexi's list of suspects had just gained another name. Why Fuller would want to murder an investor was less clear and would require more research. Perhaps she'd actually told him that she'd had a last minute change of heart. But she couldn't imagine Fuller resorting to murder because of it.

'Okay, Mr Fuller.' Alexi extended her hand. 'Thanks for your time. If you think of anything else that might help, perhaps you'd give me a call.'

She handed him a card with just her name and mobile number printed on it. It gave no indication as to her profession. He pocketed the card without looking at it.

'When you find Natalie, ask her to call me about Nova, will you?'

'I'll do that. Presumably you've left messages for her.'

'Several, but she's not answering.'

'Where did you leave them?'

'Excuse me?'

'On her mobile, or landline?'

'Oh, both.'

Unless he'd left a message on Natalie's landline before she went missing and she'd deleted it, then that was the first lie she could call him on, Alexi thought. Whether it was the only lie he'd told her was another matter, but Alexi's mild suspicions about Fuller had just gone up several notches. Interviewees who had something to hide often embellished the truth in an effort to appear helpful. It was the small details that caught a person out and Fuller had just stumbled over a tripwire.

'Right, thanks then.'

'Er, sure I can't interest you in Nova? He's going to make quite an impression on the racing world, you just mark my words.'

So why are you having so much trouble getting backers? 'Sorry,' Alexi replied, shaking her head. 'I don't have that sort of money.'

He continued to stand by Super Nova's door as she walked away, still absently stroking the horse's neck. Tod waved to her from across the yard. She waved back as she climbed into her car and drove away.

'Well, Cosmo,' she said. 'That was interesting. Two things stood out. First off, he didn't once ask me why I was investigating, or what my connection was to Natalie. Odd, don't you think? And secondly, he used the phrase "to tell you the truth". And what do we know about people who talk like that? That's right, baby: it's a pretty safe bet they're lying through their pointy little teeth. And he didn't ask if the police were involved, or any of the questions you'd expect from a concerned friend, or even a decent person. Not that he's decent. And he was far too full of himself, but still...'

* * *

Alexi was still chatting aloud when she pulled up at the side of Natalie's cottage, cut the engine, and rummaged in her bag for the key.

'Okay, Cosmo,' she said, releasing his leash and leaning across to open the passenger door for him. 'You and I are not leaving here until we find Natalie's hiding place. It's a small cottage. How hard can it be?'

Cosmo streaked from the car, hissing and growling like the panther he sometimes pretended to be. Alexi tensed. He only ever got like that when he sensed the presence of someone he *especially* didn't like. Alexi was unsure what to do. Stay in the car and call for help, or go and investigate? Who could she call, and what could she tell them? *My cat thinks there's someone here who shouldn't be?*

That settled it. Apart from not wanting to be sectioned, passivity didn't sit well with Alexi. Besides, Cosmo hadn't attacked anyone for several days – not since that little game he'd played with the postman back in Battersea – and was probably getting withdrawal symptoms. She grabbed a spanner from the glove box of her car, just in case Cosmo needed any help. She slid her phone into the front pocket of her jeans and found a travel-size can of hairspray at the bottom of her bag which went into the other pocket. Carrying pepper spray in England was against the law, but there was nothing that said a girl shouldn't be prepared for a bad-hair day.

She tucked her bag beneath the seat and climbed from the car, clicking the doors locked and pocketing the key. Then she walked around to the front of the cottage, following the racket Cosmo was making.

Gerry Seaton leaned against the bonnet of a shiny Mercedes

C Class, casting wary glances at Cosmo, who attempted to take nips out of his ankles in between hissing at him like a snake on steroids.

* * *

Jack met his client in the lobby of a Newbury hotel and imparted the good tidings. His investigations had uncovered the name of the employee who was using customers' credit card details for his own purposes. It happened more frequently than Joe Average realised, but no one got away with it for long. Jack didn't see any need to point out to his client that he could easily have discovered the employee's identity without expensive help from the Fenton-Maddox Investigation Agency. Everyone has to eat.

He returned to the office by late morning, glad that Cassie was out on a case of her own. Alexi had identified what he should have seen for himself long before now. By letting Cassie get too close at the time of his divorce, then going into a business partnership with her, he'd given the impression that he wanted more from her than that. He slapped his forehead with the heel of his hand. He was an idiot! He'd talk to her about it today, if she came back before he needed to leave for Lambourn again, and clear the air. It was sometimes necessary to be cruel to be kind. Worse-case scenario, if their partnership became untenable, he'd just have to re-establish himself – again – but this time on his own.

He completed the paperwork on the case he'd just cleared up and emailed the client his final account. He checked the progress on a few other on-going enquiries, made phone calls relating to them, and updated his notes. Then he called Natalie's shrink. He was with a client but called Jack back half-an-hour later.

'Obviously, I can't tell you anything about the sessions I had with my client, Mr Maddox, but I do share your concern as to her whereabouts. Disappearing doesn't sound like something she would do.'

'Did she mention anyone she was particularly close to? Someone she might have run off to see if they were in trouble.'

It was a forlorn hope, and Jack knew it. She wouldn't have gone without her car. Unless she'd been picked up, of course.

'Even if she did... I'm sorry, but—'

'I'm not asking you to name names, doctor. It was a non-specific question.'

The shrink's prevarication confirmed Jack's feelings about the uselessness of his profession and he hung up, none the wiser. The solicitor's office was another matter. He was put straight through to the guy who handled Natalie's affairs. Apparently he'd been warned by the concerned Athena at Mayfair Escorts to expect his call. Since that establishment provided him with a lot of work, it stood to reason that he would be as helpful as possible.

'Still no news of Natalie?' he asked.

'Unfortunately not. Is there anything you can tell me that might help?'

Jack was leaning precariously back in his swivel chair, feet propped on his desk, thinking he was chasing another dead end. He was stunned out of his lethargy when the solicitor replied in the affirmative.

'I've been thinking about that since receiving Athena's call, and actually there is one thing that isn't bound by confidentiality,' he said.

Jack sat bolt upright and his feet hit the floor with a resounding thud. 'Tell me.'

'It happened a few months before Natalie retired from the agency. I received a call from another solicitor asking me if I represented Natalie. He knew her date of birth, national insurance number, and a few other official details that enabled me to confirm we were talking about the same person.' Jack felt his blood pressure spike, the way it always did when he caught a break in a case. 'It transpired this other solicitor represented the estate of a woman who'd just died. She had left Natalie a bequest, which he wanted me to pass on to my client.'

'Are you able to tell me what the bequest was?'

'No, unfortunately not.' Jack's blood pressure returned to normal. Another brick wall. 'Because I don't know. It was a thick bundle of papers. Natalie opened them in my office. She only glanced at them but became very agitated and, as I say, shortly after that, she gave up working for the agency.'

'Do you know the name of the person the other solicitor represented?'

'Oh yes.' He paused. 'The dead woman was Laura Brooks, Natalie's natural mother.'

15

'Miss Ellis,' Seaton said with a flash of even white teeth. This time Alexi wasn't taken in by the charisma and stood facing him, the spanner concealed in the sleeve of her sweater. 'Fancy seeing you here.'

Cosmo arched his back and his caterwauling got louder: a cross between a growl and an angry mewl. Alexi had never seen him react quite so aggressively but, then again, she'd never found herself in such a potentially threatening situation before. Beneath all that glossy charm, Seaton definitely had a dark side to his character.

'I thought you'd never been to Lambourn and didn't know where Natalie lived?' Alexi said scathingly.

'Can we talk inside? Since you're here, I assume you have keys. I can't think straight with that racket going on.' He nodded towards Cosmo who obligingly growled a little louder.

Alexi shook her head. 'I don't think so.'

'I'm no danger to anyone. Besides, you have a pretty ferocious guard cat there.'

'Shame Natalie didn't have him around when you killed her.'

Seaton expelled a long sigh. 'I. Did. Not. Kill. My. Daughter.' He enunciated each word, slowly.

'Just like you didn't know where she lives?'

Alexi was no longer frightened, but mad as hell that Seaton had turned up, presumably to look for whatever it was that Natalie had on him. She had to admire his nerve, doing so in broad daylight. Nerve or desperation? She ought to call the police and she ought to do it now, but she'd never been big on taking the sensible course of action. Besides, Seaton was right about one thing. Having a pissed-off feline on the prowl was a good way to persuade Seaton to explain himself. Not that she had the slightest idea how to make Cosmo attack on command, or if he even would, but Seaton didn't know that.

'Hey, Cosmo,' she said, snapping her fingers.

The cat gave one final warning hiss and, to her astonishment, retreated. He walked over to Alexi and bumped and twined around her legs, purring as he rubbed his head against her calves.

'A most unusual feline,' Seaton said, nodding towards Cosmo. It wasn't a warm day but Alexi noticed the sweat on his brow. Yeah, good cat, she thought, making a mental note to reward Cosmo with extra tuna that evening. 'Where's your partner?'

'On his way.'

But she could tell he didn't believe her. She should ring Jack now. He was only twenty-odd miles away and never paid much attention to speed cameras. If he thought it was an emergency, he'd probably get to her in ten minutes or less. But if she rang him, Seaton would know for sure that he *wasn't* actually on his way. He probably wouldn't be caught unawares by Cosmo for a second time. Besides, if he had a weapon – a knife, or even a gun – she couldn't see him hesitating to use it on Cosmo.

'Can we talk inside?' he asked for a second time.

Alexi folded her arms, still clutching the spanner firmly in one hand. 'How did you know where Natalie lived?'

'The last time I met her to hand over money, it was in a pub in Clapham. Presumably it was familiar territory for her, what with the agency she worked for being based there. Anyway, I left first, then doubled back, followed her to her car and took the registration number.'

That was careless of Natalie. In her shoes, Alexi would have made sure she didn't park anywhere near their meeting place. Presumably she thought she had Seaton where she wanted him, too scared of the hold she had over him to fight back.

'And you had a friend somewhere, probably a policeman at your swanky golf club, run the number for you?'

'I just wanted it to stop, and make it up to Natalie in some way if I possibly could. Make her understand that I was ashamed and genuinely sorry.' He paused. 'I wanted to tell her she's the sole beneficiary of our will and that nothing would give my wife greater pleasure than to see her again, if we could just find a way to put the past behind us.' He dropped his head and kicked at the gravel beneath his feet. 'I know what you think of me, and I don't expect you to believe me, but it's true.'

The media's darling putting on a convincing show, a brutal rapist trying to cover his tracks, or genuine contrition? Probably a combination of all three, Alexi decided.

'You imagined Natalie would return home and not tell your wife the truth about why she ran?' Alexi opened her eyes wide in disbelief, unsure if the man was naïve or too used to getting his own way to see the bigger picture. 'How do you imagine Fay would have felt when she learned how Natalie had been making her living?'

'Perhaps Natalie would have spared her that knowledge. And

all the other stuff, too. She could have made something up about why she ran, for Fay's sake. After all, it was me she wanted to punish, and she sure as hell achieved that ambition.'

Alexi didn't think anything the self-centred bastard said could have surprised her, but he'd just managed it. She rolled her eyes. All that twaddle about his wife's feelings and she had almost... almost fallen for it. 'Why are you here? Come to revisit the scene of the crime?'

'I wanted to see where she lives, and if there was any sign of her.'

Alexi rolled her eyes. 'Of course you did.'

'She never lost her love of flowers.' He glanced at the lovely garden. 'She got that passion from Fay.'

Alexi didn't respond. Had he really thought she'd be won over by a little nostalgia and a sad smile? And yet, part of her still wanted to believe he regretted what he'd done, the damage he'd caused to two lives – Natalie's and his wife's. Damn, he was good! She reminded herself he would only tell her what he wanted her to hear, and that certainly wouldn't be the truth. She neither liked nor trusted him, but if they'd met under different circumstances, she would probably have been charmed by him.

'I suppose you were hoping to get into her cottage and find all the incriminating stuff she has on you,' Alexi said, finding her voice.

'In broad daylight?'

His reasonable tone only made him seem more dangerous. She felt vulnerable and exposed but knew better than to show it. Not a single car had passed the cottage during the time they'd been having their confrontation. No one had passed it on foot or horseback, either. Natalie had chosen her secluded hideaway a little too well.

'Unless you can tell me anything useful about what

happened to Natalie, then I think you'd better go. My partner and I haven't told the police about Natalie blackmailing you. Yet. So they don't know you paid her to keep silent, but I figure they will take an active interest in her disappearance if they ever learn of it.'

It was a hollow threat and they both knew it. 'How would that make Natalie look?'

'More to the point, what would they say at the golf club?' Alexi shot back. 'I doubt your police contacts will stand by you if there's a whiff of *that* sort of scandal attaching to your name. Murder and rape trumps blackmail in the high-stakes crime game.'

'Please let me know if you discover what's happened to Natalie,' he said politely as he opened his car door. 'And if I can help you in any way... well, I don't suppose you would want my help.' He offered her one of his charming smiles and slid into the driving seat. 'I hope to hear from you soon with good news.'

'Don't hold your breath,' Alexi muttered as he reversed into the lane and drove away.

No matter how genuine his contrition seemed, it didn't alter the fact that Natalie had to have something that would incriminate him if it ever came to light. She watched his car disappear around the corner. Only when it was out of sight did she release the breath she'd been holding and uncross her arms, which were shaking.

'That went well, baby,' she said aloud, bending to stroke Cosmo's head. 'Come on. We're not scared of that big bully, are we? And we're not going to let him upset us. Let's get this search on the road.'

Alexi returned to her car to grab her bag. She then approached the cottage's front door and fiddled with the strange locks, hampered by her shaking fingers. She dropped the keys and some colourful language but finally managed to get the door open. She went straight to the kitchen, poured a glass of water from the tap, and downed it in two gulps. Gradually her heart-beat returned to a more normal rate and she was able to think about her confrontation with Seaton without trembling.

'Bullies hate being confronted,' she told Cosmo, who was stalking along the work surfaces. The cottage smelt musty so Alexi opened the back door to let in some fresh air.

'Now, Cosmo,' she said, staring speculatively around the pristine kitchen. 'Where do you think she hid her papers? In the cottage, or in her workroom out the back?' Cosmo rubbed his head beneath her hand. 'Hmm, that's what I think, too. She had customers in and out of the workroom, but this was her private space, so we should concentrate on the cottage.'

Alexi shoved the spanner into the back pocket of her jeans before putting the kettle on and making herself a mug of instant coffee, needing the caffeine hit. She found a tin of pilchards in a cupboard. Figuring that Cosmo would need to recharge his batteries following his busy morning, she peeled back the lid and decanted the contents into a bowl which she placed on the floor. Cosmo stalked across to it, sniffed suspiciously, then settled down to consume his snack.

While Cosmo cleared the bowl and then set about fastidi-ously washing his face, Alexi investigated every nook and cranny in the kitchen. She reasoned that if Natalie was hiding a lot of papers, they couldn't be jammed into... well, into a jam jar. If, on the other hand, everything had been put onto a memory stick, it could be hidden just about anywhere and she might never find it.

* * *

A half-hour later, Alexi stood back with her hands on her hips, convinced the kitchen hid nothing more incriminating that a few cans of food past their sell-by date. She moved on to the lounge, which took considerably longer to search, mainly because there were so many books lining the walls. She removed each of them and flipped through the pages to see if anything had been slipped between them and also felt along the shelving for any hidden nooks, feeling as though she was featuring in an old-fashioned spy film.

Nothing.

The floor and the rest of the walls were solid and there was nothing hidden beneath the seat cushions or stuck to the bottom of the sideboard. She even checked inside the chimney, disturbed an old bird's nest when she poked upwards with a stick and received a face full of soot for her trouble.

She made her way to the cloakroom and washed her sooty hands and face.

'This is disheartening,' she told Cosmo. 'Perhaps I should have let Cheryl come along and help me. Besides, I could use the company. No offence, babe, but our conversations sometimes get a bit one-sided.'

Cosmo blinked his hazel eyes twice and preceded her towards the staircase, knowing without needing to be told that their next port of call would be Natalie's bedroom. By then it was mid-afternoon and Alexi's stomach growled, reminding her she'd forgotten to bring anything with her for lunch.

'It won't kill me to skip a meal,' she muttered, standing on the threshold to the bedroom and looking around her, wondering where to start.

This sleuthing business wasn't as easy, or as glamorous, as they made it out to be on the telly. Alexi chided herself to get on with it with a reminder that as things stood, no one would take

Natalie's disappearance seriously, especially when her previous line of work came to light, along with the fact that she was a blackmailer. It was down to Alexi to come up with irrefutable proof that something bad had happened to her.

Alexi had been able to remain detached while searching the other rooms, but pawing through another woman's personal apparel somehow seemed like an invasion of privacy. Cosmo felt no such qualms and stalked into Natalie's dressing room, where he leapt onto the shelf full of sweaters and curled up on one.

'Cosmo! You'll leave hairs everywhere. Come on now, I need your help. I know this is the shelf where we found Natalie's bank statements and it's very clever of you to remember that, but...' Alexi clapped a hand over her mouth. 'Oh my god! Cosmo, you're a genius!' She grabbed his face between her hands and plastered kisses over it. 'I'd been wondering why we found those statements in such an odd place. She was about to file them away, wasn't she? But she didn't because... because the phone rang, the doorbell disturbed her... something. She put them down, they got buried beneath her sweaters somehow, and she forgot about them. Which means we're getting warm, baby boy. Jump down, I need to check this out.'

Cosmo sent Alexi an appraising look, then leapt down from the high shelf and stalked from the room. Alexi lost no time in removing everything, which is when she noticed that the shelf wasn't as deep as the ones above it, but the lower ones were equally shallow. Euphoria swept through her. She was definitely onto something. The hiding place was ingenious. She doubted whether the police would have found it, even if they did a systematic search of the premises. She tapped the back wall, producing a hollow sound to confirm her suspicions. But there was no obvious way to remove the panel and get to the goods behind it.

'I'm not giving up now,' she said aloud, feeling carefully for any hidden catches. She removed the spanner from her back pocket, thought for a minute, then put it aside. 'Don't be stupid,' she muttered. 'This calls for something a little more subtle.'

Alexi slipped back down to the kitchen and rummaged in a drawer, looking for something flat to slip between the panel and the wall that would enable her to prise the panel away. Natalie obviously had a clever way of separating the two but Alexi was too impatient to try and figure it out. Instead, she found a small, flat-headed screwdriver which would do the job nicely, causing minimal damage.

She ran back up to the dressing room, carefully applied the tip of the screwdriver to the slight gap between panel and wall, and put pressure on it. The panel came loose with a loud cracking noise and fell away. Her heart thumping, Alexi slid her hand into the deep space that opened up to her, and pulled out an old-fashioned concertina file bursting at the seams with papers.

'Yes!'

Alexi punched the air with a clenched fist before placing the file on the floor and returning her hand to the gap. There were more files that looked as though they contained official papers. There was also a heavy bag that she struggled to bring through the gap. Eventually doing so, she placed it on the floor and unzipped it. Bundles of banknotes spilled onto the floor: all used, all twenties and fifties.

'My god!' Alexi covered her gaping mouth with her hand. 'Who the hell was she blackmailing?'

Whoever it was, she'd obviously only banked a fraction of her ill-gotten gains. Alexi was now more curious than ever to get to the bottom of things. A cursory glance at Natalie's bank papers convinced her that the answers lay not there but in the concertina file.

She left everything else where it was and carried the file to Natalie's bed. It was meticulously organised, just like everything else about Natalie's life appeared to be. Alexi removed the contents one section at a time and placed each one on a different part of the bed. Then she went through them, forcing herself to be methodical. There wasn't room for all the papers and her, so she sat cross-legged on the carpeted floor and started to read. She was tempted to ring Jack and tell him what she'd found but since she wasn't yet sure what she *had* found, she restrained herself, not wanting to appear needy.

The oldest section of the file contained diaries, written in the round hand of a teenager. A veritable treasure trove which would undoubtedly lend a clue as to what Natalie had over her adoptive father. It would take ages to read through them and Alexi wanted to get a snapshot of what else was hidden away before she started on them.

She gasped when she came across a letter from a solicitor, and a bequest from Natalie's birth mother, a lady called Laura Brooks.

'So, she found you,' Alexi muttered aloud, reading through the letter. 'Oh my god!'

Its contents made spine-chilling sense. Everything fell into place and she knew now what must have happened to Natalie.

And why.

* * *

Jack glanced at his watch, saw that it was after 3 p.m. and thought about checking in with Alexi. Then he heard the down-stairs door open, which meant Cassie was back. He put his phone down. It could wait. If Alexi had found anything important, she'd have called him.

Wouldn't she?

Jack still didn't like or trust reporters, in general, but there were exceptions to every rule.

'Hey, Cas,' he said when she walked in. 'How's it going?'

'I'm working a new case,' she replied, dumping her bag on her desk and fixing him with a considering look.

'Anything I should know about?'

'It's more my area than yours.'

'Okay. Coffee's just made.'

'Thanks.' She went into the alcove that served as a kitchen and poured herself a cup. 'How about your credit card business?'

'Done and dusted. I've even invoiced the client.'

'I'm impressed.'

'Because I solved the case?'

'No, stupid. Because you sent the invoice.'

She perched a buttock on the edge of her desk and sat facing him, sipping at her coffee, the underlying tension impossible to ignore.

'I'm surprised to see you here,' she said.

'I work here.'

'I know that, but I was starting to wonder if you'd forgotten.'

'My sister needed my help.' When she sent him a cynical look, Jack almost lost it. 'You think I should have left her hanging?'

She planted a fisted hand on her hip. 'Your sister?' she asked with attitude.

'Stop it, Cas. I pull my weight around here. What I do in my own time is down to me.'

'It's not what you do, but who, that bothers me.'

'It's never been that way between us,' he said, addressing the elephant in the room.

'It would have been, eventually.' Her belligerence gave way to pathos. 'We're a great team. I understand what makes you tick *and* I lent a shoulder when you needed one.'

'Christ, Cas, don't do this!' Jack ran a hand through his hair. 'If I've given you the wrong signals then I'm sorry. I'm not in the market for a serious relationship. Not now, perhaps not ever again. Besides, you can do a damned sight better than me.'

'Oh, please!' She threw her hands in the air. 'It's not you, it's me. Is that the best you can do?'

'I don't know what—'

'It's the reporter woman.'

'She's got a name.'

Cassie appraised him through narrowed eyes. 'Yeah, she does, and it's spelt Trouble.'

Jack held on to his temper by the sheer force of his will. 'You and I work well together, but my private life's my own. If you can't accept that then—'

'I hear you,' she said sullenly. 'It's not that I'm begging, or asking you for anything you're not prepared to give. It's just that I hate to see you making a fool of yourself, but I guess that's your call.'

'Right.' He treated her to an economical smile. 'Are we good to keep working together?'

She returned his smile, but he could see it took her a lot of effort. 'Sure. I get the message.'

Tension still fogged the atmosphere, but at least Jack had made his position clear. He was dying to get back to Lambourn and see what Alexi was up to, but figured that would be a bad move so soon after their frank exchange of views. He'd stay another hour, do some internet surfing and see what he could find out about Natalie's mother, Laura Brooks. Cassie immersed herself in her own work and the only sound was the clacking of fingers on keyboards. Until Jack found something that caused him to elevate from his chair.

'Oh my god!' he yelled, picking up the phone and dialling Alexi's number.

'What's wrong?' Cassie asked, looking up.

'I know what happened to Natalie, and Alexi's just put herself directly in the firing line.'

* * *

'Jack needs to know about this.'

Alexi spoke aloud, her voice barely audible above the sound of her disjointed breathing. Drawn by a stronger force than the need to communicate with Jack, she didn't reach for her phone. Instead her attention remained focused on the damning letter from Natalie's mother that made such chilling sense of everything Natalie had done since reading it herself. A simple document that had dramatically changed the course of Laura's child's life in ways she couldn't possibly have anticipated or intended. Unwittingly, Laura had provided Natalie with an outlet for all that pent up anger and resentment, with catastrophic consequences.

Alexi read the letter again, more slowly, allowing sufficient time for her addled brain to absorb the implications. She wanted to be sure she hadn't misunderstood anything the first time because a compelling need to know had made her read the next paragraph before she'd properly digested the contents of its predecessor.

She came to the end and lowered the letter onto her lap, tears stinging her eyes at this poignant message from beyond the grave. The icy chill freezing her bloodstream gave her some idea of just how profoundly affected Natalie must have been by the brutal reality of a past she wasn't supposed to know anything about.

The way she had so patiently and meticulously planned her revenge made perfect sense to Alexi who, now that she knew Natalie's secret, herself felt exposed and vulnerable. She was surrounded by Natalie's papers and money, there was a killer on the loose, and she was very much alone.

Self-preservation kicked in. She'd give Jack a quick call, tell him what she'd discovered, then pack all this stuff into her car and hotfoot it back to Hopgood Hall. There was safety in numbers. She'd share it all with Jack and between them they would decide what to do about it. Not that there was any real question about their next move. Natalie was dead. Any lingering hopes to the contrary dissipated the moment she started reading that letter. A letter that would give the police more reason than enough to launch a murder enquiry, even without a body, and arrest the man who must be the murderer.

She pulled the phone from her pocket and nearly jumped out of her skin when it rang in her hand. She saw Jack's name on the screen and almost laughed with relief. Talk about telepathy.

But before she could take the call, the phone was wrenched from her fingers and thrown across the room. She looked up, her heart pounding, directly into the cold eyes of a killer.

She screamed but there was no one to hear her.

16

'A reporter?' Graham Fuller growled. 'I should have made the connection.'

He towered over her, his features twisted into an impenetrable mask of resentment. Anger radiated from him, competing with the smell of alcohol on his breath. She sent him a defiant look but refrained from comment.

'You looked familiar.' Fuller's aggrieved voice filled the silence. 'But all those questions about Natalie distracted me, just like they were supposed to.'

'But then you remembered.' Alexi's own voice sounded commendably calm. 'I had no idea I had such a diverse readership.'

'I saw Tod wave to you. When he told me who you were, I knew you'd do my work for me. People like you never can mind their own bloody business.' His gaze briefly encompassed the mess surrounding Alexi. Before she could take advantage of his momentary distraction, he fixed her with an icy glare, his lips stretching into what could either have been a smile or a grimace.

'Don't even think about it,' he said, speaking softly but sounding infinitely more threatening than if he'd been ranting.

'What are you doing here?'

'What do you think?'

Alexi didn't see much point in beating around the bush. 'You want your daughter's papers.'

'That interfering bitch wasn't my daughter.'

'Actually, she was.'

'I knew you'd come around here snooping once you left the yard. Snooping is what you lot do the best. I think this proves my point.' He encompassed Alexi's find with a wide sweep of one hand. 'I wondered where her stuff was but when she refused to tell me and I couldn't find anything here myself, I thought she might have invented it all.'

Alexi stared up into the dead eyes of the man who had undoubtedly killed his own daughter. She hadn't known Natalie personally, but had lived her life vicariously for the past few days, which made her loss feel personal.

Just her luck that her phone had rung at the exact time Fuller came up the stairs. The noise of the ringtone and the hammering of Alexi's heart when she discovered the horrifying truth had masked the sound of his footsteps. He'd caught her unawares and Alexi knew with absolute clarity that he couldn't afford to let her live.

Fuller would have come in through the open back door. How stupid of her not to have locked herself in. Not that that would have kept him out for long, but at least his breaking in would have given her advance warning.

'Natalie *was* your daughter,' Alexi replied, swallowing her fear and meeting Fuller's gaze head on. 'Your father ordered her mother to abort, and gave her the money to pay for the procedure. He told you to walk away, which is what you did. After all, impressing the man so you could take over his empire was all that mattered to you. If you thought about Laura at all after your fling, you simply assumed that she'd followed orders, just like everyone in your dysfunctional family always has. But she wasn't a member of your family and couldn't bring herself to kill her baby. So she had the child and put her up for adoption.'

'Evidently,' he said, sounding disinterested. His gaze focused upon the bundles of money spilling across the carpet. 'Glad to see she didn't get to spend my money.'

'You're a callous bastard!' Alexi knew it was a mistake to let her emotions show but couldn't seem to help herself. 'You impregnated a fifteen-year-old girl who would do absolutely anything for you because she was horse mad, and a promising rider, hoping to become a three-day eventer. You were the son of an influential trainer and promised to help Laura kick-start her career. She was flattered, but too young to understand that all you really wanted to do was get into her knickers...'

Alexi was too choked up to continue. Talk about history repeating itself. Natalie's mother must have been scared and confused, and needed him more than ever at that difficult time. Laura was only fifteen when Fuller had impregnated her, just as Natalie had only been fourteen when her adoptive father had raped her. No wonder Natalie acted in the way that she had when she discovered the truth. She still hadn't got past what Seaton had done to her, and then she found out her birth mother's tragic story. It would be enough to tip anyone over the edge.

That would be why she gave up on being an escort, moved here, and methodically put her plan into action. Seaton first, then her father.

'You own Super Nova.' Alexi said and Fuller simply nodded. 'You noticed the chance to own a really good horse but by then your daughter was blackmailing you to the extent that you needed a partner to take some of the strain. Natalie pretended that was why she kept coming to your yard and you hated not being able to control her. She wanted to flaunt her hold over you, rub your nose in it and watch you squirm. That must have hurt.'

'She was a vindictive little bitch.' His upper lip curled back into a disdainful sneer. 'She had no idea what she was getting herself into.'

Alexi flexed a brow. 'Was? Where is she now?'

'Somewhere you'll never find her.'

'I found *you* and put two and two together. It's taken me two days.'

'Congratulations.'

'That must be why she spread the word about buying a share of a racehorse on Facebook. A public declaration only she could enjoy that told the world she fully intended to screw her miserable father for every penny she could get.'

He made a scoffing sound at the back of his throat. 'Don't worry about Natalie. She's beyond help. It's your own skin you should be worrying about.' He snorted. 'I've had just about all I can take from interfering females.'

A chill crept down Alexi's spine. She had been counting on Cosmo to distract him but there was no sign of him, and she had nothing to fight back against Fuller with. He was older than her, but taller and considerably stronger, and the alcohol didn't seem to have dulled his reactions. She wouldn't get to stand up before he overpowered her. She had that mini-sized can of hairspray in her pocket still, but she probably wouldn't be able to get to it because he was watching her intently. She'd left her spanner on a shelf in the dressing room. She could see it: so near yet so far. It was her only hope. She had to get to it.

Somehow.

'You couldn't let Natalie live,' Alexi said, playing for time.

'Having an illegitimate child was no big deal, not even back in the seventies, but Laura was underage. If that could be proved, then not only would your precious reputation be in tatters but you could also do jail time.' She sent him a snide smile. 'So you had to silence her for good.'

'What's the game?' he replied, sneering. 'Keep him talking until reinforcements arrive? That old ploy?' Well yes, actually. Alexi had hoped that by not answering Jack's call, it would bring him running. Or else Cosmo would give up his pursuit of the rodent population in Natalie's garden and realise she needed his help. 'Forget it!'

'You have a wife and family, don't you? Grown kids and, didn't I hear somewhere that you married into money?' Alexi expelled a hollow laugh. 'Bet your wife didn't realise what she was getting herself into.'

'Shut up!'

Alexi locked gazes with him, refusing to back down. 'Truth hurts, does it? She probably doesn't know that you pass inside information to racing scouts, either.'

He glared at her, his mouth literally falling open. 'How—'

'You should choose your meeting places more carefully.'

'And you should worry about yourself.' He recovered quickly and took control of the situation. 'Collect all this stuff up and put it in the bag with the money. Quickly.'

Alexi moved slowly, taking every opportunity to glower at him. In actual fact, it was the moment she'd been waiting for. She didn't think he'd seen the spanner. His attention was all on the money. Greed would hopefully be his downfall.

'You won't get away with this. Killing Natalie is one thing. She had a chequered past and no one to miss her.' Alexi moved closer than necessary to the dressing room as she scooped up the piles of cash. 'I, on the other hand, have a whole newsroom of people waiting to hear from me, to say nothing of my friends here. *And* an editor who already knows I suspect you.'

'You only just found all this stuff. If you'd known before now you would have turned it over to the police.'

'Journalists guard their stories more closely than you look after your pampered horses. And when I'm missed, this place will be swarming with police.'

'Who said anything about killing you? If I can destroy what Natalie had on me, no one will believe your wild story, nor will they care, and I'll sue your paper for a large fortune if it prints one unsubstantiated word.'

Alexi wasn't buying it. She knew very well that he couldn't risk letting her live. The moment she was free of him, she would get a copy of Natalie's birth certificate and go to the authorities with what she knew. If he'd heard of her reputation as a journalist then he would be aware that once she got her teeth into a juicy story she never let it go. Alexi cocked her head to one side, hope igniting. She'd just heard something. It sounded like a battering ram hitting a solid wooden door.

Cosmo, please!

It must have been the wind because the sound didn't come again and Alexi's hope died with it. Fuller obviously heard the noise, too. He took his eyes from her for a second and moved a step closer to the open door, peering around it. Alexi didn't hesitate. She leapt to her feet, lunged for the spanner and raised it above her head, ready to strike him with all the force she could muster.

He must have sensed her presence because he turned with lightning speed and aimed a vicious blow to her stomach. She deflated like a burst balloon, clutching her mid-section with one hand as she crumpled to her knees, having the presence of mind to keep hold of the spanner.

'Pass it over.'

He grinned as he extended a hand, clearly enjoying himself, and Alexi had no choice. She reluctantly gave him the spanner and he threw it onto the bed.

'I don't have any particular argument with you and don't want to cause you unnecessary pain.' His expression hardened. 'But I will if you try anything like that again.'

'You expect me to do as I'm told and simply let you kill me? The world has moved on since the days when you compromised a fifteen-year-old and then walked away without a backward glance.' She summoned up a defiant look. 'Women fight back when they're cornered nowadays.'

'It takes two.'

'Oh, please! You were eighteen, she was a star-struck kid.' Alexi sent him a disgusted look. 'Just as a matter of interest, how much did Natalie take you for?'

At first, Alexi thought he wouldn't tell her. That would mean admitting a woman had got the better of him and this guy was definitely a misogynist. 'A hundred grand,' he said shortly. 'She found out that's how much I'd paid for Nova and said a daughter ought to be worth as much as a horse.' He screwed up his features. 'She was wrong. The horse would have given me a decent return on my investment.'

She shot him a withering look. 'You're despicable.'

'And you're trying your transparent distraction tactics again.' He smirked. 'Get this stuff into the bag. Now!'

Alexi was still bent over, nursing her stomach, not having to feign light-headedness. The guy certainly packed a punch. But she couldn't give way to the pain. She was on her own, needed to get the better of the man who stood between her and the door, and needed to do it now. He'd run out of patience. Chances were he intended to kill her here and dump her body elsewhere. He was definitely in self-preservation mode and she was collateral damage.

She lurched towards the bed, grabbed the spanner and ran at Fuller with the determination of a woman fighting for her life. She felt his fetid breath peppering her face as he laughed and lashed at her with a thumping right hook, connecting severely with her temple. Her world span. She saw stars but refused to let go of the spanner. She raised it, unsure how much strength she could put behind the blow.

'You're quite a spirited little thing, aren't you?'

He laughed again, enjoying himself as he reached for the spanner. This situation was manna from heaven for a bully of Fuller's ilk. But that was okay. For once, he was doing precisely what she wanted him to. Mentally thanking Patrick for insisting she find the time for self-defence classes, she whirled in a semi-circular motion and her foot connected hard with the side of Fuller's face.

'What the—'

He shook his head, dazed, taken completely by surprise. But her satisfaction was short-lived when he surprised her with the speed of his retaliation, chopping viciously at the back of her knee with his booted foot. She cried out and fell to the ground. He followed her down, seeming to forget about the spanner. Her heart sank. She hadn't even slowed him down.

He grabbed one of her wrists and held it above her head, half-covering her body with his own, making sure he kept his groin clear of her one working knee and both of her feet. Hold the spanner, or let it go and try to jab a finger into his eye?

Before he could grab her other hand, she twisted her body sideways and bit down as hard as she could on the fleshy part of the arm pinning her wrist. He howled and slapped her face so hard that her head snapped back and made painful contact with the leg of the iron bedstead. Alexi felt her strength sap as more of his body weight pinned her down, forcing the air from her lungs, making it a struggle to breathe. This was it. She'd enraged him and he really was going to kill her.

His hands circled her neck and slowly squeezed. She saw stars and all the fight drained out of her. It would be easier to close her eyes, surrender to the inevitable and wait for the end to come.

'That's it, honey,' her aggressor said in a sing-song voice. 'Now you're getting it. When it comes right down to it, women are no different to horses. They just need a firm controlling hand to remind them who's boss.'

The pressure on her neck gradually increased. Very gradually, like he got a kick out of this and wanted to make it last. Images of Natalie filled her head, urging her to fight, always to fight. She saw Fay Seaton's face, too. She would never know peace if she didn't learn the truth about Natalie's struggles.

More banging from downstairs spurred her on. She was sure now that it must be Cosmo. He'd been shut out but hadn't given up on her so she wouldn't give up on herself. Using every vestige of her rapidly dwindling strength, Alexi lifted her free hand. Fuller noticed but had obviously forgotten about the spanner and simply laughed at her. Infuriated when she caught a glimpse of his smug smile, Alexi bashed the spanner against the side of his skull, surprised at how much strength she was able to put behind the blow. Even more surprised when she heard the sound of splintering bone.

Fuller cried out, a combination of surprise and pain, but the pressure on her neck didn't ease.

* * *

Jack floored the accelerator as he drove back to Lambourn, his gut telling him Alexi was in trouble. He'd checked with Cheryl, who confirmed she hadn't returned to Hopgood Hall.

Jack squealed to a halt in front of Natalie's cottage. Alexi's car was parked where she usually left it. Everything seemed tranquil. Perhaps he'd over-reacted.

His concerns returned when he rang the front doorbell and no one answered. Because Alexi wasn't in the house, or because something was preventing her from getting to the door? Perhaps she was in the workshop. Jack went around the back and his concerns multiplied when he encountered a snarling Cosmo hurling his body repeatedly against the kitchen door. He saw Jack and let out a blood-curdling yowl.

The moment Jack opened the door, the cat streaked through it and bounded up the stairs. Jack followed right behind him and burst into Natalie's bedroom, his worst fears realised. Fuller was on top of Alexi, his hands around her throat. She was motionless. There was blood pouring from a crack on the side of Fuller's head and a manic look in his eyes. Cosmo hurled himself onto the man's back and scratched at his eyes from behind, making the most terrifying noise.

Fuller's hands had left Alexi's neck, but she still wasn't moving. Fuller got up and stumbled around the room, blood now pouring from scratches to his face as well as his skull. There were papers everywhere, as well as loads of cash, and Fuller was disturbing it all with his blind blundering. Jack solved the problem by planting his fist squarely in the centre of the man's face and knocking him out cold. Satisfied that he wouldn't be going anywhere any time soon, he crouched beside Alexi and felt for a pulse, terrified there wouldn't be one to find. Cosmo sat on her opposite side, making piteous, human-like sounds as he stroked her face with a paw.

'Alexi,' he said softly, touching her forehead, willing her to open her eyes.

He tried to get his phone out of his pocket and call the emergency services with one hand and continue holding hers with the other. He could already see dark bruising forming around her neck, another bruise on her cheek and a cut to her temple. But at least she was breathing, albeit shallowly and unevenly. He put his call through to 999 and told them to hurry.

'Fuller.'

* * *

Jack almost jumped out of his skin. He'd looked away from her at the exact moment she'd opened her eyes and her voice, shallow and croaky, was the most welcome sound he'd ever heard.

She blinked up at him. 'The bastard was going to kill me,' she rasped.

'It's okay. You and Cosmo got him first.'

At the sound of his name and Alexi's voice, Cosmo purred loudly and rubbed his head gently against Alexi's uninjured cheek.

'He's saying sorry for not getting to you sooner. So am I.' Jack ran his free hand through his hair. 'Christ, Alexi, I never should have left you alone.'

'I can... can—' She burst into tears.

'Shush. An ambulance is on its way, and so are the police.'

'Before the police... there's some stuff here we need to hold on to.'

The effort it took for her to talk was obviously taxing her strength. 'Don't worry about that.'

'You don't understand...'

His reassurances only appeared to make her more agitated. 'What is it?'

'There's Natalie's diaries from when Seaton raped her... and Jack, she was writing a manuscript. Must keep them.'

'Okay, I'll get them.'

'Copy all the stuff from her mother.'

Jack didn't know what she'd found, but was rapidly piecing it together. He needed to work quickly, remove the stuff the police didn't need to know about, and copy the stuff that would enable them to prosecute Fuller.

'I'm on it.'

Jack didn't want to leave her side, but the papers clearly mattered to her more. He was distracted by the sound of Fuller regaining consciousness. Cosmo prowled across to sit over him and gave a warning growl.

'Don't even think about it,' Jack told him as he gathered up the scattered papers and quickly sorted out the ones that he thought would need to be copied. 'Scratch his eyes out if he moves a muscle, Cosmo.'

Half-an-hour later, Natalie's photocopier had been pressed into service, the papers Alexi wanted were safely stowed in Jack's car, and the cottage was crawling with police and paramedics. One of the latter dealt with Alexi's head wound.

'Probably won't need stitching,' he told her. 'Head wounds always bleed a lot, but the cut's not deep. However, that bang on the head might have left you with a concussion and you've got a bruised larynx. Best come back in the ambulance with us. We'll get you checked out in casualty. You'll need an X-ray.'

She closed her eyes and nodded once, like she was too tired to argue.

17

Alexi felt as though she was floating on a chemically induced high. If this was death, it wasn't so very bad. Then voices that were very much of this world broke through the misty fog inside her brain, causing anxiety to nag her back to consciousness. There was something important she had to finish. She reluctantly forced her eyelids open and had absolutely no idea where she was. Everything was white: white walls, white ceiling, white bedcovers, and an antiseptic smell that made her want to gag. Except she couldn't because her throat hurt like hell.

So did all the rest of her.

Then it all came crashing back. She was in hospital. But she had no idea how long she'd been there or if anything was seriously wrong with her. Fuller. What had happened to him? Thinking made her head ache. She wanted to close her eyes again and find a way back to that fluctuating sleep that had ended far too soon. But she couldn't do that. Now that she'd remembered her ordeal, each time she closed her eyes she could feel Fuller's hands around her neck, the pressure on lungs that felt as though they would burst like over-inflated balloons, the cold determination in his hard, flat eyes as he slowly choked the life out of her. The overwhelming temptation she had felt to let her life slide away because the effort to fight back was beyond her.

In a panic, she turned her head to one side and saw a large male figure sprawled in the chair beside her bed, engrossed in whatever he was reading.

'Jack,' she whispered.

'Hey, you're awake.' He sent her a megawatt smile. 'How do you feel?'

'What time is it? How long have I been here?'

'It's early morning. They gave you something to make you sleep. You were getting agitated, trying to talk. The nurse just came in and said you should be awake soon.'

'Have you been here all night?' she asked, her voice croaky and raw.

'Where else would I be?'

She tried to sit up. Every bone in her body protested but Jack helped her, then bolstered the pillows behind her. He handed her a cup with a drinking straw and she greedily allowed water to trickle down her bruised throat. Never had water tasted sweeter.

'You're going to be fine,' he said. 'A lot of bruises and a swollen knee—'

'Fuller kicked it from beneath me when I tried to attack him.'

'I should have been there!' He grasped her hand and gave it a gentle squeeze. 'I'd like to see him try and kick me around.'

'Why? You didn't know he was—'

'I knew there was something off about him when I overheard his conversation in the men's room, and we knew Natalie had had a lot of contact with him. I should have put it together sooner. If I'd got to you just a minute or two later, I...'

'How did you know?'

'Once I got the name of Natalie's birth mother from her solic-itors and did some digging, I found a few old articles about Laura Brooks online. She had a promising career as a junior three-day eventer. When I made the connection to horses and Fuller's father's yard, it all fell into place.'

She thought about that for a moment but was distracted when Jack moved. 'What are you doing?'

'Ringing for the nurse. She told me to let her know if you woke up.'

The nurse responded to the bell, checked Alexi's vital signs, and nodded her satisfaction.

'Would you like a cup of tea and something light to eat?' she asked.

'What I'd like is to go home,' she said, not very graciously.

'The doctor will have to discharge you and he won't do that until you've had something to eat and drink.'

'Okay then, tea would be good. Thanks.'

'I'll be right back,' she said, to Jack, not to her.

'You didn't need to stay. That chair looks uncomfortable,'

'I've slept in worse places.' He winked at her. 'Besides, you're getting VIP treatment. A private room with a police guard outside the door, no less. I had to lie and say I was your signifi-cant other.'

On the evidence she'd seen so far, Alexi figured he could probably have charmed the nurses into letting him do anything he wanted to.

'Tell me what happened after they brought me here.'

'It was pandemonium. At first the plod were a bit overawed by Fuller, what with him being akin to a local god. They seemed to think I was the aggressor and wanted to slap the cuffs on me.'

Alexi spontaneously laughed, but regretted it. 'Don't say

anything amusing,' she said, choking and reaching for the water. 'It hurts.'

The nurse interrupted them and placed a tray over Alexi's knees. Rather anaemic-looking scrambled eggs and tea.

'Eat up,' Jack said, holding a forkful of the unappetising eggs to her lips, 'and I'll tell you some more.'

The eggs tasted as cardboardy as they looked but the warm tea soothed her throat and made her feel a little better.

'It took me a while to make the uniforms understand what they were dealing with. Cosmo didn't help, of course. When they took you off, he created merry hell because he couldn't go with you. No one could get near him, except me, so I put him in my car—'

'Did your upholstery survive?'

'Of course. Cosmo and I understand one another completely. Anyway, I put him in the car, safe in the knowledge that no one would get near the papers I'd copied, or the diaries and stuff I'd already taken from the cottage, with Cosmo standing guard over them. Then I went back inside and patiently explained it all. Eventually... eventually,' he said with an exaggerated sigh, 'they realised what they were dealing with, got their act together, and a murder squad came out from Reading nick. They read Natalie's mother's letter, I then told them who you were and what Fuller had tried to do, and he was taken away in handcuffs.'

'Damn, I wish I'd seen that.'

'Sorry sweetheart, but at least he's under lock and key. He was swearing blue murder when they took him away, asking all and sundry if they knew who he was, threatening to sue for wrongful arrest... all the usual. Then he demanded a lawyer.'

'He hasn't admitted anything?'

'Not yet.'

'Damn!' Alexi shook her head, close to tears of frustration.

'Unless he tells them where he hid Natalie's body, it might never be found.'

'Shush, don't get worked up. We'll find her.'

'I hope we do.' She sighed. 'Is that Natalie's manuscript?'

'Yes. Very poignant stuff.'

'We need to get out of here. Cheryl and Drew—'

'I went back there first and dropped Cosmo off. They know you're all right.'

They were interrupted by the doctor. He examined Alexi and wanted her to stay with them another day. She refused and so by mid-morning she was in Jack's car, on the way back to Hopgood Hall. The swelling in her knee had subsided sufficiently for her to be able to hobble under her own steam. She didn't want to think about the bruises to her face and neck, or the bash she'd taken to the head, to say nothing of the bruise forming on her belly where Fuller had punched her.

'The police will want to talk to you once we get back,' Jack warned her as he drove.

'That's okay. I have a few things to say to them.'

The moment Jack pulled his car into the forecourt at Hopgood Hall, Cheryl and Drew, along with Cosmo and Toby, came bounding out to meet them.

'We've been beside ourselves.' Cheryl engulfed Alexi in a cautious hug.

'You should see the other guy,' she replied, giving Drew a kiss on the cheek and slowly bending to greet Cosmo.

'Let's get you inside,' Jack said, sliding an arm around her waist and helping her to walk the short distance.

* * *

'So Fuller had no idea he actually had a daughter,' Cheryl said when they were all seated around the kitchen table drinking tea. 'Well, not Natalie, anyway. He has other kids with his American wife.'

'Did Natalie's mother pursue her dream and make it in three-day eventing?' Drew asked.

Alexi shook her head. 'According to the letter she left for Natalie, her heart went out of it after the way she was treated at the hands of the Fullers and she saw a very different, ugly side to the equestrian world.'

'I'll just bet she did,' Cheryl said, grinding her jaw.

'Just like Natalie's career choices were derailed after what Seaton did to her,' Drew added. 'No wonder Natalie was so determined to get her revenge.'

'Fatal revenge,' Alexi said softly. 'Laura took an office job and finished up marrying her boss, a widower old enough to be her father.'

'She probably felt comfortable with an older man who was willing to look after her,' Drew said pensively. 'More in control. Natalie's life was all about being in control as well. Two abused women doing what they could to protect themselves, and then fighting back.'

'Yes,' Alexi agreed, her voice hoarse, raspy. 'They didn't have any children of their own and her husband died ten years ago. Then, a year before Natalie moved here, her mother discovered she had terminal cancer. She'd never forgotten her only child, and set about trying to find her. She got investigators onto it, and they probably found out all the stuff that Jack and I did.'

'Did they ever meet?' Cheryl asked, her eyes filling with tears.

'No,' Alexi replied. 'I guess Laura figured it was too late to mend that particular fence.'

'But she left that letter,' Cheryl pointed out, 'to be given to Natalie upon her death. She assumed Natalie would want to know about her start in life and the reasons why her mother couldn't keep her.'

Cheryl made it sound as though she desperately wanted to believe Natalie died fighting for justice for two generations. Alexi couldn't fault her friend's reasoning.

Except that she could.

Instead of blackmail, Natalie could have gone to the police, or better yet, to the media with all the information she'd gathered on Seaton and Fuller. Trial by media was way more effective nowadays. By going to the papers, Natalie would have been viewed as the victim that she was. So too would the mother whom she'd never met, and Seaton and Fuller would both have done jail time. But because she turned to blackmail, she would be seen as a manipulative woman with a grudge to bear.

'Do you think her mother's soul-cleansing was the right way to set the record straight?' Drew asked, standing behind Cheryl and absently massaging her shoulders with one large hand. 'She was no longer around to answer Natalie's questions, and couldn't have known what the consequences would be.'

'Having read the letter several times, I'd say she was conflicted,' Jack replied.

'Don't the police have the letter?' Cheryl asked.

Jack winked at her. 'We might have kept a copy.'

'And all of Natalie's childhood diaries, as well as the manuscript she was writing,' Alexi added.

'Best not to mention that to the police,' Jack warned. 'There's nothing there that impinges upon Fuller's culpability and we don't want Fay Seaton to learn about her husband's perversions from Natalie's diaries. If she has to hear it at all, it would be better coming from us.'

'Did Fuller admit to murdering Natalie?' Cheryl asked.

'He did to me,' Alexi replied. 'But Jack says when the police took him away, he was denying everything.'

Cheryl rolled her eyes. 'Of course he was.'

'And he's probably got a fancy lawyer who will try and muddy the waters,' Drew said, curling his lip in disgust. 'If they find out Natalie was an escort, that will open a whole new can of worms.'

'That's another reason why it's better not to let the police see Natalie's diaries and manuscript,' Jack replied. 'It would cast Seaton in the role of alternative suspect. Especially if they delve into his financials and discover she blackmailed him, too.'

'Fuller's lawyer will have his work cut out to cast doubt on his guilt,' Alexi rasped, 'because Natalie was very thorough. She'd managed to get a sample of Fuller's DNA and paid a private lab to compare it to her own. There's a ninety-nine point seven per cent chance that Fuller's her biological father. Her mother also included a sample of her own DNA with the letter she left for Natalie. He won't be able to talk his way out of that one.'

'Where are those samples now?' Jack asked.

'Being held by the lab that ran the tests, along with the original results.'

'She really wasn't taking any chances,' Cheryl said. 'Good for her.'

'There was a ton of cash hidden in the house,' Jack said, yawning. 'The police have all that.'

'Natalie took Fuller for a hundred grand.' Alexi said. 'The same amount as he paid for Super Nova.'

'Kind of poetic justice, when you think about it,' Drew mused, turning to the stove to heat up some soup for their lunch.

'Yeah, she only banked small parts of it and, I'm guessing here, laundered the rest through her business. That would be one of the reasons why she set it up, and explains why it was already in the black.'

Drew served them with Marcel's homemade soup and Alexi surprised herself by feeling hungry again.

Jack's phone rang.

'That was the lead detective in the murder squad,' he told Alexi. 'He needs to come and talk to you. Might as well get it out the way. They'll be here in an hour, which gives you time for that bath you said you wanted.'

'Sure.'

'I'd best hide this evidence,' he said, pointing to the diaries and manuscript he'd brought back from the hospital. 'And I have a few bases to cover. I'll be a few minutes.'

'Jack,' Alexi said, her croaking voice halting him before he was halfway across the room.

'Yes.' He turned to look at her, his eyes dark and intense. 'What is it?'

'Thanks.'

He looked surprised. 'For what?'

'Oh, I don't know.' She cautiously shrugged. Even that small gesture caused half the nerve endings in her battered body to protest. 'Let me see. Saving my life is probably worth acknowledging.'

He swallowed and took a step towards her, as though he wanted to say more. Then he appeared to remember Cheryl and Drew were both there and the moment of mutual awareness passed.

'Any time,' he said flippantly.

"You'll have one hell of an inside story to write when this is all over,' Cheryl remarked as she and Alexi watched Jack leave the room.

Astonishingly, that thought hadn't even occurred to Alexi.

Well, maybe not so astonishing, given that she'd just narrowly escaped being Fuller's second victim. She held that thought as she turned to the kitchen mirror, wincing as she assessed her appearance. A dressing on her temple covered the gash where she'd hit her head on the bedstead. There was already a dark reddish tinge surrounding it. The same was true of her cheek, where Fuller's hand had struck it so violently.

She instinctively touched the dark marks ringing her neck like an ugly collar and closed her eyes for an expressive moment, waiting for the nausea caused by delayed shock and visual realisation to dissipate.

'Come on,' Cheryl said softly from behind her. 'I'll help you with that bath.'

18

Jack ran up to his room, phoned Cassie, gave her an abbreviated version of events and told her she'd have to cope without him for a day or two. He'd been in no mood to handle her tantrum the previous day and was surprised when she accepted what he told her now with calm resignation.

Next Jack called his sister, told her the same story and warned her to expect a visit from the police.

'They'll check into Natalie's background and will want to know why I got involved,' he told her. 'It's best they hear the truth from me.'

'Of course you need to be straight with them. Don't worry about me. I'm just so glad your friend survived.'

Jack phoned Reading nick next. As luck would have it, there was a uniformed sergeant on desk duty, one who'd been there forever and owed Jack a favour from the days when Jack had been seconded to Reading as part of a fraud investigation. Technically, Jack was a person of interest, as they say, in a murder case. Make that a potential murder case. Still no body. Even so, the sergeant shouldn't tell him anything.

'Fuller's being interviewed now,' the sergeant said. 'He's lawyered up and so far hasn't said much. How's the woman he tried to throttle?'

'Recovering, but it was a close call.'

'I dunno.' Jack could imagine the sergeant scratching his balding head. 'You think you've seen it all when you've been in this game as long as I have, but I never would have pegged Fuller for a villain.'

'Can't trust anyone these days.'

Jack told the sergeant he owed him a drink and hung up. Then he sat back and had a good think about their conversation, more convinced than ever that if Fuller didn't confess and tell them where he'd hidden the body, he might well get away with murder. He would go down for rape of a minor and for attempted murder, but how long for? His brief would dig up all the sordid details of Natalie's past. How she blackmailed her biological father until he was in danger of going under financially. Everything would get spun, glossed over, and Fuller might not pay the ultimate price.

'Not on my watch,' Jack said aloud, grimly determined.

His next call was to Athena at Mayfair Escorts, warning her that Natalie was dead and she would undoubtedly receive a visit from the police.

'I'm glad Alexi's okay,' she said, her voice low and full of melancholy at the sad news she had just learned.

'I'll send her your regards. Thanks for thinking of her.'

'She made quite an impression upon me.'

Me too.

Jack had some time to kill before the police arrived so decided to dig a little deeper into Fuller's background. Jack thought about talking to Fuller's lads living in Drew's annexe but decided against it. Fuller's place would be buzzing with rumour and speculation about the future of the yard. The lads wouldn't be human if they didn't worry about indiscretion costing them their jobs. Besides, if the police discovered Jack had interfered in the investigation by talking to the lads before they could, he would only piss them off unnecessarily.

Jack absorbed himself in some of the endless articles he found online about Fuller. And very interesting reading they made too.

'Well, well,' he muttered, reaching for his phone and calling Cassie again. 'Hey,' he said when she answered. 'If you were serious in your offer of help, can you do some digging for me?'

'Sure. What do you need?'

Jack told her.

* * *

When Alexi, dressed in a simple sheath dress and flat shoes, re-entered the kitchen, Jack was the only person in it. He had Cosmo on his lap and was stroking his back with smooth swoops of his large hand.

'Hey,' he said, looking up and smiling at her. 'Feel better?'

'A little.' She poured herself a coffee from the pot sitting on the counter.

'He was trying to open the kitchen door when I got there,' Jack said, nodding in Cosmo's direction.

'I left it open. Fuller must have come in that way and closed it behind him.'

'Right. It's one of those handles that you push down. Cosmo was leaping up at it. I figure he was trying to land on the handle and force it down.'

'I think he must have been a human in a previous life. He certainly thinks like one.'

'He loves you. Wants to protect you.'

Alexi took a sip of her coffee. The warm, rich liquid trickling down her throat was soothing. 'You've read Natalie's diaries and I haven't,' she said, taking the chair next to his. 'Are you going to make me guess what Natalie had on Seaton?'

He grimaced. 'Her diaries were touchingly naïve, up until the day that changed her life. She was excited about going to that do with her dad and critical of her mum for not attending . Natalie couldn't understand how anything could be more important than a glamorous awards event in a posh hotel but was really stoked about taking her mum's place. She had a new dress and all her friends were envious.'

'Poor kid.'

'Right. Her description of what happened that night is as harrowing as it is detailed including, significantly, details of a birthmark on Seaton's privates.'

'Ah,' Alexi replied, nodding slowly. 'The smoking gun.'

'Quite. Anyway, she really was an innocent and believed Seaton when he told her afterwards that she'd brought it on herself. She hated herself after that and I don't think she ever really got to like who she became. Well, perhaps not until recently and then, as we know, her every action was guided by the DNA of human motivation—'

'Otherwise known as revenge,' Alexi said softly.

'Right. If she hadn't gone to that damned navel-gazer and if he hadn't encouraged her to explore her past, things might have turned out very differently.'

'I agree Natalie's past would have been better left alone. But don't lose sight of the fact that Seaton did ruin her life and she didn't want to let go of her anger. Something had to give. I'm just glad she had the stamina to run away when she was still a teenager, even if she did finish up doing what she did. At least that was on her own terms.' Alexi placed an elbow on the table and leaned the uninjured side of her face in her cupped hand. 'I keep worrying that Fuller will use his influence to wheedle his way out of this.'

'The same thought occurred to me, so I did a little digging. I found some interesting stuff, so I got Cassie to dig deeper still.'

'I know that look.' Alexi smiled. 'I take it all is not what it seems in the Fuller household.'

'When are things ever what they seem? Okay, here's the short version. Fuller's father—'

'The one who wanted Laura to abort her baby?'

'Yeah, that charmer. He was a very successful trainer back in his day and ruled his yard with a crop of iron. He was a bully who had no time for personal weaknesses and everyone was scared of him, including his kids.'

'Which is why Graham Fuller walked away from Laura and toed the parental line.'

'That's the way I see it. Anyway, the prodigal son obviously redeemed himself because Daddy dearest passed his business over to Graham. But Graham has slowly run it into the ground because—'

'Because he has a drinking problem. I smelled it on his breath when I saw him... blimey, was it only yesterday morning? Anyway, it was early and he'd already had a fortifier or six.'

'There've been some problems. Horses not being entered in races, or being entered in the wrong ones. Owners stuck with him because of his reputation but talk has spread about booze, a short fuse, and some fairly public rows. Quite a few of them have now taken their horses away.'

'I noticed a few of the boxes in his yard were empty. I assumed the horses were out... wherever it is that they go.'

Jack grinned, presumably at her ignorance.

'Fuller married a rich American, and they have two grown kids. A daughter who works in Newbury as a management consultant. Doesn't want anything to do with horses and seldom returns home. The son is following the family tradition and being groomed to take over the training yard... if it survives.'

'They have financial problems, don't they?'

'Yeah. Fuller was asked to look at Super Nova on behalf of his then owner. Fuller knew a good thing when he saw it, talked the horse down, persuaded the owner to sell at a bargain price and used his wife's money to buy the colt for himself.'

'Very ethical.'

'Quite. The owner in question got into a big bust-up with Fuller over it when he found out Fuller had done the dirty on him.'

'Fuller didn't care because Super Nova would restore his fortune and his reputation. Then Natalie came along and demanded money with menaces, as they say in your old profession. She left him with no choice but to try and sell a share or two in his talented horse so that his wife didn't have to find out about the blackmail.'

Jack nodded. 'That's my take. Cassie took a peep at his bank accounts. He's up to his eyes in debt. Overdrawn to the limit, blah, blah. And he had no idea how often Natalie would come back for more, or if she would decide to go public with what he'd done once she'd bled him dry. He couldn't let it go on.'

'Oh, Natalie!' Alexi sighed. 'She should have come to me. I'd have got justice for her.'

'I suspect Fuller's wife knows he's been arrested by now, and probably some of the details. Whether or not she chooses to stand by him is another matter. She might stick it out for the sake of her kids, or she might cut and run. If she runs, without her money Fuller can kiss bye-bye to his expensive lawyer.'

'Let's hope that happens then. If it does, there's more chance of him pleading guilty and telling the police where he's hidden the body.'

'With what they have against him, his best bet is to cut a deal in return for a lighter sentence. At least that would avoid the additional embarrassment of a trial.'

Cheryl and Drew joined them and Jack updated them on his findings.

'There was a lot of talk when his stable lads' accommodation mysteriously burned down and the fire didn't touch anything else,' Cheryl told them.

'The fire investigators were all over it but couldn't prove anything, especially because they knew about a very public argument with an unhappy owner and his threats to take revenge. In the end, the insurers had to pay out.'

'Fuller is always behind in paying us for the accommodation we now provide for his lot,' Drew added. 'If we didn't need the dosh so badly, I'd tell him to take a hike. I'm sick of constantly chasing him for it.'

'We're gonna have to think of an easier way for you to make ends meet when this is all over,' Alexi said.

'Believe me,' Cheryl replied with feeling. 'If you can do that, you can live here rent free forever.'

Alexi laughed. 'Beware what you wish for.' She fiddled with her empty cup. 'Oh, by the way, with all the excitement, I forget to mention that Seaton turned up at Natalie's cottage yesterday.'

Jack gaped at her. 'You have got to be kidding me.'

'He claimed concern about Natalie—'

'And you fell for that?' Jack looked horrified.

'Of course not, but subsequent events have convinced me he didn't kill Natalie. All he wanted was to recover any incriminating evidence she had against him.'

'I think our visit must have prompted Seaton to act,' Jack said. 'He started to wonder if Natalie was actually dead, which is what we implied. If so, the police would get involved eventually and might find that evidence, which would put his name squarely in the frame. He had to get it back to keep himself in the clear and to stop his wife from finding out.'

Alexi nodded. 'I think you're right.'

'That'll be the police,' Drew said, standing to answer the front door bell. 'Use the upstairs lounge to talk to them, Alexi. You won't be disturbed there.'

'They might want to talk to you two as well,' Jack warned. 'You reported Natalie's disappearance and they'll want you to confirm you asked Alexi to look into it.'

'No problem,' Cheryl replied. 'But I can't guarantee I won't tear them off a strip for not taking us seriously.' Her expression sobered. 'If they had, Natalie might still be alive.'

Alexi knew that wasn't the case, but understood her friend's frustration, her need to blame someone else as well as Fuller.

* * *

'Are you feeling better, Ms Ellis?' the inspector asked, giving Cosmo a wide berth and wincing when he caught sight of her necklace of bruises. 'I hear you had a lucky escape.'

'I feel okay,' she replied cautiously, shaking the man's outstretched hand.

The detective constable produced a digital camera and with Alexi's permission took close-ups of her neck, and then the interview started. They didn't separate Jack and Alexi, treating them as victims and would-be witnesses. They went over everything several times, recording the conversation. They weren't aggressive, and implied the case was all but wrapped up.

'What's Fuller's reaction?' Jack asked when the tape was switched off. 'Off the record.'

The inspector shrugged. 'He's lawyered up and isn't talking. The arrogant sod seems to think he can walk away from all this.'

'Ain't gonna happen,' Jack replied, flexing his jaw.

'Count on it.' The inspector stood and shook each of their hands. 'I'll call and arrange for you to come in and sign your statements. But it can wait until Ms Ellis is properly back on her feet.'

The moment the detectives went downstairs to speak with Cheryl and Drew, Cosmo came out from beneath his chair and jumped onto Alexi's lap.

'What now?' Alexi asked, absently stroking him.

'How about a drive to Woldingham?'

'I like the way you think,' Alexi flashed a slow smile. 'It's not a journey I relish the thought of, but I think we should be the ones to break the news to Fay Seaton before the police get around to her.'

'Right.'

'Okay, but how much are we going to tell her?'

'All of it,' Jack replied, with a grimace. 'We owe it to Natalie.'

They waited for the police to leave. Then they went back downstairs and told Cheryl and Drew what they planned to do.

They walked outside and Jack opened the passenger door of his car for Alexi. Then he opened the rear door for Cosmo, who had made it crystal clear he had no intention of being left behind again.

19

Jack pulled his car up in front of the Seaton residence and cut the engine. Seaton's car was nowhere in sight.

'Ready?' he asked, reaching across to squeeze Alexi's hand.

'As I ever will be.'

They rang the bell but no one answered.

'Don't say she's out, too.' Alexi had psyched herself up for the interview and wanted to get it over with.

'Let's go round the back.'

Fay was down the end of the large garden, pruning something. She looked up when she heard them approach and smiled.

'Oh, hello again.' Alexi noticed hope flare in her eyes and hated what they were about to do to her. 'Do you have more news? About Natalie, I mean. Let's go into the house. It will be more comfortable talking there... oh my goodness!' Fay clasped a hand over her mouth. 'Whatever happened to you?'

'I had an accident, but I'm okay.'

'Goodness,' Fay muttered in a bewildered tone as she led them through the patio doors directly into the lounge and asked them if they would like tea. They declined. Fay sat upright in an armchair, her expression a combination of anticipation and resignation, as though a part of her sensed what she was about to hear but the rest of her wasn't ready to deal with it.

'It's bad news, isn't it?' she said softly. 'I can tell from your expression.'

'The very worst, I'm afraid.' Alexi crouched beside her, ignoring the protest from her injured knee as she took the older lady's hand. 'I'm so very sorry.'

'I think I've always known she must be dead.' Tears flowed freely down Fay's cheeks. 'It's a relief to know, in a way. How, when, did she die?'

'She was murdered.'

Fay lifted a trembling hand to her mouth. 'You hear about child abductions but you never think—'

'This didn't happen when she was a child, Fay. It was just a few days ago.'

Fay shook her head, looking lost and bewildered. 'I don't understand.'

'Up until a week ago Natalie was living in Lambourn.'

'Lambourn? Why does that sound... just a minute, that famous trainer? It was all over the news this morning. My husband was quite put out about it, which struck me as odd. He's never taken an interest in horseracing. He was arrested in connection with the disappearance of a local woman; the trainer, that is. Was the woman... was she my Natalie?'

Alexi squeezed her hand and nodded. 'I'm so very sorry.'

'But she might not actually be dead.' Hope flared in her eyes. 'They said they haven't found a body.'

'She's dead, I'm afraid,' Alexi replied. 'Fuller tried to kill me yesterday. I was in Natalie's cottage, looking for more clues about her disappearance, and he caught me there.'

'What did Natalie get caught up in?' Fay looked as though she was holding on by a whisker. But she had hidden depths, as evidenced in her determination to adopt a child against the wishes of a strong-willed husband. She was going to need all that strength of character to see her through this nightmare. 'Please tell me.'

Alexi did, explaining about Natalie's birth mother and the actions Natalie had subsequently taken.

'She must have been devastated, but blackmail...' Fay produced a handkerchief and mopped her eyes. 'And that doesn't explain why she left here when she was fourteen. I need to know what I did to drive her away.'

It was typical of the woman's self-effacing attitude that she automatically assumed the blame was hers.

'About that, Fay. Do you remember that award do Natalie went to with your husband?'

'Of course. She was so excited. She had a new dress. She was very off with me because she thought I should have put Gerry's interests ahead of my own and gone as well. She was too young to understand... I wasn't good in those sorts of situations. Gerry was better off without me cramping his style.'

Ah, Alexi thought, so she knew, or suspected, that her husband played away from home and tried not to mind. As gently as she could, Alexi explained what had happened.

'No!' All colour drained from Fay's face and she looked on the point of passing out. 'Don't say such things. I refuse to listen. I don't believe a word of it.'

'Get her some water, Jack.'

He returned from the kitchen with a glass and Alexi held it to Fay's lips. 'Take deep breaths and try to stay calm. Drink some water, it will help.'

'My husband is far from perfect,' she managed to splutter,

anger overcoming shock. 'But he loved Natalie and would *never* do something so terrible.'

'We can prove it,' Alexi said softly.

'See for yourself.' Jack handed her the incriminating diary, opened to the appropriate page.

She gasped when she saw the pink cover decorated with pictures of ponies. 'That's Natalie's! Where did you get it?'

'I found it in her cottage in Lambourn,' Alexi replied. 'Read those pages and tell me if you think a fourteen-year-old could possibly make something like that up.'

Fay reached for a pair of glasses and started to read. Sobs racked her body before she was halfway down the page. The diary fell from her fingers. Alexi enfolded the older woman in her arms and simply let her cry.

'I've lived with that monster all these years and didn't have a clue. How could I not have known? How could Natalie not have told me? Surely she knew I would do anything for her.'

They allowed Fay to rant and ask questions to which they had no answers. Eventually she asked one they could reply to, one which they would much prefer not to answer since it would cause Fay more pain.

'I can understand now why she ran away again, after they brought her back that first time. What I don't know is how she managed to support herself. She was only just fifteen.'

Alexi told her the brutal truth. Fay had stopped crying and took it with surprising calm.

'She lost all respect for herself, I suppose, discovered that men liked her and so used that to her advantage.' She sighed. 'She was the sweetest little girl, but Gerry's actions made her grow up overnight.'

'It is *not* your fault,' Alexi replied. 'Never think that.'

'We needed to tell you all this,' Jack said, 'because the police will discover who she was sooner or later and will want to talk to you. We didn't want it to come as a complete shock.'

'Thank you for that, anyway.' She straightened her spine, a determined expression pushing aside her bewilderment. 'I know now what I must do.'

Before Alexi could ask what she meant by that, Jack spoke. 'Natalie contacted your husband a while back and extracted money from him as well, just after she gave up working at the agency and moved to Lambourn.'

'I hope she took the bastard for every spare penny he had,' she replied aggressively, her jaw trembling with emotion.

'Will you be all right?' Alexi asked. 'Is there anyone we can call to be with you?'

She looked at Alexi as though she'd grown a second head. 'Do you honestly think I intend to spend another moment beneath this roof with that pervert?'

'But your life, your garden—'

'Is just a garden. I want to see where Natalie lived these past few years, and what sort of a life she'd made for herself. I... I also want to be close by if her body's found. I failed her in life. I don't aim to fail her in death as well. Will you take me back with you?'

'Of course,' Alexi replied, giving her shoulders a gentle squeeze, 'if that's what you'd like. You can stay in my friends' hotel. It was Cheryl who asked me to look for Natalie. She was Natalie's friend and will be able to tell you a lot more about her than I can.'

'Thank you.'

'Shall I help you pack?' Alexi asked. 'We need to do it now. We don't want your husband to come home and find us here.'

'Whereas I would welcome the confrontation,' Fay replied

* * *

Twenty minutes later, Jack carried a suitcase down the stairs for Fay and Alexi toted the only other bag she intended to take.

Fay scribbled a note, placed in the centre of the kitchen table, that said:

gone away for a few days F

'That'll shake him,' she said, a flash of defiance temporarily pushing aside the despair in her eyes.

'He'll suspect you know about Natalie,' Jack warned her. 'Because, excuse me for saying so, but as far as I can tell, Natalie is the only thing you've ever defied him over.'

'So far.'

They went out to the car, which is when Alexi remembered Cosmo. Before she could remind Jack, he'd unlocked the car and opened the rear door for Fay. Cosmo, curled up asleep, opened his eyes wide as Fay slid onto the seat beside him. He blinked at her in his customary lazy, contemplative fashion, as though sizing her up.

'Oh, a cat. How nice. I love cats but Gerry would never let me have one. He's allergic.'

'Be careful,' Alexi warned, smiling when she thought about Seaton's confrontation with Cosmo the previous day. He would be even more allergic now. 'He's not very sociable.'

'Of course he is.'

Cosmo proved her point by climbing onto her lap and purring up a storm.

'Remarkable,' Alexi muttered, sharing a glance with Jack.

'Do you think Natalie was Gerry's only victim or does he make a habit out of underage girls?' Fay asked pensively, speaking for the first time as they reached the outskirts of Lambourn.

'Men with those sorts of persuasions seldom stop at one,' Jack replied.

'Then we must make the police aware of what he did to our daughter. That might encourage others to come forward.'

'I wouldn't recommend it,' Jack said. 'Quite apart from anything else, the CPS would be reluctant to prosecute because, unfortunately, Natalie is no longer alive to accuse him. Her written word wouldn't be enough to secure a prosecution.'

'And besides,' Alexi added. 'If Fuller doesn't confess to killing Natalie, his lawyer will try and find another person with a reason to silence her. She did blackmail your husband and threaten to tell the world what he did to her. That's a pretty powerful motive and might fill a jury's mind with enough doubt to acquit Fuller.'

'Possibly, but it infuriates me that Gerry should continue to get away with it.'

'We'll find another way to make him pay,' Jack assured her.

'Natalie's cottage is down that lane,' Alexi said, indicating the turning as they passed it. 'We'll show you it as soon as we can. At the moment it's still a crime scene and we wouldn't be allowed inside.'

'Thank you. You're being very kind.'

Jack's mobile rang. He used the hands-free device to take the call. 'Fuller's talking,' a voice said.

'A sergeant friend of mine at Reading nick,' Jack mouthed to Alexi. 'Right,' he said in a normal voice into the phone, 'is he putting his hand up?'

Alexi sensed Fay's tension and reached between the seats to take her hand as they both listened.

'There's been a right to-do,' the sergeant replied, chuckling. 'His wife's disowned him and is legging it back to the States, refusing to foot his legal bills. His brief heard that and disappeared faster than a fiver staked on a hundred-to-one outsider.

Our boys took the opportunity to explain a few facts of life to Fuller while he was between lawyers and made him understand he's going down for a long stretch, even if we never find Natalie's body. We've got him banged to rights for trying to throttle Ms Ellis and having underage sex with Natalie's mum. The media would crucify him.'

'Count on it,' Alexi muttered.

'Anyway, he's admitted to killing her.' There was a collective release of breath within the car. 'He says it was an accident. They were talking, got into an argument, he struck her, she fell and hit her head and... well, you know the score.'

'Did he say where she is?'

'Yeah, he says he panicked, like they all do, and instead of calling us to the scene of a fatal accident, he put her on his quad bike and took her up to Membury Woods. She's in a shallow grave. There's a team up there now.'

'Thanks,' Jack said grimly, cutting the connection.

'It's over, Fay,' Alexi said softly as they turned into Hopgood Hall's driveway.

20

There was a media frenzy in Lambourn once Natalie's body was found and identified. Fuller was charged with murder, rape of a minor, and the attempted murder of Alexi, although her name as the victim hadn't yet been released. All the hotels within a ten-mile radius were booked out and the pubs struggled to keep up with demand. Television trucks blocked the lanes and locals brave enough to venture out of doors had microphones shoved beneath their noses. If you were a villager, it followed you had to know something newsworthy. A sound bite for the six-o'clock bulletin. How hard could it be to get one?

Hopgood Hall was under siege. Drew could have let all his rooms ten times over but refrained out of respect for Fay, whom he and Cheryl had taken under their wing. The bar was packed with hacks eager for the inside story, aware it was Drew who had identified Natalie's body. Drew employed extra help to keep up with the demand for alcoholic beverages.

Some of Fuller's lads were giving interviews, seeming to think their jobs were a thing of the past so they might as well cash in somehow. Tod was amongst them but he didn't tell them much, promising to give Alexi the true insider's story of life in the Fuller concentration camp, as he called it, once the dust had settled. Part of Alexi didn't want the story. Being on the receiving end of mob-journalism had given her a very different perspective of her chosen profession and she didn't much like what she saw. Bribery, bully-boy tactics, ridiculous speculation based on the flimsiest, unsubstantiated rumours were methods used to fill airtime and column inches. It was tacky, sensationalist, and about as reliable as a politician's promise.

Alexi recognised some of her former colleagues and kept out of sight. She and Jack took refuge in the kitchen, unable to let Fay see Natalie's cottage until the media storm blew over.

Alexi's phone rang. Patrick. With a sigh of resignation, she accepted he wouldn't give up until she spoke to him, so she took the call.

'At last,' he said.

'Patrick, what can I do for you?'

'Come on! You're sitting on the story of the decade. Murder, underage sex, and...' His breathing echoed down the line. 'Is it you, the attempted murder? You were looking for a friend of Cheryl's, Drew identified the body... it all fits.'

'I'm fine.'

'The hell you are! I'm coming down.'

'No!' She swallowed. 'No, Patrick, you're not. You have a paper to run and it's a jungle down here. Hopefully the mob will move on before my name gets leaked.'

'You think that's important? About the paper, I mean. I know you don't have a high opinion of me right now, but...' He paused and she could imagine his agitated expression as he ran fingers through his hair and juggled commitments in his mind. 'Nothing matters more than you,' he said softly.

Other than scooping the opposition. Alexi chased the thought away. It was what he did. And what she would have done too not so long ago. His first thought would be for the story. Of course it would. But she knew he felt something for her as well, otherwise why pursue her? She would have to find a way to tell him that she no longer returned those feelings. Right now it didn't rank high on her list of priorities because it would be the start of a battle she didn't have the energy to fight.

'I'm fine. Really. But there's no point in coming down. All the hotels are full anyway.'

'Will you at least file your story with us? I have people down there, but you have your finger on the pulse. No one can eclipse your version of events.'

'I can't talk about most of what I know until after Fuller's been sentenced.'

'I hear he's due before Magistrates today.'

'Yes. He's going to plead guilty.'

'I'm sorry this has happened to you, Alexi, and I know this isn't the right time to ask but have you thought more about my proposition?'

'You're right, Patrick. This isn't the time.' *Coward!*

She hung up, aware of Jack's gaze fixed on her profile.

He smiled at her. 'How's Fay doing?'

'She's read all of Natalie's diaries and they've made her cry. A lot.'

'That's to be expected. Has she got the strength to tackle her manuscript?'

'She's on it now.'

Jack nodded but before he could say anything more, their conversation was interrupted by Fay herself.

'How are you doing?' Jack asked, standing to pour coffee for them all.

'I'm finding the manuscript easier because it's written with such clinical detachment,' Fay replied, sighing. 'It's almost as though she's talking about someone else's life.'

'Yes,' Alexi agreed. 'She held back on describing her feelings and stuck to the facts.'

'Which means it lacks heart. We all want to know what was going on inside of her. Well, I do, anyway. I'd suggest you write her story,' Fay said. 'But I hesitate to let the world know how badly I failed her.'

'You didn't fail her,' Jack replied. 'Speaking of which, has he been in touch again?'

Fay shook her head. Gerry had been on the phone to Fay shortly after she arrived at Hopgood Hall, demanding to know where she was. When she said she was in Lambourn, Seaton had become defensive, accusing her of listening to 'that reporter's lies' and insisting she return home. Alexi heard Fay's end of the conversation and wanted to punch the air when she calmly told him that if he came within ten miles of her, she would release Natalie's diaries to the press.

'No, I've not heard from him since. He must have seen the news and decided to keep a low profile. Natalie's identity and the fact that she was our adopted daughter hasn't yet been released, but I expect it will be any day now and Gerry knows he'll be in demand for interviews.' She curled her lip. 'What's the betting he'll preen in front of the cameras, thanking god that he finally knows where his long-lost daughter was all this time, giving him closure?'

'I certainly wouldn't bet against it,' Jack replied.

Fay nodded, drained her coffee cup, and stood up.

'I shall have to go back to Newbury tomorrow,' Jack said once Fay had left them. 'Will you be all right?'

'Of course.' She smiled at him, surprised at how much she didn't want him to go. 'The press will clear off once Fuller's been before the beak so I'm planning on showing Fay Natalie's cottage tomorrow.'

'What about you?' Jack said. He reached for the coffee again, thought better of it, and went to the fridge for a cold bottle of wine. He poured her a glass without asking if she wanted one and placed it in front of her. Alexi took a healthy swig. 'What do you plan to do now?'

'Actually, the country's growing on me. I might take a rented cottage down here. I like the area and it would be good to be close to Cheryl when she becomes a mother. I fully intend to be a hands-on godmother.'

'I think that's a great idea. Got any places in mind?'

'I've put out a few feelers with local estate agents, but until the furore of Fuller's arrest dies down...'

'I'm glad you're sticking around.' He touched her face with the tips of his fingers. Alexi waited, half hoping he'd say more. Glad when he didn't. 'Let's have dinner once the village returns to normal.'

'I'd like that.'

'Me too.'

He briefly, too briefly, touched her lips with his own. Then Cheryl joined them, which Alexi told herself was just as well.

Jack's mobile rang. He answered it, and listened for a while.

'Just a moment,' he said. 'I'll pass you to Ms Ellis. She can help you.' Alexi flexed a brow in enquiry. 'It's Natalie's solicitor.'

'Oh, right.' Alexi took Jack's phone. 'Alexi Ellis. How can I help you?'

'The name's Denton. I represented Natalie Parker's interests and was very sorry to hear what happened to her. Very sorry indeed.' He sighed. 'I understand Mrs Seaton is there with you. Could I come down and talk with her tomorrow?'

* * *

Alexi drove Fay and Cosmo to Natalie's cottage the following morning. Fay sat in Fabio's passenger seat, lacing her fingers together and twisting them until her knuckles turned white, staring straight ahead and not saying a word.

It had been harrowing for Fay to read her daughter's words. And now she would see for herself how she had chosen to live since leaving the agency. She would be able to touch her clothes, her possessions; walk through the rooms she had decorated and furnished to suit her own taste. Breathe in the essence of the woman she hadn't seen for nearly thirty years but had never stopped loving, worrying over, and wondering about.

'Here we are.'

Fay snapped out of her reverie when Alexi pulled up beside the cottage. She peered through the window, tentatively at first, but revived when she saw the lovely garden in full bloom.

'Cheryl tells me it was a right old wilderness before Natalie got her hands on it.'

Fay walked through the gate, barely sparing a glance for the cottage as she walked round the side of it and into the garden. Rose petals littered the path, their fragrant perfume almost overwhelming. Jasmine and honeysuckle fought with plumbago for pride of place on a trellis against a back wall and flowering shrubs Alexi couldn't put names to filled every bed.

Cosmo stalked ahead of them, tail aloft, almost as though patrolled the grounds to ensure there were no persons with murderous intent lurking behind the shrubbery. Satisfied on that score, he found a patch of sun and settled down to attend to his ablutions.

'Are you all right?' Alexi asked, placing a hand gently on Fay's shoulder.

Fay wiped the tears away with the back of her hand, stopped dead in the centre of a path, and turned to face Alexi, the emotion of reminiscence lending character to her face. 'She remembered the plans we had when we talked of creating a garden from scratch,' she said softly. 'She actually remembered.'

Fay spent half-an-hour in the garden and Natalie's work-room, brightening considerably at little touches that evoked memories. By the time they went into the cottage, Fay seemed more composed.

'Thank you for bringing me here, Alexi,' Fay said softly.

'My pleasure.'

'We can go now. I've taken up enough of your time.'

'Actually, we're waiting for someone.' Alexi consulted her watch. 'Natalie's solicitor needs to speak with you.'

Fay's eyes widened. 'With me? Whatever...'

The doorbell cut off Fay's astounded reaction and barrage of questions. Cosmo growled, so Alexi shooed him out into the back garden. She then went to the front door and wrenched it open. A man of about forty, of medium height and medium build who would be forgettable in a crowd, stood on the threshold. He was dressed in a lightweight, crumpled suit, an open-necked shirt, and wore aviator sunglasses which he whipped off when Alexi opened the door.

'Ms Ellis?'

'Yes. Mr Denton I assume. Do come in.'

'Sorry to be a little late.' He extracted a business card from the top pocket of his jacket, handed it to Alexi, and followed her into the cottage. 'Took a wrong turn and had to double back.'

'No problem.'

Alexi introduced Fay. Ever the hostess, Fay had set her wari-ness at Denton's arrival aside and put the kettle on the moment the doorbell rang. She was now busying herself by assembling a tray with coffee cups. Alexi carried it through to the lounge, Fay poured and Mr Denton then got right down to business.

'I'm sorry for your loss, Mrs Seaton,' he said. 'I liked your daughter very much. She was a good person.'

'Thank you.' Fay swallowed. 'Did you know her well?'

'I looked after her business affairs for a number of years.'

'I see.'

'Actually, Mrs Seaton, as I told Ms Ellis, Natalie left very detailed instructions regarding her funeral wishes.'

Fay blinked rapidly. 'How could she have known?'

'She wished to be cremated,' Denton said, extracting a sheaf of papers from his briefcase. 'She doesn't want any religious connotations. She was most specific on that point.'

'Given what happened to her,' Fay said, *sotto voce*, 'that doesn't come as a big surprise.'

'No flowers or donations to worthy causes in her name, and close friends only. No announcements in the papers.' Denton cleared his throat. 'On one point, she was most specific. She did not want... under any circumstances, Mr Seaton to be admitted to the funeral or involved in it in any way.'

Denton looked concerned that Fay would object, or have a screaming fit, when he stumbled through that provision. Instead, she straightened her spine and met Denton's gaze head on.

'You have my assurance that he will not be, Mr Denton.'

'Right, okay, well, that's good.' He offered Fay a detached smile. 'So, that just leaves the business of Natalie's will.'

Fay looked shocked. 'She made a will?'

'Indeed. She owned this cottage outright, along with all its contents. She had a healthy bank balance and thriving business.' Denton paused and leaned forward to hold Fay's gaze. 'She left all of it to you.'

Alexi's smile was as spontaneous as it was heartfelt. Fay, on the other hand, looked to be on the verge of passing out. Alexi reached across and took her hand. It was ice cold.

'Me?' Fay shook her head. 'But she must have hated me for...'

'Evidently not,' Denton replied. 'But there is one major stipulation.'

'Of course.' Fay seemed to shrink in on herself, as though she expected someone to jump out from behind a chair and yell 'got ya!'

'If Mr Seaton has any dealings with Natalie's property, then the will is revoked and everything is left to charity. I have been appointed as administrator of this rather unusual bequest. I am to have full access to all accounts, and to the property and business without prior appointment. If I find this clause has been circumvented or abused in any way, I have the power to revoke the bequest and evict you from the premises.' He smiled to take the sting out of his words. 'I hope that won't prove to be necessary and I'm sorry to sound so blunt, but Natalie was adamant.'

'I'm sure she was,' Alexi muttered when Fay didn't immediately respond.

Fay glanced at Alexi, her eyes glassy with shock. 'She didn't hate me,' she said dazedly. 'She didn't forget me. She wanted me to have all this.'

Fay burst into tears. Alexi smiled at Denton, who fidgeted in his chair and looked most uncomfortable, the way men do when women cry in their presence.

'She was offering you a way out,' Alexi explained when Fay's sobs subsided. 'She probably knew you would never leave him otherwise, or that he wouldn't let you and you had no independent means to make it happen.'

'She left this for you.' Denton stood up, handed Fay a sealed envelope, and prepared to take his leave. 'If you have no further questions, ladies, I ought to be going.'

Alexi could see that Fay had a great many but was too stunned to voice them. Instead she fingered the envelope Denton had given her, clearly wanting to open it straight away. Alexi gave her some privacy by showing Denton to the door and then wandering around the back in search of Cosmo. She found him stretched full length in a patch of sun, ever optimistic, beneath the bird feeder.

'They won't come if you make yourself so obvious,' she told him absently, her head full of Natalie's bequest.

* * *

Alexi and Cosmo stayed in the sun for a good ten minutes before they wandered together into the sitting room. Fay had the letter open and was clutching it between trembling fingers.

'Are you all right?' Alexi asked tentatively.

Fay looked up, a combination of relief and sadness clouding her expression. 'She explains it all,' she said. 'She believed him. She was convinced it was her own fault, that she'd encouraged him in some way and that I would think less of her, if I believed her at all. When she was old enough to realise it hadn't been her fault, she was already working as an escort and was ashamed of what she'd become.'

'She wanted you to be proud of her.'

'She says she could have lied to me about what she did for a living but preferred to keep her distance rather than there be more secrets between us.' Fay sighed. 'She was planning to contact me once she'd concluded her business with her natural father. She was blackmailing him and Gerry, not for herself but so she would have enough money for me to be able to move in here with her if I wanted to and help with her business.'

'She knows you would have liked that, I expect, which is why she designed the garden to your specification.'

'Foolish child! She should have told me all this years ago. I would have left Gerry in a heartbeat and lived with her in a hovel if necessary.'

'What shall you do now?' Alexi asked.

'Why, what Natalie wanted me to do, of course: I shall move in here and take over her business. And I shall also sue my husband for divorce and take him for every penny I can.' She tossed her head. 'I'm not quite the doormat he takes me for. I've always known how much we're worth and where all his bank accounts are. Even the ones he thinks are secret. Especially those. I shall make my daughter proud of me, you just see if I don't.'

Alexi believed her.

EPILOGUE

'What do you think?' Alexi asked.

Cheryl grinned. 'I think it's perfect for you. The garden's big enough for Cosmo to stake his claim but not unmanageable.'

'Or I can get a man in.' Alexi grinned. 'I'm not that much of a changed character. A window-box still stretches my horticultural abilities.'

The friends joined Cosmo on the patio and sat in the sun, enjoying a moment's peace and quiet. It was the first they'd had for some time. In the two weeks since Natalie's funeral, life had been hectic. Fay was doing okay. She'd moved into Natalie's cottage and taken over her business. A girl from the village was doing the arrangements while Fay did what she did best and concentrated on ensuring the garden thrived.

The funeral itself had been conducted in accordance with Natalie's wishes, with Jack's solid and reassuring presence helping Alexi to keep her demons at bay. Fuller's name was on everyone's lips, the reverberations echoing far beyond Lambourn, reminding her of her ordeal. She put a brave face on things but clearly didn't fool Jack, who barely left her side the entire day.

Gerald Seaton created quite a fuss, wanting to attend. Fay had told him he would be bodily removed if he attempted it, right in front of the press contingent covering the event. The threat was enough to keep him away. Denton was there to ensure fair play. Athena De Bois attended and Alexi saw her and Fay in deep conversation at the small reception held at Hopgood Hall afterwards. Darren Walker, the man Natalie had dated three times, was also invited. He and Fay had a great deal to say to one another, too, and Alexi understood they'd arranged to have dinner together soon. Alexi was glad. Fay was already making new friends and building an independent life for herself.

Fay had insisted that Alexi write Natalie's story. At first luke-warm about the idea, it had grown on Alexi. She needed to do something while she decided on her future, and this was a story that needed to be told. She already had a publisher interested.

Patrick had been down, they'd had dinner together, and she had told him his offer of employment was a no-go. He seemed sad yet resigned, still convinced she would have enough of the country sooner rather than later and promising to keep the offer open indefinitely. When she was ready he would make it happen. Somehow.

She diverted him by pitching a story that she really did want to write: a three-part series for the *Sentinel* focusing on the effects of incest on its victims and how it impacted the rest of their lives. She had two people willing to contribute. One who had put it behind her and moved on, one who had been in and out of therapy for years and couldn't get past it, and Natalie, the avenging angel. The world now knew of Alexi's involvement in Natalie's case and it wouldn't take a rocket scientist to piece together the part Gerald had played in it, even if she couldn't actually name him or Natalie in the article. It would be the ultimate revenge – the ultimate closure – for Fay.

And for Natalie, too.

She still thought Seaton was getting off too lightly and fumed because she couldn't do more to name and shame him. He'd ruined Natalie's life but was now doing the media rounds, painting himself as a victim. Natalie's murder had broken up his marriage and it was all Fuller's fault. Fay was furious. She knew he was doing it to get back at her. He would have to agree to her terms for the divorce and couldn't claim a half-share of her inheritance, off-setting it against what he must pay her, partly because she'd sued for divorce *before* she knew of the inheritance.

Seaton continued to plague Fay with entreaties, promises, and then demands. In the end, she had threatened him with a restraining order and since then he'd gone deathly quiet.

Cheryl and Alexi tore themselves from the sunny patio and re-joined the letting agent who was patiently waiting for them in the sitting room.

'I'll take it,' Alexi told him. 'How soon can I move in?'

Having told the agent she would call at his office to sign the lease agreement the following day, Alexi drove Cheryl back to Hopgood Hall.

'Oh god!' Cheryl shuddered when she heard shouting coming from the kitchen. 'I'd better go and see what's wrong this time.'

'Leave him to it,' Alexi said, heading for the kitchen. 'You'll only encourage his bad behaviour otherwise. Come on, I'll make some tea.'

'Thanks,' Cheryl said, when Alexi placed a cup in front of her a short time later.

'What's happening about the annexe?' Alexi asked. 'Any news about the future of Fuller's yard?'

'More owners have withdrawn their horses,' Cheryl replied. 'And some of the lads have already been poached.'

'What will you do?'

Cheryl sighed. 'I wish I knew.'

'Are you up for suggestions?'

'Speak!'

'We... ll, I was just wondering if you've considered using your lovely home as a retreat.'

'Conferences, you mean?' Alexi nodded. 'We don't have the facilities. Besides, most conferences are at weekends and that's when we're busiest.'

'Not necessarily. I shall be living down here and I happen to know a lot of people who'd pay through the nose to attend journalist workshops hosted by yours truly, modesty notwithstanding. And I have other colleagues from different aspects of the business who would probably contribute. Then there are creative writing retreats, stuff like that. With the right marketing, it could work.'

'I'll talk to Drew about it, but I already know he's desperate enough to try anything.'

'And what about the annexe? Do you really want to keep that monstrosity?'

'Of course not, but—'

'Why not replace it with a proper extension, in keeping with the main part of the house?'

Cheryl flashed a sarcastic smile. 'And pay for it, how?'

'Hear me out.' Alexi paused to sip at her tea. 'You don't want the tennis courts back. They're a pain in the backside to maintain and no one used them anyway. You said that yourself. But you could have a lovely conference centre on that site, use aged bricks so it blends in better with the main building, get land-scape gardeners to put in courtyards and pretty little bits... and, I don't know, but I'm sure you get my drift.'

Cheryl shrugged. 'There's no harm in dreaming.'

'Hey, pay attention, I'm serious. I was thinking of Marcel and how to keep him. His star's in the ascendency, so lots of wanna-be chefs would pay good money to come here and be yelled at by him.' She spread her hands. 'It takes all sorts. Anyway, you could open your restaurant at lunchtimes and flog their efforts cheaply enough to attract a crowd.' Alexi grinned. 'A crowd who would stump up for wine to accompany the food. Marcel could boss his students about and feel important, and you could reap the benefits.'

'It's a lovely idea, Alexi, but it would cost a fortune to build the conference centre and finish it to the required standard. We just can't—'

'No, but I can.'

'Seriously?' Cheryl blinked. 'Why would you?'

'I need an investment opportunity. My flat in town has already been let for twice the amount I'll be paying in rent down here, I have the money I inherited from my mum sitting in the bank earning diddly squat, my redundancy pay-out has nothing to do, and now the publishers are talking a hefty advance for Natalie's story.'

Cheryl swallowed, looking warily interested. 'You really are serious?' She covered Alexi's hand. 'Thank you, but even if we were tempted, it would be years before we could repay you.'

'Hey, I'm not an easy touch. If you go into business with friends, it needs to be on an official footing. I'd want a binding contract that allowed you to pay back my capital in a timescale that wouldn't keep you awake at night *and* pay me a handsome dividend from the profits.'

'You're overwhelming me, Alexi. I can't—'

'Think about it. Talk to Drew.'

'What if Marcel decides to leave anyway?'

'His ego won't allow it. Anyway, you might want to offer him a share in the profits, which would bind him in.'

Cheryl caught an errant tear on her forefinger as it trickled down her face. 'Why would you do this, Alexi?'

'I know a good opportunity when I see one. Besides, someone has to take care of my godchild's interests.'

Cheryl grinned. 'The idea has merit but it's so ambitious it takes my breath away. Still, if you really mean it, I'll run it past Drew.'

'Don't run it past him, convince him.' Alexi squeezed her friend's hand. 'It's the only way. Don't allow his silly pride to stand in the way of your dreams.'

Cheryl's smile widened. 'You're right,' she said. 'Men don't always know their own minds. It's down to us to make sure that they do.'

'And I shall be here to back you up.'

'And see more of Jack, perhaps?' Cheryl suggested, a sparkle in her eye.

'Jack works in Newbury,' Alexi said. 'Besides, I'm off men. They're more trouble than they're worth.'

Cheryl leaned over awkwardly, her expanding belly restricting her movements, and kissed Alexi's cheek. 'Keep telling yourself that,' she said, chuckling.

ACKNOWLEDGEMENTS

My thanks to all the wonderful Boldwood team and, in particular, to my talented editor, Emily Ruston.

ABOUT THE AUTHOR

E.V. Hunter writes bestselling cosy murder mysteries. She has also written revenge thrillers as Evie Hunter. For the past twenty years she has lived the life of a nomad, roaming the world on interesting forms of transport, but has now settled back in the UK.

Sign up to E.V. Hunter's mailing list here for news, competitions and updates on future books.

Follow E.V. Hunter on social media:

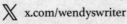 x.com/wendyswriter

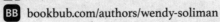 facebook.com/wendy.soliman.author

bookbub.com/authors/wendy-soliman

ALSO BY E.V. HUNTER

The Hopgood Hall Murder Mysteries

A Date To Die For

A Contest To Kill For

A Marriage To Murder For

A Story to Strangle For

Revenge Thrillers by Evie Hunter

The Sting

The Trap

The Chase

The Scam

The Kill

The Alibi

Poison
& Pens

POISON & PENS IS THE HOME OF
COZY MYSTERIES SO POUR YOURSELF
A CUP OF TEA & GET SLEUTHING!

DISCOVER PAGE-TURNING NOVELS FROM
YOUR FAVOURITE AUTHORS &
MEET NEW FRIENDS

JOIN OUR
FACEBOOK GROUP

BIT.LYPOISONANDPENSFB

SIGN UP TO OUR
NEWSLETTER

BIT.LY/POISONANDPENSNEWS

Boldwᴏᴏd

Boldwood Books is an award-winning fiction publishing company seeking out the best stories from around the world.

Find out more at www.boldwoodbooks.com

Join our reader community for brilliant books, competitions and offers!

Follow us
@BoldwoodBooks
@TheBoldBookClub

Sign up to our weekly
deals newsletter

https://bit.ly/BoldwoodBNewsletter